THE COMPLETE BOOK OF
HOME PLANS

CONTENTS

59 CHARLEVOIX CREEK Plan #651-055D-0215
Photos courtesy of Nelson Design Group.

8 SWEET VALLEY Plan #651-032D-0520
Photos courtesy of Drummond Designs.

The Complete Book of Home Plans is published by HDA, Inc., 944 Anglum Road, St. Louis, MO 63042. All rights reserved. Reproduction in whole or part without written permission of the publisher is prohibited. Printed in the U.S.A. © 2013.

Artist drawings and photos shown in this publication may vary slightly from the actual working drawings. Some photos are shown in mirror reverse. Please refer to the floor plan for accurate layout. All plans appearing in this publication are protected under copyright law.

Reproduction of the illustrations or working drawings by any means is strictly prohibited. The right of building only one structure from the plans purchased is licensed exclusively to the buyer and the plans may not be resold unless by express written authorization.

For questions call 1-800-367-0921 or e-mail at plans@hdainc.com.

Current Printing 5 4 3 2 1

10 AVALON PLACE Plan #651-13S-0014
Photos courtesy of Atlanta Plan Source.

Follow House Plans and More on:

WHAT'S THE RIGHT PLAN FOR YOU?

Many factors play a role in what home plan is best for you and your family. To help you get started, we have pinpointed some of the major factors to consider when searching for your dream home. Take the time to evaluate your family's needs and you will have an easier time sorting through all of the home plans offered in our book.

Choosing a home plan is an exciting but difficult task.

Budget:

The first thing to consider is your budget. Many items take part in this budget, from ordering the blueprints to the last doorknob purchased. When you find your dream home plan, visit our website at houseplansandmore.com to get a cost-to-build estimate to ensure that the finished product will be within your cost range.

Family Lifestyle:

After your budget is deciphered, you need to assess you and your family's lifestyle needs. Think about the stage of life you are at now, and what stages you will be going through in the future. Ask yourself questions to figure out how much room you need now and if you will need room for expansion. Incorporate in your planning any frequent guests you may have, including elderly parents, grandchildren or adult children who may live with you. Here are some questions that can help access your type of lifestyle:

Are you married? Do you have children? How many children do you plan on having? Are you an empty-nester? Does your family entertain a lot? If so, think about the rooms you will need to do so. Will you need both formal and informal spaces? Do you need a gourmet kitchen? Do you need a game room and/or a wet bar?

Experts in the field suggest that the best way to determine your needs is to begin by listing everything you like or dislike about your current home.

Floor Plan Layouts:

When looking through our home plans, imagine yourself walking through the house. Consider the flow from the entry to the living, sleeping and gathering areas. Does the layout ensure privacy for the master bedroom? Does the garage enter near the kitchen for easy unloading? Does the placement of the windows provide enough privacy from any neighboring properties? Do you plan on using furniture you already have? Will this furniture fit in the appropriate rooms? When you find a plan you want to purchase, be sure to picture yourself actually living in it.

Exterior Spaces:

There are many different home styles ranging from Traditional to Contemporary. Flip through and find which style most appeals to you and the neighborhood in which you plan to build. Also think of your site and how the entire house will fit on this site. Picture any landscaping you plan on incorporating into the design. Using your imagination is key when choosing a home plan.

Choosing a home plan can be an intimidating experience. Asking yourself these questions before you get started on the search will help you through the process. With our large selection of multiple styles we are certain you will find your dream home in the following pages.

FOLLOW US

Pinterest

follow us at pinterest.com/houseplansmore/

MOST POPULAR REPIN!

This stunning kitchen photo from Plan #082S-0002 is the most pin-worthy!

facebook

follow us at facebook.com/HousePlansandMore

From fan favorites like "House Plan of the Day," to surveys, polls, stunning photo albums, trivia and fan special offers, stay connected to House Plans and More on facebook and enjoy everything there is to love about homes and beautiful architecture everyday!

You Tube

follow us at youtube.com/user/houseplansandmore

MOST POPULAR VIDEO!

View amazing videos featuring the most beautiful homes in the world!

DON'T FORGET...

Follow @HousePlansMore for the latest industry news, special offers and house info.

View remarkable photos from House Plans and More on the home design website houzz.com.

Follow us on google+ and see all that House Plans and More has to offer.

Follow us on tumblr to check houseplansandmore.com's most attractive photos and great articles.

WHY STOCK PLANS?

Building a home from scratch presents many opportunities to showcase a homeowner's creativity, individuality, and dreams turned into reality.

With this opportunity, also comes many challenges and questions that tend to crop up. Location, size, and budget are all important to consider, as well as special features and amenities. When one really examines everything that must be determined, it can become overwhelming to search for your dream home. But, with the ease of purchasing a stock plan such as the homes presented throughout this book, the time and money saved will allow you to build your dream home faster and most likely for less money than drawing a home design completely from start to finish.

The variety of stock plans available is truly impressive, encompassing the most up-to-date features in square footage, room dimensions, layout, and amenities homeowners want today. With some patience and determination, browsing the house plans presented throughout this book can allow you to find and easily purchase a wonderful design faster than ever before. Plus, all the house plans featured are customizable. For example, perhaps you see a stock plan that is just about perfect, but you wish the mudroom was a bit larger. Rather than go through the cost and time of having a customized home design, you could submit a home plan modification and have your new dream hhome ready to go in no time. Also, many of these home plans include a materials list, helping to eliminate unknown costs from developing during construction.

See why it has never been easier to build your dream home from a stock plan such as these. With this book along with our website, houseplansandmore.com, you can uncover the perfect home plan by style, size, budget, and other features. With all these tools, you'll soon have the home plan of your dreams in your reality!

PLAN FEATURES

1,909 total square feet of living area

Width: 54'-0" Depth: 38'-0"

Energy efficient home with 2" x 6" exterior walls

The absolutely brilliant exterior has bright windows, a stone facade, and a large porch with beautiful detail

The charming kitchen has a double sink, an efficient dishwasher, and direct access to the inviting rear deck

Two bedrooms have ample closet space, a full bath with a spacious vanity, and a cozy linen closet that is highly convenient

3 bedrooms, 2 1/2 baths, 2-car garage

Basement foundation

Price Code F

Second Floor
655 sq. ft.

© Copyright by designer/architect

First Floor
1,254 sq. ft.

Lovely rear deck

houseplansandmore.com

PLANFEATURES

3,909 total square feet of living area

Width: 77'-4" Depth: 62'-4"

Energy efficient home with 2" x 6" exterior walls

The entry opens into the great room and offers a grand first impression with a 15' ceiling

A massive pantry and snack bar island enhance the kitchen that is open to the formal dining room and cozy hearth room

The lower level is comprised of three secondary bedrooms, a recreation room and entertaining area with wet bar

4 bedrooms, 2 full baths, 2 half baths, 1-car garage, 2-car side entry garage

Walk-out basement foundation

Price Code G

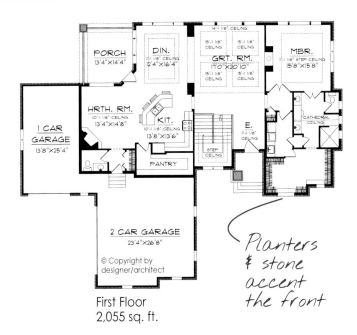

Planters & stone accent the front

First Floor
2,055 sq. ft.

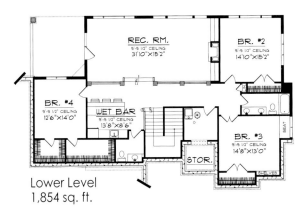

Lower Level
1,854 sq. ft.

Photo, above: Elegant ivory furnishings create a sharp contrast against the dark wood beamed ceiling treatment highlighted above in the great room.

Photo, right: The antique white cabinets add a terrific Country French influence to the interior of the kitchen.

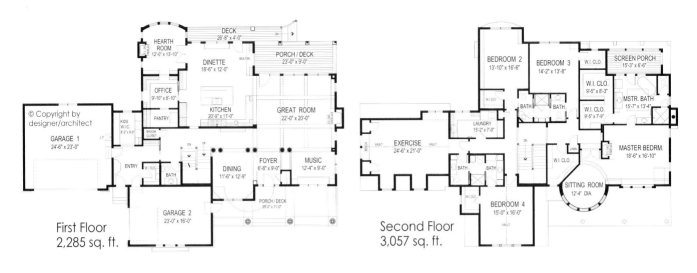

First Floor
2,285 sq. ft.

Second Floor
3,057 sq. ft.

Lower Level
2,092 sq. ft.

Awesome indoor sport court!!

Photo, below: Sipping your morning coffee in the comfort of the private master bedroom sitting room is sure to make for the perfect beginning of a new day.

PLANFEATURES

7,434 total square feet of living area

Width: 88'-6" Depth: 62'-0"

Energy efficient home with 2" x 6" exterior walls

A circular sitting room invites the owner into their lovely master bedroom equipped with a generous master bath and private screen porch

The gorgeous great room features a fireplace, a wall of windows and access to the deck

Entertaining is a breeze on the lower level including several game areas, a wet bar and full bath

4 bedrooms, 4 1/2 baths, 2-car garage, 1-car side entry garage

Walk-out basement foundation

Price Code S2

CEDARWOOD

PLAN FEATURES

1,475 total square feet of living area

Width: 43'-0" Depth: 36'-6"

The family room features a 10' high ceiling and prominent corner fireplace

The kitchen with an island counter and garden window makes a convenient connection between the family and dining rooms

A hallway leads to three bedrooms all with large walk-in closets

A covered breezeway joins the main house and the garage

The full-width covered porch entry lends a country touch

3 bedrooms, 2 baths, 2-car detached side entry garage

Slab foundation, drawings also include crawl space foundation

Price Code B

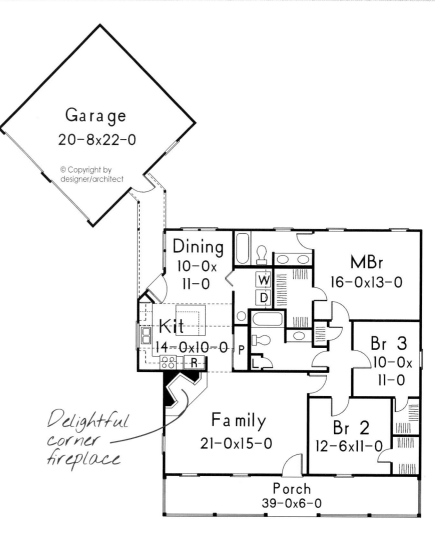

Garage
20-8x22-0

© Copyright by designer/architect

Dining
10-0x11-0

MBr
16-0x13-0

W
D

Kit
14-0x10-0

P

Br 3
10-0x11-0

Delightful corner fireplace

Family
21-0x15-0

Br 2
12-6x11-0

Porch
39-0x6-0

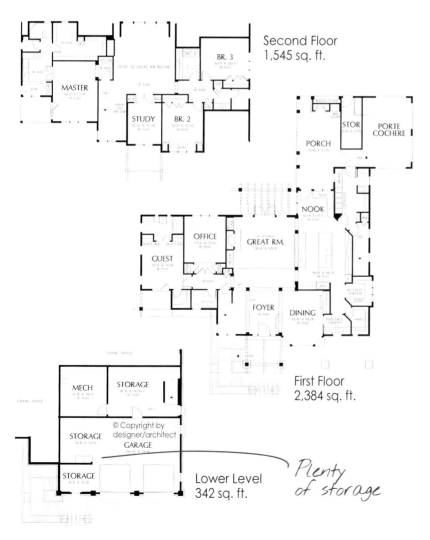

Second Floor
1,545 sq. ft.

First Floor
2,384 sq. ft.

Plenty of storage

Lower Level
342 sq. ft.

PLANFEATURES

4,271 total square feet of living area

Width: 80'-6" Depth: 78'-0"

Enjoy the outdoors with the exquisite rear porch featuring a cozy fireplace to warm guests on cold nights

The master bedroom has many amenities including a spa tub, two separate sinks and a large walk-in closet with space designated for a safe

There is ample storage space located on the lower level and a convenient staircase leading to the first floor

4 bedrooms, 3 full baths, 2 half baths, 2-car drive under garage

Partial crawl space/walk-out basement foundation

Price Code S1

PLANFEATURES

5,864 total square feet of living area

Width: 129'-8" Depth: 110'-2"

The amazing family room has a corner fireplace and is just steps away from the octagon-shaped wet bar with multiple windows brightening the area

Luxury abounds in the master bath including his and hers walk-in closets and separate vanity areas

A large back porch is perfect for entertaining and can be accessed through the master bedroom, kitchen and family rooms

4 bedrooms, 4 full baths, 2 half baths, 4-car side entry garage

Slab foundation

Price Code S7

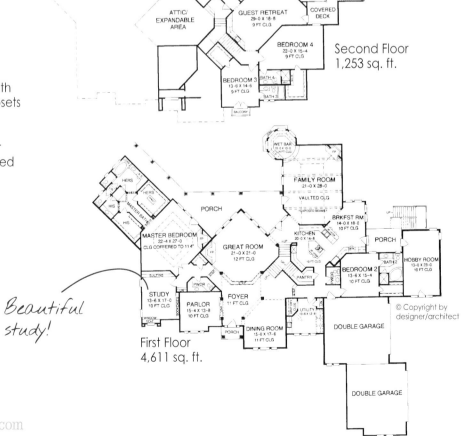

Beautiful study!

Second Floor
1,253 sq. ft.

First Floor
4,611 sq. ft.

© Copyright by designer/architect

PLANFEATURES

2,889 total square feet of living area

Width: 42'-0" Depth: 79'-6"

Stone, a striking turret and decorative roof lines accent this home and give it a European flair

The luxurious first floor offers a massive great room, plush master suite, quiet office and access to the outdoor living porch furnished with a stone hearth fireplace

The second floor consists of three bedrooms, a shared bath and handy computer center

The second floor bonus room has an additional 378 square feet of living area

4 bedrooms, 2 1/2 baths, 2-car garage

Crawl space or slab foundation, please specify when ordering

Price Code E

First Floor
1,819 sq. ft.

Amazing outdoor fireplace!

Second Floor
1,070 sq. ft.

© Copyright by designer/architect

houseplansandmore.com

PLANFEATURES

2,523 total square feet of living area

Width: 90'-4" Depth: 48'-4"

The entry featuring a high ceiling leads to a massive vaulted great room with a wet bar, plant shelves, pillars and a fireplace with a harmonious window trio

The elaborate kitchen with bay and breakfast bar adjoins the morning room with a fireplace-in-a-bay

The vaulted master bedroom features a fireplace, book and plant shelves, a large walk-in closet and double baths

3 bedrooms, 2 baths, 3-car garage

Basement foundation, drawings also include crawl space and slab foundations

Price Code D

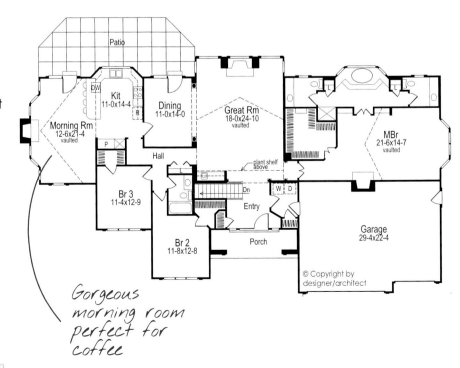

Gorgeous morning room perfect for coffee

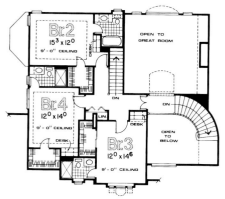

Second Floor
1,020 sq. ft.

PLANFEATURES

3,623 total square feet of living area

Width: 76'-8" Depth: 68'-0"

The exquisite master bedroom includes a sitting area with built-in bookcases and a fireplace

The spacious great room features a fireplace wall with an entertainment center, bookcases and a wet bar

Each secondary bedroom includes a walk-in closet, a built-in desk and a private bath

4 bedrooms, 4 1/2 baths, 4-car side entry garage

Basement foundation

Price Code F

First Floor
2,603 sq. ft.

© Copyright by designer/architect

Private sitting area in the master bedroom

MONTCLAIRE

PLAN #651-001D-0007

2,874 total square feet of living area

Width: 83'-0" Depth: 52'-2"

The large foyer opens to the family room with a massive stone fireplace and open stairs to the basement

4 bedrooms, 2 1/2 baths, 2-car side entry garage

Basement foundation

Price Code E

WILLOW CREEK

PLAN #651-020D-0007

1,828 total square feet of living area

Width: 64'-0" Depth: 62'-0"

Energy efficient home with 2" x 6" exterior walls

4 bedrooms, 2 baths, 2-car garage

Slab foundation, drawings also include crawl space and basement foundations

Price Code D

KINSLEY

PLAN #651-007D-0049

1,791 total square feet of living area

Width: 68'-0" Depth: 48'-4"

2" x 6" exterior walls available, please order plan #651-007E-0049

4 bedrooms, 2 baths, 2-car garage

Basement foundation, drawings also include crawl space and slab foundations

Price Code C

ASHMONT WOODS

PLAN #651-007D-0060

1,268 total square feet of living area

Width: 38'-8" Depth: 48'-4"

2" x 6" exterior walls available, please order plan #651-007E-0060

3 bedrooms, 2 baths, 2-car garage

Basement foundation, drawings also include crawl space and slab foundations

Price Code B

houseplansandmore.com

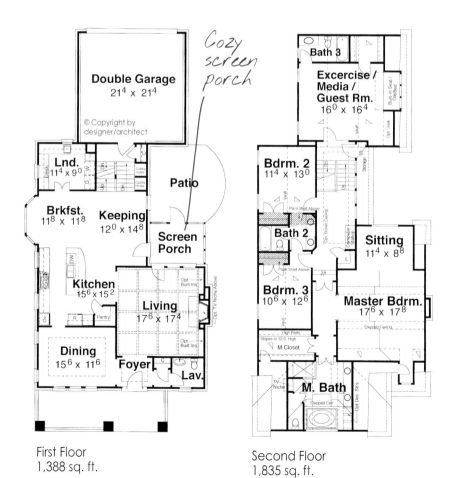

Cozy screen porch

Double Garage
21⁴ x 21⁴

© Copyright by designer/architect

Lnd. 11⁴ x 9⁰

Patio

Brkfst. 11⁸ x 11⁸

Keeping 12⁰ x 14⁸

Screen Porch

Kitchen 15⁶ x 15²

Living 17⁶ x 17⁴

Dining 15⁶ x 11⁶

Foyer

Lav.

First Floor
1,388 sq. ft.

Bath 3

Excercise / Media / Guest Rm. 16⁰ x 16⁴

Bdrm. 2 11⁴ x 13⁰

Bath 2

Sitting 11⁴ x 8⁸

Bdrm. 3 10⁶ x 12⁶

Master Bdrm. 17⁶ x 17⁸

M.Closet

M. Bath

Second Floor
1,835 sq. ft.

PLAN FEATURES

3,223 total square feet of living area

Width: 38'-0" Depth: 79'-0"

The kitchen, breakfast and keeping rooms combine creating an open environment to enjoy

A screen porch is ideal for outdoor living and has access to the living and keeping rooms

A built-in computer station on the second floor is the perfect place for children to do schoolwork

4 bedrooms, 3 1/2 baths, 2-car rear entry garage

Partial basement/slab foundation

Price Code F

houseplansandmore.com

Photo, above: At dusk, the amazing rear view of this home showcases two levels of unbelievable outdoor living spaces just steps away from interior spaces loaded with warmth and ambiance. Whether you choose the large covered deck with outdoor fireplace or the lower level patio for peaceful relaxation or entertaining, these spaces will never disappoint.

Photo, right: Upon entering the foyer, a spectacular stage is set. Gorgeous views straight ahead in the great room and outdoors can be seen. Plus, the second floor balcony and its detailed splendor tops off the entire scene, making it truly unforgettable.

Remarkable library loft!

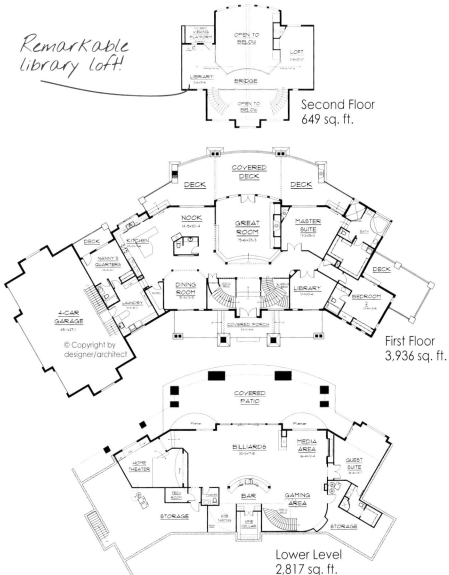

Second Floor
649 sq. ft.

First Floor
3,936 sq. ft.

© Copyright by
designer/architect

Lower Level
2,817 sq. ft.

Photo, above: The massive marble-topped island in the kitchen controls the traffic flow, while offering prime workspace and casual dining options.

Photo, below: Open and spacious, the lower level provides plenty of amenities when entertaining such as a billiards area, wet bar and media room. And, a three-sided fireplace warms all of the surroundings equally.

PLANFEATURES

7,402 total square feet of living area

Width: 154'-8" Depth: 87'-9"

Energy efficient home with 2" x 6" exterior walls

The first floor is filled with luxury including a stunning staircase, sunken great room, enormous master suite, open kitchen, cozy nanny's quarters and breathtaking outdoor living

Enjoy the quiet library and loft on the second floor

Entertain in style on the lower level complete with a media area, a home theater, a massive bar and billiards area

4 bedrooms, 4 full baths, 2 half baths, 4-car side entry garage

Basement or walk-out basement foundation, please specify when ordering

Price Code S4

houseplansandmore.com

PLAN FEATURES

4,790 total square feet of living area

Width: 116'-0" Depth: 88'-0"

Transfer easily from work to play as the home office adjoins the great room via the wet bar

A separate media room/playroom shared between two bedrooms completes the second floor

The four-car garage has additional storage and/or workshop space with a built-in bench and shelves, as well as a dedicated barbecue porch

The bonus room above the garage has an additional 789 square feet of living area

4 bedrooms, 6 1/2 baths, 4-car side entry garage

Crawl space foundation

Price Code S1

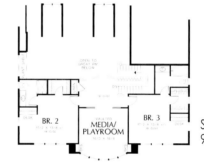

Second Floor
990 sq. ft.

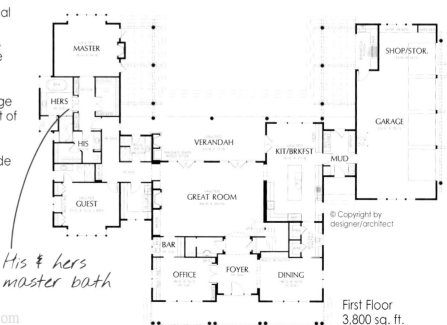

His & hers master bath

First Floor
3,800 sq. ft.

© Copyright by designer/architect

houseplansandmore.com

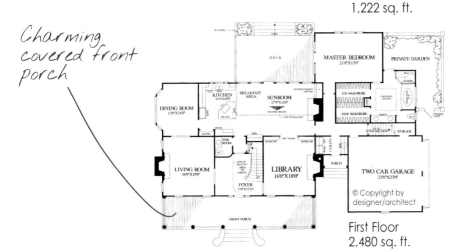

Second Floor
1,222 sq. ft.

Charming covered front porch

First Floor
2,480 sq. ft.

© Copyright by designer/architect

PLANFEATURES

3,702 total square feet of living area

Width: 82'-0" Depth: 60'-7"

Step onto the grand front porch that enters into a lovely two-story foyer

The delightful sunroom features a wall of windows, high ceiling, fireplace and built-in entertainment center

The master bedroom has a bath perfect for relaxing with a coffered ceiling, access to a private garden and a large whirlpool tub overlooking the garden

The future recreation room on the second floor has an additional 561 square feet of living area

4 bedrooms, 3 1/2 baths, 2-car side entry garage

Crawl space foundation

Price Code E

houseplansandmore.com

PLANFEATURES

2,113 total square feet of living area

Width: 40'-0" Depth: 42'-0"

Formal living and dining rooms combine to the left of the foyer for an elegant entertaining atmosphere

At the rear of the house, the family room, breakfast area and kitchen flow together for a casual gathering space

All the bedrooms are located on the second floor for extra peace and quiet

4 bedrooms, 2 1/2 baths, 2-car garage

Basement foundation, drawings also include walk-out basement foundation

Price Code B

Second Floor
1,033 sq. ft.

Bedroom #3 10-0 x 12-0
Bedroom #2 10-8 x 12-0
Master Bedroom 15-10 x 14-5
Vaulted Ceiling
Bedroom #4 12-4 x 9-9
Open To Below

Open family & breakfast room

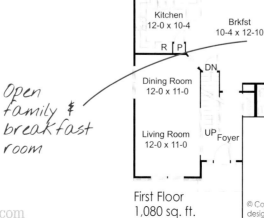

Deck 12-0 x 12-0
Kitchen 12-0 x 10-4
Brkfst 10-4 x 12-10
Family Room 11-0 x 15-4
Dining Room 12-0 x 11-0
Living Room 12-0 x 11-0
Foyer
2-Car Garage 19-5 x 19-4

First Floor
1,080 sq. ft.

© Copyright by designer/architect

PLANFEATURES

2,565 total square feet of living area

Width: 40'-4" Depth: 58'-0"

Energy efficient home with 2" x 6" exterior walls

The first floor bedroom, perfect for a master suite has a wonderful see-through fireplace enjoyed by the whirlpool tub and the master bedroom alike

A large and well-organized laundry room offers lots of cabinetry, a sink and counterspace

The second floor landing is spacious and has a substantial window for taking in views

3 bedrooms, 2 1/2 baths, 2-car garage

Basement foundation

Price Code G

© Copyright by designer/architect

15'-0" x 16'-0"
4,50 x 4,80

12'-6" x 16'-2"
3,75 x 4,85

10'-10" x 11'-4"
3,25 x 3,40

10'-2" x 14'-8"
3,05 x 4,40

6'-8" x 6'-8"
2,00 x 2,00

19'-8" x 21'-0"
5,90 x 6,30

10'-0" x 11'-0"
3,00 x 3,30

First Floor
1,680 sq. ft.

Second floor living room

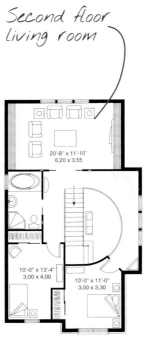

20'-8" x 11'-10"
6,20 x 3,55

10'-0" x 13'-4"
3,00 x 4,00

10'-0" x 11'-0"
3,00 x 3,30

Second Floor
885 sq. ft.

houseplansandmore.com

PLANFEATURES

1,333 total square feet of living area

Width: 36'-0" Depth: 44'-6"

Energy efficient home with 2" x 6" exterior walls

A vaulted ceiling and a wood stove create a warm, yet spacious feeling to the great room

The second floor studio has an appealing open railing looking down to the great room

A private bedroom and bath complete the second floor

2 bedrooms, 2 baths

Crawl space foundation

Price Code B

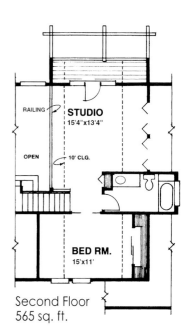

Amazing deck space!

First Floor
768 sq. ft.

© Copyright by
designer/architect

Second Floor
565 sq. ft.

PLAN FEATURES

5,079 total square feet of living area

Width: 88'-1" Depth: 77'-3"

Energy efficient home with 2" x 6" exterior walls

Art niches and arched soffits add elegance and style throughout the first floor of this luxurious home

A vestibule sets off the master bedroom complete with a large bay window, access to the rear deck, built-in cabinets, a walk-in closet and a plush bath

The lower level is just as stunning as the first floor with a family room, wet bar, exercise room and three additional bedrooms

5 bedrooms, 4 1/2 baths, 3-car garage

Walk-out basement foundation

Price Code S1

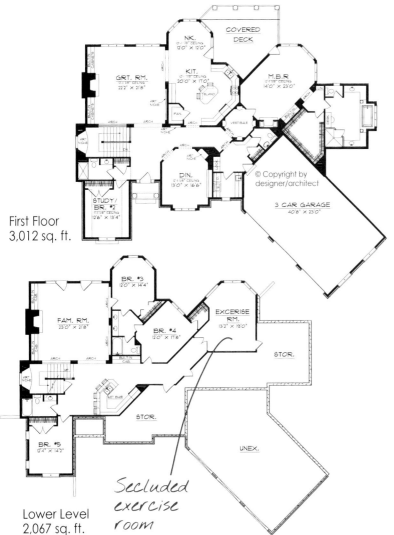

First Floor
3,012 sq. ft.

Secluded exercise room

Lower Level
2,067 sq. ft.

PLAN FEATURES

4,121 total square feet of living area

Width: 89'-0" Depth: 104'-0"

An 11' boxed ceiling, a media center, a wet bar and a cozy corner fireplace make the hearth room/den the center of activity

The master suite is full of amenities including a corner fireplace, a luxury bath, an exercise room and a unique reinforced storm closet for shelter

An immense home theater/game room and bonus room on the second floor provide an additional 1,826 square feet of living space for entertaining and fun for the whole family

3 bedrooms, 3 baths, 3-car side entry garage

Slab or crawl space foundation, please specify when ordering

Price Code S1

houseplansandmore.com

28

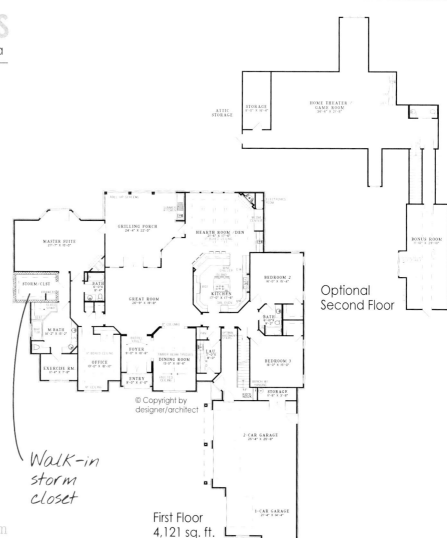

Walk-in storm closet

Optional Second Floor

© Copyright by designer/architect

First Floor
4,121 sq. ft.

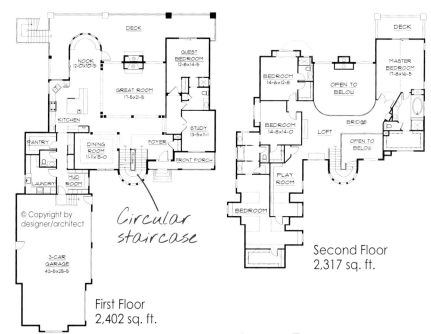

Circular staircase

© Copyright by designer/architect

First Floor
2,402 sq. ft.

Second Floor
2,317 sq. ft.

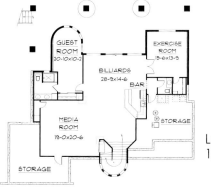

Lower Level
1,578 sq. ft.

PLANFEATURES

6,297 total square feet of living area

Width: 68'-0" Depth: 106'-6"

The circular staircase is dabbled with windows on various levels enhancing the beauty of the home with natural sunlight

Off one of the second floor bedrooms is a spacious playroom with potential for many uses

The lower level has exceptional entertaining space including a billiards room with wet bar and a media room

6 bedrooms, 5 full baths, 2 half baths, 3-car side entry garage

Basement or walk-out basement foundation, please specify when ordering

Price Code S1

houseplansandmore.com

Photo, above: Something rarely seen in the kitchen is a wall of cheerful windows. Here, this kitchen is flooded in sunlight and enjoys gorgeous outdoor views.

Photo, right: The perfectly decorated formal dining room has an elegant, yet inviting feel with the utmost amount of class for entertaining in grand style.

houseplansandmore.com

Luxurious pool & spa!

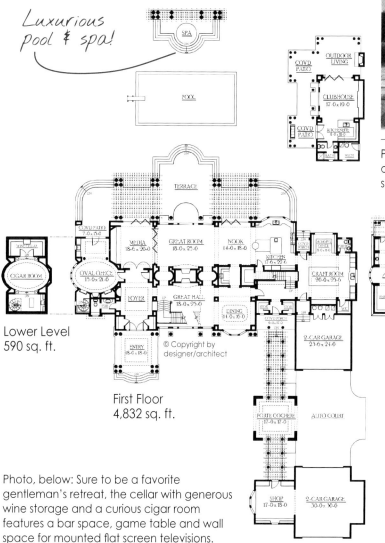

Lower Level
590 sq. ft.

First Floor
4,832 sq. ft.

© Copyright by
designer/architect

Photo, above: Several Roman columns decorate the outdoor stone whirlpool spa designed to provide a retreat.

Clubhouse
640 sq. ft.

Second Floor
3,758 sq. ft.

Photo, below: Sure to be a favorite gentleman's retreat, the cellar with generous wine storage and a curious cigar room features a bar space, game table and wall space for mounted flat screen televisions.

PLANFEATURES

9,820 total square feet of living area

Width: 126'-0" Depth: 94'-0"

Energy efficient home with 2" x 6" exterior walls

The soothing oval office has an amazing spiral staircase that accesses the lower level cigar room with double-door entry to the wine cellar

A majestic terrace, an elevated spa, a pool and clubhouse with covered patio are the many amenities that make outdoor living truly exceptional

Grand open spaces are celebrated in the remarkable great room, nook and kitchen

4 bedrooms, 6 full baths, 2 half baths, 4-car garage

Crawl space foundation

Price Code S1

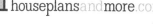
houseplansandmore.com

PLANFEATURES

4,064 total square feet of living area

Width: 78'-0" Depth: 52'-4"

Energy efficient home with 2" x 6" exterior walls

Sleek lines add a contemporary feel to the front of this home

The three-sided fireplace creates a cozy feeling to the kitchen, breakfast and hearth rooms

Decorative columns grace the corner of the formal dining room and help maintain an open feeling

4 bedrooms, 3 baths, 3-car garage

Walk-out basement foundation

Price Code G

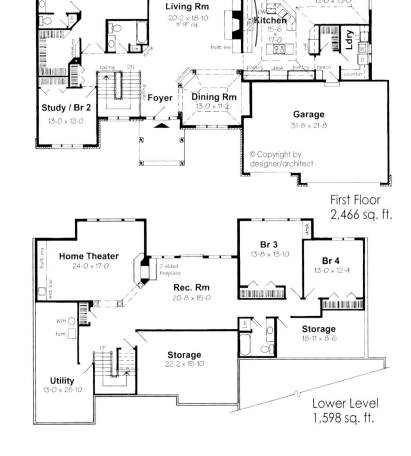

Highly functional & modern Kitchen

First Floor
2,466 sq. ft.

Lower Level
1,598 sq. ft.

houseplansandmore.com

PLANFEATURES

3,102 total square feet of living area

Width: 54'-6" Depth: 83'-7"

The great room is flooded with light by four large windows and is warmed by the inviting fireplace

There is plenty of space and a raised counter with stool seating in this open and airy kitchen

Along with two bedrooms, the second floor also features a media room for entertaining and a bonus room above the garage

The bonus room on the second floor has an additional 468 square feet of living area

4 bedrooms, 2 full baths, 2 half baths, 3-car side entry garage

Basement foundation, drawings also include crawl space and slab foundations

Price Code S1

Expansive eating bar!

© Copyright by designer/architect

First Floor
2,112 sq. ft.

Second Floor
990 sq. ft.

TOWERCLIFF

PLAN #651-001D-0119

1,285 total square feet of living area

Width: 48'-0" Depth: 43'-8"

Energy efficient home with 2" x 6" exterior walls

3 bedrooms, 2 baths

Crawl space foundation, drawings also include basement and slab foundations

Price Code B

LA VALENCIA

PLAN #651-007D-0046

1,712 total square feet of living area

Width: 67'-0" Depth: 42'-4"

The stylish stucco exterior enhances curb appeal

3 bedrooms, 2 1/2 baths, 2-car garage

Crawl space foundation

Price Code B

houseplansandmore.com

34

WESTPORT

PLAN #651-007D-0008

2,452 total square feet of living area

Width: 70'-8" Depth: 70'-4"

The vaulted master bedroom includes transomed windows, a walk-in closet and a luxurious bath

3 bedrooms, 2 1/2 baths, 3-car garage

Basement foundation

Price Code D

BAKERSVILLE

PLAN #651-053D-0053

1,609 total square feet of living area

Width: 50'-0" Depth: 54'-0"

Efficient kitchen includes a corner pantry and adjacent laundry room

Entry opens into large living area with fireplace

4 bedrooms, 2 baths, 2-car garage

Walk-out basement foundation, drawings also include crawl space and slab foundations

Price Code B

PLANFEATURES

4,099 total square feet of living area

Width: 72'-0" Depth: 78'-0"

The large kitchen with center cooktop island overlooks the cozy family room with corner fireplace

An amazing private master bath boasts a peninsula whirlpool tub with built-in flat screen television and a walk-through shower behind it

The second floor media room is the perfect spot for watching a favorite film

4 bedrooms, 3 1/2 baths, 3-car drive under side entry garage

Basement foundation

Price Code S1

Comfortable screen porch

© Copyright by designer/architect

First Floor Plan:

- COV. PRCH
- MUD ROOM 8'1"x7'6"
- UTIL. 8'1"x8'6"
- FAMILY ROOM 16'4"x18'6"
- KITCHEN 16'2"x14'2"
- SCREEN PORCH 19'6"x16'
- SITTING 12'3"x9'1"
- MA. BATH
- MASTER SUITE 17'x16'8"
- 15'9"x19'4"
- 16'4"x12'6"
- 1/2 BA.
- MA. CLOSET
- LIVING ROOM 19'9"x22'
- BEDROOM 2 13'2"x12'5"
- 9'6"x5'4"
- BA. 3
- DINING ROOM 14'10x14'
- FOYER 8'3"x14'
- STUDY 12'3"x14'
- BEDROOM 3 15'5"x12'5"
- PORCH 32'x8'

First Floor
3,163 sq. ft.

Second Floor Plan:

- MEDIA ROOM 17'5"x31'6"
- BA. 4
- HALL
- BEDROOM 4 12'10"x14'8"

Second Floor
936 sq. ft.

houseplansandmore.com

FOXBURY

PLAN FEATURES

1,845 total square feet of living area

Width: 83'-0" Depth: 42'-4"

Roof dormers add great curb appeal

Vaulted dining and great rooms are immersed in light from the atrium window wall

The breakfast area opens onto the covered porch

Functionally designed kitchen

2" x 6" exterior walls available, please order plan #651-007E-0010

The lower level has an additional 889 square feet of optional living area

3 bedrooms, 2 baths, 3-car garage

Walk-out basement foundation, drawings also include crawl space and slab foundations

Price Code C

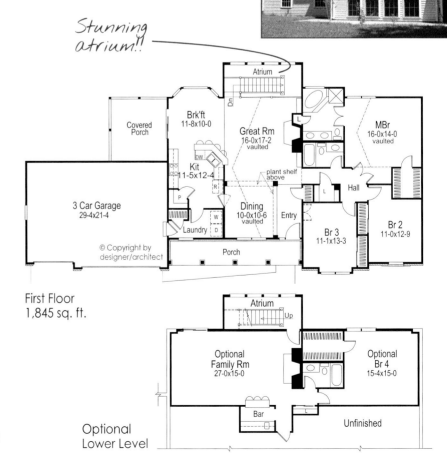

Stunning atrium!!

First Floor
1,845 sq. ft.

Atrium

Covered Porch

Brk'ft
11-8x10-0

Great Rm
16-0x17-2
vaulted

MBr
16-0x14-0
vaulted

Kit
11-5x12-4

plant shelf above

Hall

3 Car Garage
29-4x21-4

Dining
10-0x10-6
vaulted

Entry

Br 3
11-1x13-3

Br 2
11-0x12-9

Laundry

Porch

© Copyright by designer/architect

Optional Lower Level

Atrium

Up

Optional Family Rm
27-0x15-0

Optional Br 4
15-4x15-0

Bar

Unfinished

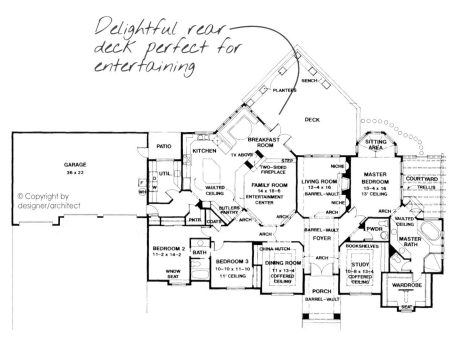

PLANFEATURES

2,880 total square feet of living area

Width: 115'-11" Depth: 57'-2"

Energy efficient home with 2" x 6" exterior walls

Varied ceiling heights throughout this home add spaciousness

The charming master bedroom features a bayed sitting area, view to the courtyard and an exquisite master bath

An interesting barrel vaulted living room ceiling is a unique focal point

3 bedrooms, 2 1/2 baths, 3-car garage

Crawl space foundation

Price Code E

Delightful rear deck perfect for entertaining

© Copyright by designer/architect

Photo, above: This photo provides a unique view as interior light illuminates the lower deck and the stunning stone chimney's facade.

Photo, right: This home is overflowing with outdoor living space between the upper and lower decks and the dedicated outdoor kitchen. However, none of these rival the private gazebo, the best spot for taking in nature, enjoying a view, or even napping in the afternoon shade. It's a retreat center never far from home.

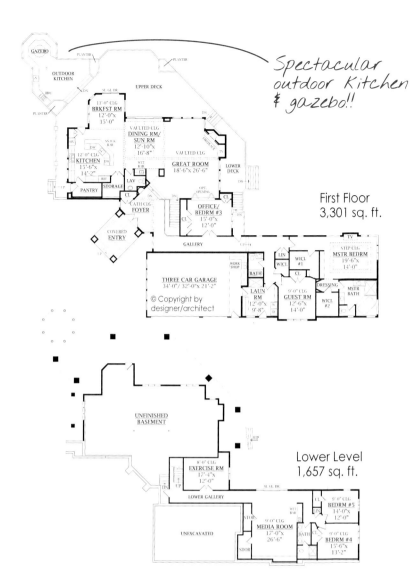

Spectacular outdoor Kitchen & gazebo!!

First Floor
3,301 sq. ft.

© Copyright by designer/architect

Lower Level
1,657 sq. ft.

Photo, above: This vaulted entry welcomes guests with stunning skylights above.

Photo, below: The kitchen island defines the space without inhibiting the open feeling that has been created throughout the first floor. The use of light and dark stained wood, along with a variety of other earth tones, creates a fresh approach that allows this home to perfectly merge with its outdoor surroundings.

PLANFEATURES

4,958 total square feet of living area

Width: 106'-4" Depth: 75'-10"

Energy efficient home with 2" x 6" exterior walls

The covered entryway and double front doors create a breathtaking welcome from the outdoors

Multiple deck levels add a unique and functional element

The outdoor kitchen and gazebo resemble a place of retreat, yet the main kitchen is directly accessible

A wet bar is centrally located on both floors, allowing an easy transition from dinner time to relaxing by the fireplace or down in the media room

5 bedrooms, 3 1/2 baths, 3-car side entry garage

Walk-out basement foundation

Price Code S4

 houseplansandmore.com

FORESTLAND

PLAN #651-011D-0004

1,997 total square feet of living area

Width: 60'-0" Depth: 51'-0"

Energy efficient home with 2" x 6" exterior walls

A spa tub and shower enhance the master bath

4 bedrooms, 2 1/2 baths, 3-car garage

Crawl space foundation

Price Code D

SIESTA HILL

PLAN #651-047D-0048

2,660 total square feet of living area

Width: 66'-4" Depth: 74'-4"

The well-designed kitchen has a center island

4 bedrooms, 3 baths, 2-car side entry garage

Slab foundation

Price Code E

40

JAMIESON

PLAN #651-021D-0001

2,396 total square feet of living area

Width: 72'-0" Depth: 60'-0"

Energy efficient home with 2" x 6" exterior walls

A generously wide entry welcomes guests

4 bedrooms, 2 baths, 2-car garage

Slab foundation, drawings also include basement and crawl space foundations

Price Code E

BONNIE BRIAR

PLAN #651-065D-0074

1,698 total square feet of living area

Width: 51'-8" Depth: 61'-8"

The functional kitchen enjoys a walk-in pantry and a delightful angled snack bar

Warmth and charm radiate from the corner fireplace through the combined living areas, and a covered porch offers outdoor enjoyment

3 bedrooms, 2 baths, 2-car garage

Basement foundation

Price Code B

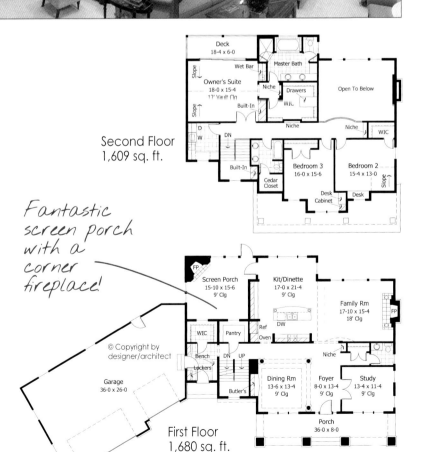

Second Floor
1,609 sq. ft.

Deck
18-4 x 6-0

Wet Bar

Master Bath

Slope

Owner's Suite
18-0 x 15-4
12' Vault Clg

Niche

Drawers

Open To Below

Built-In

WIC

Niche

Niche

WIC

D
W

DN

Built-In

Bedroom 3
16-0 x 15-6

Bedroom 2
15-4 x 13-0

Cedar Closet

Slope

Desk Cabinet

Desk

Fantastic screen porch with a corner fireplace!

FP

Screen Porch
15-10 x 15-6
9' Clg

Kit/Dinette
17-0 x 21-4
9' Clg

Family Rm
17-10 x 15-4
18' Clg

FP

WIC

Pantry

Ref

DW

Oven

Niche

© Copyright by designer/architect

Bench
Lockers

DN

UP

Garage
36-0 x 26-0

Butler's

Dining Rm
13-6 x 13-4
9' Clg

Foyer
8-0 x 13-4
9' Clg

Study
13-4 x 11-4
9' Clg

Porch
36-0 x 8-0

First Floor
1,680 sq. ft.

PLAN FEATURES

3,289 total square feet of living area

Width: 98'-4" Depth: 55'-8"

Decorative columns define the dining room and provide an elegant first impression upon entering the home

A screen porch off the kitchen includes a corner fireplace creating a cozy atmosphere

At the garage entrance, a bench, lockers and a walk-in closet keep everything organized

3 bedrooms, 2 1/2 baths, 3-car side entry garage

Walk-out basement foundation

Price Code F

houseplansandmore.com

Photo, above: The owner's bedroom, located on the second floor for privacy, has an elegant tray ceiling and breezy ceiling fan.

Photo, right: A towering window wall in the great room shrouds the entire space with warm sunlight.

 houseplansandmore.com

COMP
6'-0" X 6'-0"

DINETTE
11'-6" X 15'-0"

HEARTH
12'-0" X 15'-0"

GREAT ROOM
17'-0" X 19'-0"

PANTRY

MUD

BA
7'-0" X 11'-0"

KITCHEN
20'-0" X 8'-6"

DINING
13'-0" X 15'-0"

GARAGE
32'-0" X 24'-0"

ENTRY
7'-6" X 12'-0"

STUDY
11'-0" X 12'-0"

© Copyright by
designer/architect

PORCH

First Floor
1,948 sq. ft.

BATH
15'-0" X 7'-3"

OWNER'S BED
14'-6" X 17'-6"

WIC
15'-0" X 6'-3"

OPEN TO
BELOW

LAUN
10'-6" X 8'-3"

BED RM 4
11'-0" X 12'-6"

BED RM 3
11'-0" X 11'-6"

BED RM 2
11'-0" X 11'-6"

BATH

BATH

BATH

LOFT
11'-0" X 13'-0"

Second Floor
1,785 sq. ft.

French doors open to a charming study

FUTURE BED RM
EXERCISE RM
12'-0" X 13'-3"

FUTURE REC AREA
22'-0" X 11'-0"

FUTURE FAMILY RM
21'-0" X 19'-0"

FUTURE BATH

FUTURE BAR

MECHANICAL

STORAGE
19'-0" X 12'-0"

Optional Lower Level

Photo, below: The cozy hearth room easily shares its fireplace with the more formal great room. This spot is the ideal place to watch a movie with family and friends right in the heart of the home.

PLANFEATURES

3,733 total square feet of living area

Width: 66'-0" Depth: 55'-0"

Energy efficient home with 2" x 6" exterior walls

A grand open kitchen has a massive center island with a double sink and casual dining space

A great computer nook off the dinette is the perfect spot for the students in the family

Double doors off the entry lead into a private study ideal for a home office

The optional lower level offers an additional 1,948 square feet of living area

4 bedrooms, 3 1/2 baths, 3-car garage

Walk-out basement foundation

Price Code S1

houseplansandmore.com

PLAN FEATURES

2,037 total square feet of living area

Width: 55'-0" Depth: 41'-0"

Energy efficient home with 2" x 6" exterior walls

An expansive area is designed to create the optimum space for family gatherings

The first floor master bedroom encourages privacy and convenience

A sink and large countertop in the laundry room provides maximum efficiency

4 bedrooms, 2 baths, 2-car garage

Basement foundation

Price Code F

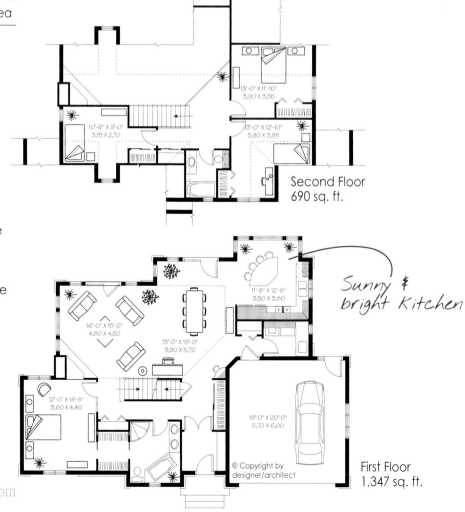

Second Floor
690 sq. ft.

Sunny & bright Kitchen

© Copyright by designer/architect

First Floor
1,347 sq. ft.

CHLOE

PLAN#651-121D-0007

1,308 total square feet of living area

Width: 46'-0" Depth: 34'-0"

A tall ceiling and warming fireplace in the great room appeal to every homeowner

3 bedrooms, 2 baths, 2-car detached garage

Basement foundation

Price Code AA

SOPHIA

PLAN#651-121D-0027

2,453 total square feet of living area

Width: 54'-4" Depth: 66'-0"

A sunny bay window with rear patio access is featured in the vaulted breakfast area

The master bedroom features a luxurious bath with a corner tub and a spacious walk-in closet

3 bedrooms, 2 baths, 2-car garage

Basement foundation

Price Code C

GABRIELLA

PLAN#651-121D-0019

2,814 total square feet of living area

Width: 73'-0" Depth: 75'-4"

The kitchen features a center island with an eating bar for casual meals and a planning center

3 bedrooms, 3 1/2 baths, 2-car side entry garage

Basement foundation

Price Code D

AVERY

PLAN#651-121D-0030

2,156 total square feet of living area

Width: 76'-4" Depth: 52'-0"

A handy walk-in pantry and efficient breakfast bar can be found in the sizable kitchen

3 bedrooms, 2 baths, 2-car garage

Basement foundation

Price Code B

houseplansandmore.com

SHADYPARK

PLAN #651-011D-0008

1,728 total square feet of living area

Width: 55'-0" Depth: 48'-0"

Energy efficient home with 2" x 6" exterior walls

The vaulted great room features an oversized fireplace and a built-in wall for a media center

2 bedrooms, 2 baths, 3-car garage

Crawl space foundation

Price Code C

WYNEHAVEN

PLAN #651-048D-0004

2,397 total square feet of living area

Width: 60'-6" Depth: 71'-8"

The kitchen features an island with eating bar and opens into the breakfast and family rooms

3 bedrooms, 2 1/2 baths, 2-car garage

Slab foundation

Price Code E

COOPERS MILL

PLAN #651-028D-0004

1,785 total square feet of living area

Width: 56'-0" Depth: 42'-0"

The cozy breakfast area is convenient to the kitchen

3 bedrooms, 3 baths, 2-car detached garage

Basement, crawl space or slab foundation, please specify when ordering

Price Code C

KINGS CROSSING

PLAN #651-065D-0103

1,860 total square feet of living area

Width: 64'-2" Depth: 44'-2"

The extended counter in the kitchen offers extra dining space

A bayed breakfast area is open to the great room and kitchen creating a spacious atmosphere

3 bedrooms, 2 baths, 2-car garage

Basement or walk-out basement foundation, please specify when ordering

Price Code C

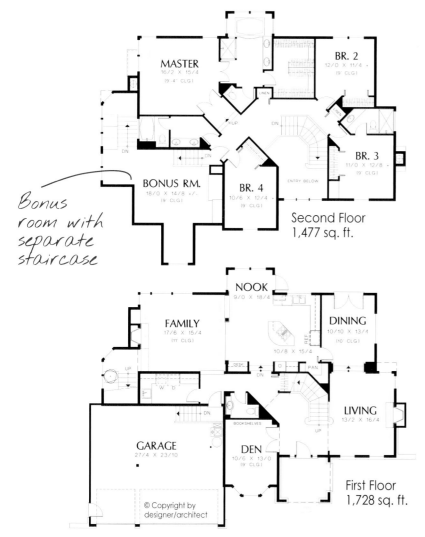

Bonus room with separate staircase

MASTER
16/2 X 15/4
(9'-4" CLG)

BR. 2
12/0 X 11/4
(9' CLG)

BR. 3
11/0 X 12/8
(9' CLG)

BONUS RM.
18/0 X 14/8 +/-
(9' CLG)

BR. 4
10/6 X 12/4
(9' CLG)

Second Floor
1,477 sq. ft.

NOOK
9/0 X 18/4

FAMILY
17/6 X 15/4
(11' CLG)

DINING
10/10 X 13/4
(10' CLG)

10/8 X 15/4

LIVING
13/2 X 16/4

GARAGE
27/4 X 23/10

DEN
10/6 X 13/0
(9' CLG)

First Floor
1,728 sq. ft.

© Copyright by designer/architect

PLANFEATURES

3,205 total square feet of living area

Width: 63'-0" Depth: 52'-0"

The den features a cheerful bay window making this great as a sunny home office

A secondary staircase is located near the casual family room and leads to the second floor bonus room

The master bath features a stunning box bay window with an oversized tub

The bonus room on the second floor has an additional 382 square feet of living area

4 bedrooms, 3 1/2 baths, 3-car garage

Crawl space foundation

Price Code F

houseplansandmore.com

CONCORD GROVE

PLANFEATURES

1,189 total square feet of living area

Width: 36'-0" Depth: 35'-8"

All bedrooms are located on the second floor for added privacy

The dining room and kitchen both have views of the patio

The convenient half bath is located near the kitchen

The master bedroom has a private bath

3 bedrooms, 2 1/2 baths, 2-car garage

Basement foundation

Price Code AA

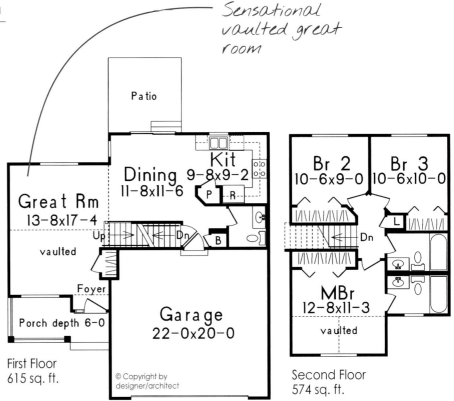

Sensational vaulted great room

First Floor
615 sq. ft.

© Copyright by designer/architect

Second Floor
574 sq. ft.

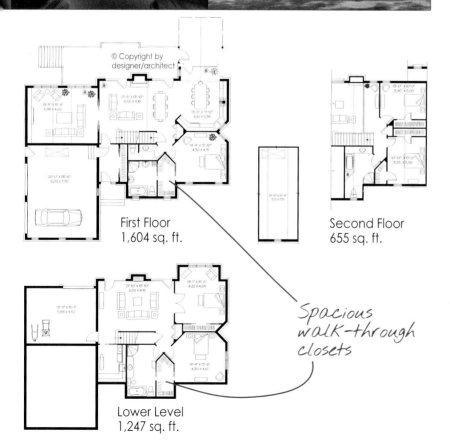

© Copyright by designer/architect

First Floor
1,604 sq. ft.

Second Floor
655 sq. ft.

Lower Level
1,247 sq. ft.

Spacious walk-through closets

PLANFEATURES

3,506 total square feet of living area

Width: 59'-0" Depth: 49'-8"

Energy efficient home with 2" x 6" exterior walls

This home has so much character with features such as rounded windows, a screened porch, a stone facade, and a decorative railing

The large kitchen has a center island with seating, dual sinks with a window and immense counterspace

Two bedrooms on the second floor have ample closet space, a full bath with large vanity, and a linen closet

The bonus room on the second floor has an additional 307 square feet of living area

5 bedrooms, 3 1/2 baths, 2-car side entry garage

Walk-out basement foundation

Price Code H

houseplansandmore.com

PLANFEATURES

3,347 total square feet of living area

Width: 74'-0" Depth: 62'-0"

This stunning home features an impressive two-story foyer that leads directly into the spacious great room, with a wall of windows to showcase a beautiful backyard view

The open kitchen with hearth room is a spacious gathering spot for entertaining

The study/office off the foyer can be closed off with French doors and used as a quiet workspace

4 bedrooms, 3 1/2 baths, 3-car garage

Basement foundation

Price Code S1

Second Floor
1,558 sq. ft.

Gorgeous wall of windows!

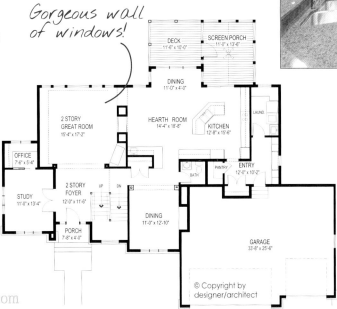

First Floor
1,789 sq. ft.

© Copyright by designer/architect

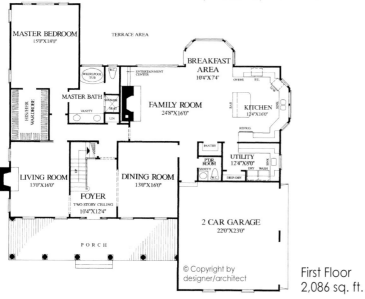

Plenty of storage

Second Floor
1,094 sq. ft.

BEDROOM 4
16'8"X12'0"

BATH 4

BATH 3

BATH 2

FUTURE REC ROOM
22'0"X16'4"

BEDROOM 3
13'0"X16'0"

OPEN TO BELOW

BEDROOM 2
13'0"X12'4"

WALK IN CLOSET

DECK

STORAGE

First Floor
2,086 sq. ft.

MASTER BEDROOM
15'0"X18'0"

TERRACE AREA

WHIRLPOOL TUB

ENTERTAINMENT CENTER

BREAKFAST AREA
10'4"X7'4"

OVENS

MASTER BATH

FAMILY ROOM
24'8"X16'0"

KITCHEN
12'4"X16'0"

HIS/HER WARDROBE

REFRIG

PANTRY

P'DR ROOM

UTILITY
12'4"X8'0"

DRIP-DRY

DRY WASH

LIVING ROOM
13'0"X16'0"

DINING ROOM
13'0"X16'0"

FOYER
TWO STORY CEILING
10'4"X12'4"

2 CAR GARAGE
22'0"X23'0"

PORCH

© Copyright by designer/architect

PLANFEATURES

3,180 total square feet of living area

Width: 62'-0" Depth: 61'-10"

Beautiful columns and amazing windows create distinct curb appeal

Enter into a dramatic two-story foyer brightened by multiple windows

The U-shaped kitchen has a center island with eating bar and is just steps away from the bayed breakfast area

A walk-in closet and private bath with whirlpool tub are some of the amenities in the master bedroom

The future recreation room on the second floor has an additional 372 square feet of living area

4 bedrooms, 4 1/2 baths, 2-car side entry garage

Partial crawl space/walk-out basement foundation

Price Code E

houseplansandmore.com

PLANFEATURES

7,100 total square feet of living area

Width: 90'-5" Depth: 78'-0"

A popular summer kitchen can be found on the covered patio overlooking the space designated for a pool

A gorgeous staircase in a circular turret ascends to the second floor creating quite a dramatic statement

A unique V.I.P. suite is the perfect place for guests featuring a lavish bath, a walk-in closet and direct access to the pool and patio

Framing - only concrete block available

6 bedrooms, 7 1/2 baths, 3-car garage

Slab foundation

Price Code S1

Second Floor
3,172 sq. ft.

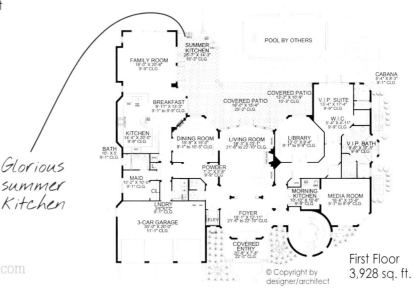

Glorious summer Kitchen

First Floor
3,928 sq. ft.

© Copyright by designer/architect

houseplansandmore.com

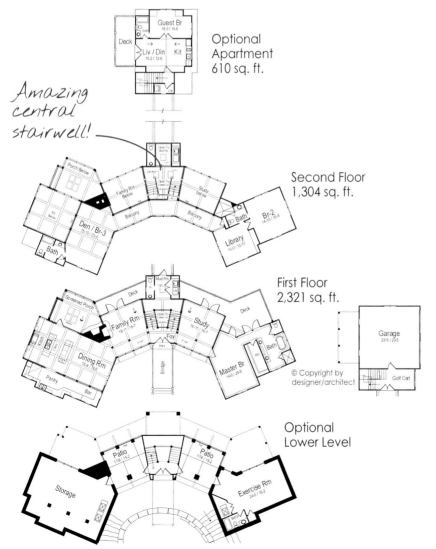

Amazing central stairwell!

Optional Apartment 610 sq. ft.

Second Floor 1,304 sq. ft.

First Floor 2,321 sq. ft.

Optional Lower Level

© Copyright by designer/architect

PLANFEATURES

3,625 total square feet of living area

Width: 106'-7" Depth: 50'-1"

The grand stairwell captures attention upon entering the foyer

The two-story kitchen has suspended beams and glass that extend to the ceiling

A vaulted screened porch enjoys a stacked stone fireplace and skylights

The optional lower level has an additional 818 square feet of living area

3 bedrooms, 3 1/2 baths, 2-car detached side entry garage

Crawl space or basement foundation, please specify when ordering

Price Code S6

houseplansandmore.com

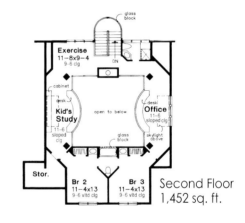

PLAN FEATURES

4,220 total square feet of living area

Width: 66'-0" Depth: 65'-0"

This two-story home is designed perfectly to suit the needs of a busy family featuring an "US" room, activity area, multi-purpose room and even a kid's study

Spacious garden spaces surround this home creating pleasant outdoor living areas perfect for relaxing

Interesting architectural details exist on the second floor with curved glass block walls around the staircase and curved built-in desks in both the office and kid's study

3 bedrooms, 4 1/2 baths, 2-car garage

Basement foundation

Price Code H

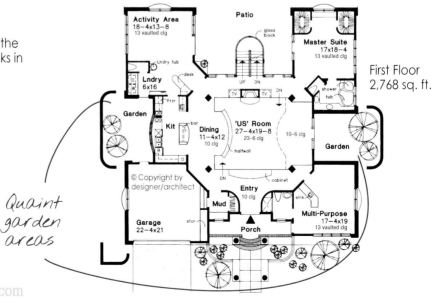

Second Floor 1,452 sq. ft.

First Floor 2,768 sq. ft.

Quaint garden areas

houseplansandmore.com

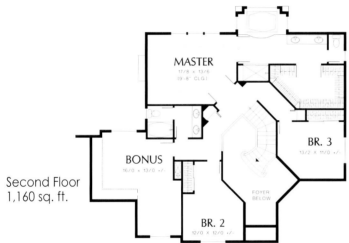

MASTER
17/8 x 13/6
(9'-8" CLG.)

BR. 3
13/2 x 11/0 +/-

BONUS
16/0 x 13/0 +/-

FOYER
BELOW

Second Floor
1,160 sq. ft.

BR. 2
12/0 x 12/0 +/-

*Open family
room with
a handsome
fireplace!*

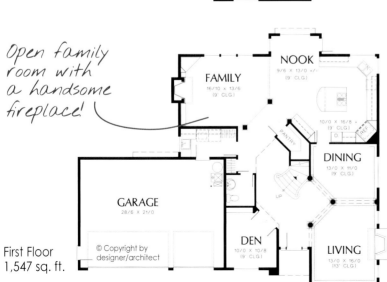

NOOK
9/6 x 13/0
(9' CLG.)

FAMILY
16/10 x 13/6
(9' CLG.)

PANTRY

DINING
13/0 x 11/0
(9' CLG.)

GARAGE
28/6 x 21/0

© Copyright by
designer/architect

UP

DEN
10/0 x 10/8
(9' CLG.)

LIVING
13/0 x 16/0
(113' CLG.)

First Floor
1,547 sq. ft.

PLAN FEATURES

2,707 total square feet of living area

Width: 60'-0" Depth: 50'-0"

Double doors off the front entry lead to a private den

A prominent angled staircase ascends to the second floor where all the bedrooms can be found

The master bath includes an oversized tub in a box bay window flooded in sunlight

The bonus room on the second floor has an additional 288 square feet of living area

3 bedrooms, 2 1/2 baths, 3-car garage

Crawl space foundation

Price Code E

houseplansandmore.com

Photo, above: The living room's large bay window and decorative ceiling treatment create a formal space with a comfortable atmosphere.

Photo, right: The breakfast bar provides a gathering place without inhibiting the view of the family room beyond, while wood paneling brings warmth to this spacious kitchen's functional atmosphere.

Splendid outdoor Kitchen

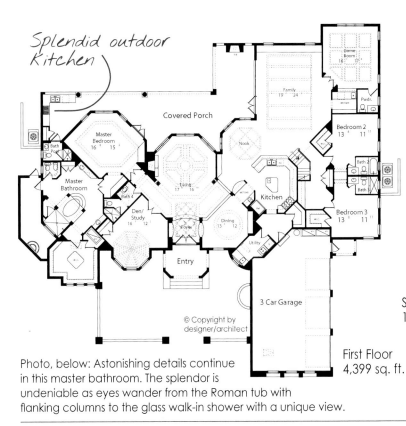

Covered Porch

Master Bedroom 16'⁸ 15'⁸

Bath

Master Bathroom

Bath 4

Den/ Study 16'⁸ 12'

Foyer

living 17'⁸ 16'

Nook

Kitchen

Dining 13'⁸ 12'

Utility

Entry

3 Car Garage

Family 19'⁸ 24'

Game Room 16'⁶

Pwdr.

Bedroom 2 13'⁴ 11'¹¹

Bath 2

Bath 3

Bedroom 3 13'⁸ 11'¹¹

© Copyright by designer/architect

First Floor 4,399 sq. ft.

Photo, below: Astonishing details continue in this master bathroom. The splendor is undeniable as eyes wander from the Roman tub with flanking columns to the glass walk-in shower with a unique view.

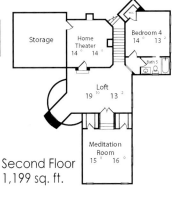

Photo, above: The open family room features tall windows that provide beautiful views and porch access.

Storage

Home Theater 14'⁰ 14'⁰

Bedroom 4 14'⁰ 13'²

Bath 5

Loft 19'¹⁰ 13'²

Meditation Room 15'⁰ 16'⁰

Second Floor 1,199 sq. ft.

PLAN FEATURES

5,598 total square feet of living area

Width: 96'-4" Depth: 100'-4"

The master suite is a cavernous place of retreat with private doors to the covered porch and a master bath centered around the spa tub

This spacious home offers entertainment on multiple levels, with a game room and wet bar located off the family room and a home theater on the second floor

Strategic placement of bay windows increases functional space, adding charm and creativity to commonly used areas, such as the den and living room

4 bedrooms, 6 1/2 baths, 3-car side entry garage

Slab foundation

Price Code J

 houseplansandmore.com

PLANFEATURES

1,536 total square feet of living area

Width: 36'-0" Depth: 43'-8"

Energy efficient home with 2" x 6" exterior walls

Sliding glass doors in the master bedroom lead to a terrific screened porch offering a quiet place to retreat

The galley-style kitchen is compact, yet convenient

A sunny dining area extends off the kitchen

3 bedrooms, 2 1/2 baths

Pier foundation

Price Code C

Cheerful rear screened porch

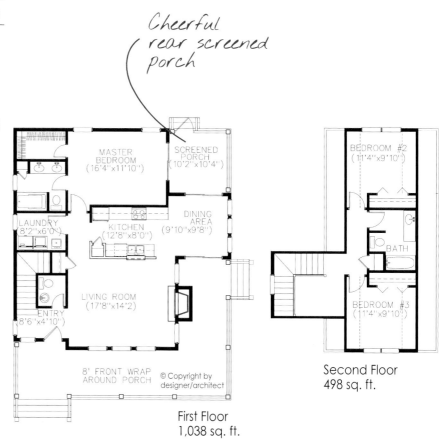

First Floor
1,038 sq. ft.

Second Floor
498 sq. ft.

© Copyright by designer/architect

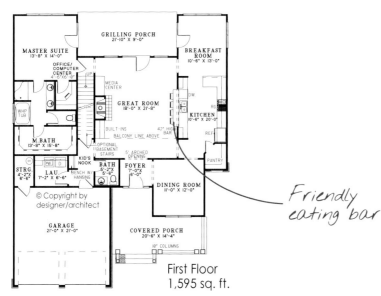

Second Floor
875 sq. ft.

First Floor
1,595 sq. ft.

Friendly eating bar

© Copyright by designer/architect

PLANFEATURES

2,470 total square feet of living area

Width: 47'-4" Depth: 58'-8"

Rustic shutters and shingle siding add a great custom feel to the exterior of this home

An extended counter in the kitchen has enough dining space for four people to gather around and enjoy a meal

A media center is designed next to the fireplace in the cozy great room

The bonus room above the garage offers an additional 389 square feet of future living area

4 bedrooms, 2 1/2 baths, 2-car garage

Slab or crawl space foundation, please specify when ordering

Price Code E

FERNVIEW

2,662 total square feet of living area

Width: 50'-0" Depth: 50'-0"

Combination living and dining rooms create an open space perfect for entertaining

The second floor loft could easily be converted to a home office or children's play room

A cozy corner fireplace warms the casual family room

4 bedrooms, 2 1/2 baths, 2-car garage

Crawl space foundation

Price Code E

Second Floor
893 sq. ft.

Cozy loft!

First Floor
1,769 sq. ft.

© Copyright by
designer/architect

SUNNYDALE

2,696 total square feet of living area

Width: 69'-0" Depth: 50'-0"

The great room features a corner design fireplace

The dining room has a 14' ceiling and beautiful sweeping views onto the curved front porch

The second floor includes a turreted recreation room, two bedrooms and a full bath

4 bedrooms, 3 baths, 2-car side entry garage

Crawl space or slab foundation, please specify when ordering; basement foundation available for an additional fee

Price Code F

Curved front porch

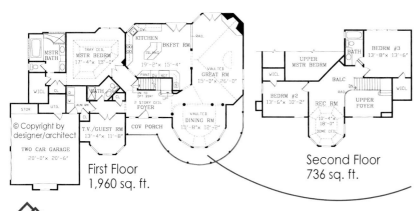

First Floor
1,960 sq. ft.

Second Floor
736 sq. ft.

© Copyright by
designer/architect

houseplansandmore.com

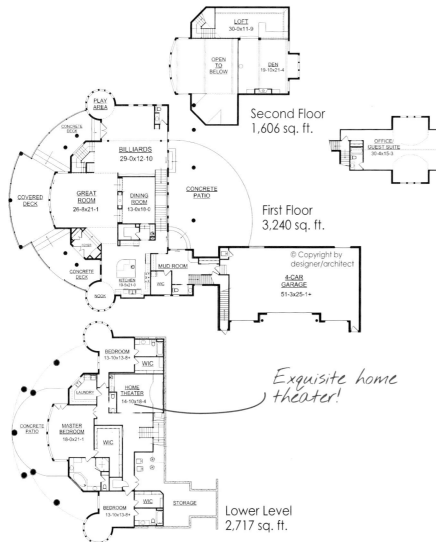

LOFT
30-0x11-9

OPEN TO BELOW

DEN
19-10x21-4

Second Floor
1,606 sq. ft.

PLAY AREA

CONCRETE DECK

BILLIARDS
29-0x12-10

CONCRETE PATIO

COVERED DECK

GREAT ROOM
26-8x21-1

DINING ROOM
13-0x18-0

CONCRETE DECK

MUD ROOM

KITCHEN
19-5x21-0

WIC

NOOK

OFFICE/ GUEST SUITE
30-4x15-3

First Floor
3,240 sq. ft.

© Copyright by designer/architect

4-CAR GARAGE
51-3x25-1+

BEDROOM
13-10x13-8+

WIC

LAUNDRY

HOME THEATER
14-10x18-4

Exquisite home theater!

CONCRETE PATIO

MASTER BEDROOM
18-0x21-1

WIC

BEDROOM
13-10x13-8+

WIC

STORAGE

Lower Level
2,717 sq. ft.

PLANFEATURES

7,563 total square feet of living area

Width: 93'-3" Depth: 139'-9"

If you enjoy the outdoors then this is the home for you - with the covered deck, patio, and copious amounts of windows, you can enjoy the outdoors from virtually anywhere in the home

The loft and den located on the second floor is a perfect getaway

Large closets throughout the home and a storage area on the lower level provide a place for everything

The monstrous master bedroom includes a large private bath and walk-in closet fit for a king

4 bedrooms, 4 full baths, 3 half baths, 4-car side entry garage

Walk-out basement or basement foundation, please specify when ordering

Price Code S3

houseplansandmore.com

DANTON

PLAN#651-111S-0005

PLANFEATURES

3,937 total square feet of living area

Width: 96'-5" Depth: 63'-11"

This eclectically styled home invites you through the courtyard into open spaces that are designed for a family who loves to entertain

This home's exterior features the use of stone, stucco and cedar as well as an interior using stone, wood, granite and subtly plastered arches

The grand foyer includes extra space with the addition of a loggia and looks upon the great room

The bonus room on the second floor has an additional 328 square feet of living area

5 bedrooms, 4 1/2 baths, 3-car side entry garage

Basement, crawl space or slab foundation, please specify when ordering

Price Code S1

houseplansandmore.com

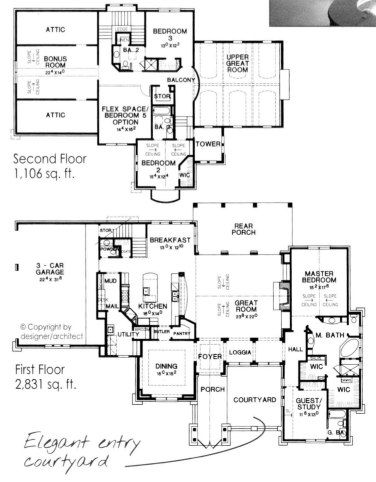

Second Floor
1,106 sq. ft.

First Floor
2,831 sq. ft.

© Copyright by designer/architect

Elegant entry courtyard

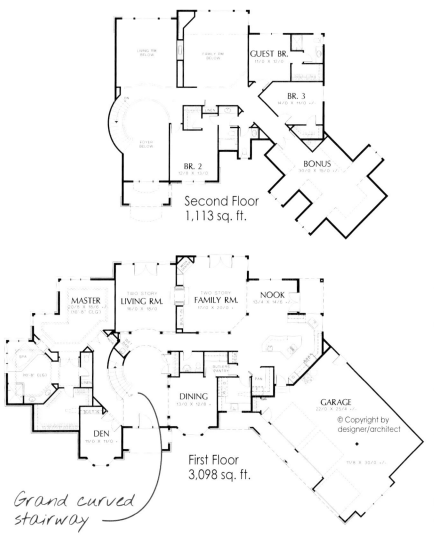

Second Floor
1,113 sq. ft.

GUEST BR.
11/0 X 12/0

BR. 3
14/0 X 11/0 +/-

BR. 2
12/8 X 13/0

BONUS
30/0 X 15/0

LIVING RM
BELOW

FAMILY RM
BELOW

FOYER
BELOW

First Floor
3,098 sq. ft.

MASTER
20/8 X 16/6
(10'-8" CLG.)

TWO STORY
LIVING RM.
16/0 X 18/0

TWO STORY
FAMILY RM.
17/0 X 20/0

NOOK
13/4 X 14/6

DINING
13/0 X 12/8

BUTLER'S
PANTRY

GARAGE
22/0 X 25/4 +/-

DEN
11/0 X 11/0

SPA

11/8 X 30/0 +/-

© Copyright by
designer/architect

Grand curved stairway

PLANFEATURES

4,211 total square feet of living area

Width: 112'-0" Depth: 70'-0"

Energy efficient home with 2" x 6" exterior walls

The master suite has every luxury including an enormous bath with a see-through fireplace placed near the spa-style tub and a huge walk-in closet

A convenient butler's pantry connects the kitchen to the formal dining room

A grand foyer is highlighted with an oversized curved staircase

The bonus room on the second floor has an additional 567 square feet of living area

4 bedrooms, 3 full baths, 2 half baths, 3-car garage

Crawl space foundation

Price Code H

houseplansandmore.com

BROOKMONT

PLAN #651-007D-0067

1,761 total square feet of living area

Width: 57'-0" Depth: 52'-2"

The great room, that opens to a pass-through kitchen, boasts a vaulted ceiling and a fireplace

4 bedrooms, 2 baths, 2-car side entry garage

Basement foundation

Price Code B

GILCREST

PLAN #651-028D-0010

2,214 total square feet of living area

Width: 68'-4" Depth: 80'-0"

The great room has built-in cabinets for an entertainment system, a fireplace and French doors leading to a private rear covered porch

3 bedrooms, 2 baths, 2-car side entry garage

Crawl space or slab foundation, please specify when ordering

Price Code D

AMBROSE TRAIL

PLAN #651-077D-0025

1,500 total square feet of living area

Width: 61'-0" Depth: 47'-4"

Energy efficient home with 2" x 6" exterior walls

3 bedrooms, 2 baths, 2-car side entry garage

Slab, basement or crawl space foundation, please specify when ordering

Price Code D

RIDGEFOREST

PLAN #651-077D-0138

1,509 total square feet of living area

Width: 61'-0" Depth: 47'-4"

A large eating area has covered porch access and is near the kitchen and vaulted great room

Cabinets flank the fireplace in the vaulted great room

3 bedrooms, 2 baths, 2-car garage

Basement, slab or crawl space foundation, please specify when ordering

Price Code D

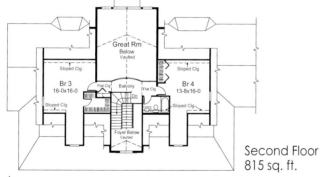

PLANFEATURES

3,782 total square feet of living area

Width: 101'-0" Depth: 50'-0"

A stylish staircase in the foyer ascends to the second floor balcony overlooking the great room below

The lower level includes a media/theater room with built-in bookshelves

The formal dining room is decorated with an impressive tray ceiling drawing the eye upward

A massive 42" direct vent fireplace and expansive window wall help bring the outdoors into the vaulted great room

2" x 6" exterior walls available, please order plan #651-121E-0004

4 bedrooms, 3 1/2 baths, 2-car garage

Basement foundation

Price Code E

Relaxed media/theater room!!

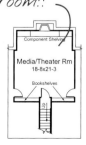

Lower Level
396 sq. ft.

Second Floor
815 sq. ft.

First Floor
2,571 sq. ft.

PLANFEATURES

3,937 total square feet of living area

Width: 77'-4" Depth: 75'-6"

An amazing walk-in closet provides an abundance of space for the homeowners in the private master bath

Off the breakfast nook is a pleasant screened porch ideal for year-round outdoor enjoyment

Double doors off the foyer lead to a den featuring a handsome decorative ceiling above

Optional lower level has an additional 1,914 square feet of living area

3 bedrooms, 3 1/2 baths, 4-car side entry garage

Basement foundation

Price Code S1

Pleasant rear screened porch & deck

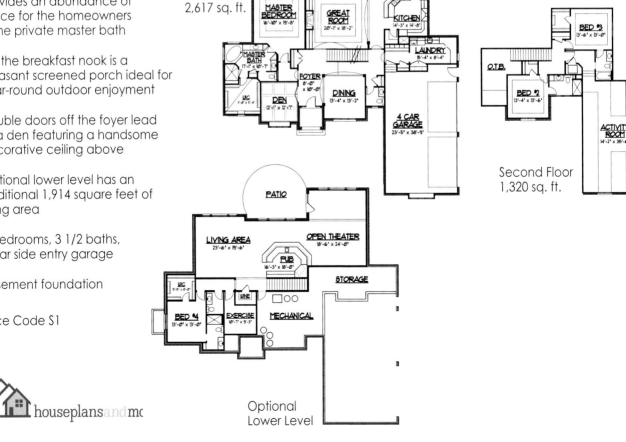

First Floor
2,617 sq. ft.

Second Floor
1,320 sq. ft.

Optional
Lower Level

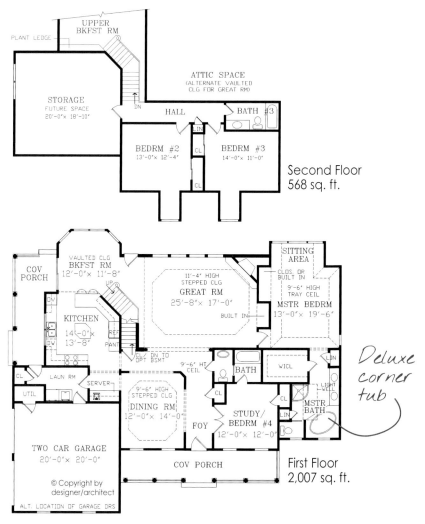

UPPER BKFST RM

PLANT LEDGE

STORAGE
FUTURE SPACE
20'-0"x 18'-10"

ATTIC SPACE
(ALTERNATE VAULTED
CLG FOR GREAT RM)

HALL   BATH #3

DN

BEDRM #2
13'-0"x 12'-4"

BEDRM #3
14'-0"x 11'-0"

CL

CL

Second Floor
568 sq. ft.

COV PORCH

VAULTED CLG
BKFST RM
12'-0"x 11'-8"

UP

KITCHEN
14'-0"x
13'-8"

11'-4" HIGH
STEPPED CLG
GREAT RM
25'-8"x 17'-0"

SITTING AREA

CLOS. OR
BUILT IN

9'-6" HIGH
TRAY CEIL
MSTR BEDRM
13'-0"x 19'-6"

BUILT IN

DW

REF

PANT

CL DN TO
OPT BSMT

9'-6" HT
CEIL

BATH

WICL

LIN

LAUN RM

SERVER

CL

9'-6" HIGH
STEPPED CLG
DINING RM
12'-0"x 14'-0"

FOY

STUDY/
BEDRM #4
12'-0"x 12'-0"

CL

LIN

MSTR
BATH

LIGHT
WELL

UTIL

CL

Deluxe corner tub

TWO CAR GARAGE
20'-0"x 20'-0"

COV PORCH

First Floor
2,007 sq. ft.

© Copyright by
designer/architect

ALT LOCATION OF GARAGE DRS

PLAN FEATURES

2,575 total square feet of living area

Width: 62'-4" Depth: 53'-6"

The master bedroom is fully equipped and has a sitting area, a built-in niche, a walk-in closet and full bath with a spa tub

A covered porch attaches to the vaulted breakfast room and is perfect for grilling

The study/bedroom #4 is a versatile space that can adapt to your family's needs

The storage/future space on the second floor has an additional 376 square feet of living area

4 bedrooms, 3 baths, 2-car side entry garage

Crawl space or slab foundation, please specify when ordering; basement foundation available for an additional fee

Price Code F

Photo, above: Casual and inviting, the great room beckons friends and family to relax within its walls and enjoy its uncomplicated design.

Photo, right: A raised island creates a quality space for dining and food preparation in the expansive kitchen.

houseplansandmore.com

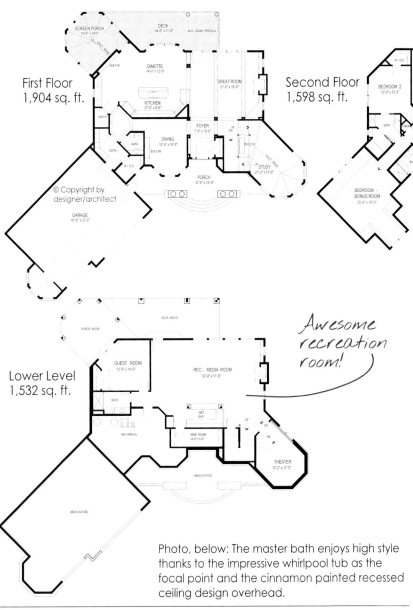

First Floor
1,904 sq. ft.

Second Floor
1,598 sq. ft.

© Copyright by
designer/architect

Lower Level
1,532 sq. ft.

Awesome recreation room!

Photo, below:
Working from
home will not
be a gloomy
thought in
this cheerful
vaulted
study lined
with large
windows.

Photo, below: The master bath enjoys high style thanks to the impressive whirlpool tub as the focal point and the cinnamon painted recessed ceiling design overhead.

PLAN FEATURES

5,034 total square feet of living area

Width: 88'-0" Depth: 82'-0"

The octagon-shaped vaulted study will peak interest when guests and family enter this stately home

The first floor features an elegant open kitchen and dinette with multiple built-in amenities

The bonus room has an additional 442 square feet of living area and can be used for a variety of purposes, including an additional bedroom

An octagon-shaped theater is the highlight of the lower level, where the family will undoubtedly spend countless hours together

4 bedrooms, 4 1/2 baths, 3-car garage

Walk-out basement foundation

Price Code S2

houseplansandmore.com

CASH CANYON

3,076 total square feet of living area

Width: 71'-0" Depth: 95'-0"

This unique home features all the living areas near each other for ease with family activities

The cheerful breakfast room enjoys views of the enormous covered rear porch featuring a corner outdoor fireplace for year-round enjoyment

The elegant master bedroom has its own sitting area and pampering spa style bath

4 bedrooms, 3 baths, 2-car rear entry garage and 1-car carport

Floating slab foundation

Price Code K

Comfortable master bath

© Copyright by designer/architect

SANDPIPER

3,098 total square feet of living area

Width: 78'-0" Depth: 75'-4"

The master bedroom is ultra luxurious with a private bath, an enormous walk-in closet and a sitting area leading to the lanai

The vaulted family room has lots of windows and a cozy fireplace

A secluded study has double closets and built-ins

The optional second floor has an additional 849 square feet of living area

Framing - only concrete block available

3 bedrooms, 3 baths, 3-car side entry garage

Slab foundation

Price Code F

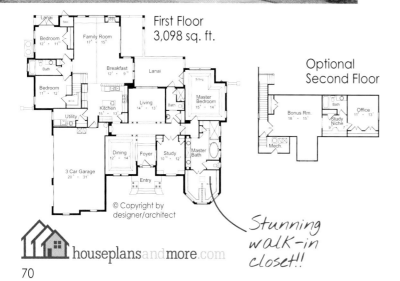

First Floor
3,098 sq. ft.

Optional
Second Floor

© Copyright by designer/architect

Stunning walk-in closet!!

houseplansandmore.com

Second Floor
620 sq. ft.

BR. 3
12/6 X 15/6

BR. 2
12/0 X 13/10

OPEN TO BELOW

SHELF

BONUS
14/8 X 41/2

First Floor
2,287 sq. ft.

CEDAR TRELLIS

PORCH
12/0 X 9/6

VAULTED
GREAT RM.
17/0 X 20/10

SPA

DINING
12/4 X 16/0

MEDIA

MASTER
14/2 X 20/0

DISPLAY
NICHE

STOR

FOYER

OPEN TO ABOVE

UP

PANTRY

OFFICE
11/0 X 10/2

MUDROOM

SEAT

GARAGE
24/0 X 35/6 +/-

© Copyright by
designer/architect

Spacious laundry room

PLAN FEATURES

2,907 total square feet of living area

Width: 98'-8" Depth: 66'-3"

Energy efficient home with 2" x 6" exterior walls

The first floor is open and airy with a vaulted great room, dining room and foyer

The master suite has a double-door entry to a spacious bathroom with dual sinks and a spa tub

The bonus room on the second floor has an additional 581 square feet of living area

3 bedrooms, 2 1/2 baths, 3-car garage

Crawl space foundation

Price Code D

houseplansandmore.com

SELKIRK

First Floor
2,461 sq. ft.

Cozy hearth room

Optional
Second Floor

2,461 total square feet of living area

Width: 71'-4" Depth: 74'-8"

The cooktop island in the kitchen has ample counterspace for easy food preparation

The luxurious master suite has a large closet with conveniently separated hanging areas

The covered deck/screened porch with vaulted ceiling creates a great outdoor gathering area

The optional second floor has an additional 518 square feet of living area

3 bedrooms, 3 1/2 baths, 3-car side entry garage

Basement foundation

Price Code D

HARTENBACH

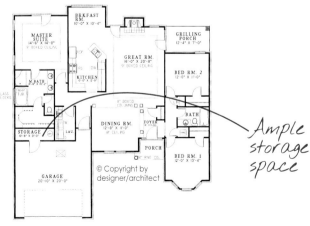

Ample storage space

1,758 total square feet of living area

Width: 54'-2" Depth: 56'-2"

The kitchen, breakfast, dining and great rooms combine for a spacious living area

A wonderful grilling porch is perfect for entertaining

The master suite boasts a private bath with whirlpool tub, spacious walk-in closet and access to the outdoors

3 bedrooms, 2 baths, 2-car garage

Slab, crawl space, basement or walk-out basement foundation, please specify when ordering

Price Code B

houseplansandmore.com

First Floor
2,049 sq. ft.

WD. DECK

NOOK
BATH CLG.
11'8" × 10'0"

BR. #2
10'-1 1/8" CLG.
11'0" × 13'2"

KIT.
10'-1 1/8" CLG.
11'8" × 14'10"

GRT. RM.
12'-1 1/8" CLG.

MBR.
11'8" CLG.
14'0" × 16'4"

PAN.

LIN.

ART NICHE   ART NICHE   ART NICHE

3 CAR GARAGE
29'8" × 21'8"

DIN.
TRAY CLG.
12'0" × 12'0"

E.

© Copyright by
designer/architect

Lower Level
1,728 sq. ft.

WET BAR
10'-8 1/2" CLG.
11'8" × 10'0"

10'6" × 14'8"

REC. RM.
10'-8 1/2" CLG.
23'0" × 14'4"

DN

BR. #3
10'-8 1/2" CLG.
15'6" × 14'4"

GALLERY
8'-8 1/2" CLG.
22'10" × 8'6"

BR. #4
8'-8 1/2" CLG.
13'4" × 13'6"

STOR.

Beautiful gallery

PLAN FEATURES

3,777 total square feet of living area

Width: 65'-0" Depth: 58'-0"

Energy efficient home with 2" x 6" exterior walls

The master bedroom provides the ultimate relaxation with a deluxe bath and walk-in closet to keep everything organized

A walk-in pantry and snack bar peninsula add efficiency to the kitchen that opens to the great room and cozy nook

The lower level is comprised of two secondary bedrooms, a recreation room and a wet bar

4 bedrooms, 3 1/2 baths, 3-car garage

Walk-out basement foundation

Price Code G

houseplansandmore.com

73

Photo, above: This view shows off the pantry door as well as the door leading to the utility room side-by-side for ease when unloading groceries from the garage.

Photo, right: The breakfast bar is just within reach of the dining room, perfect for those festive buffet-style meals or extra seating when the party is a bit larger.

houseplansandmore.com

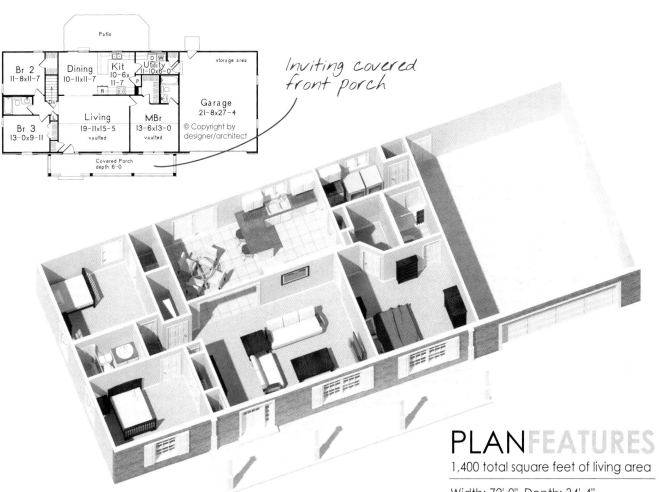

Inviting covered front porch

Patio

Br 2
11-8x11-7

Dining
10-11x11-7

Kit
10-6x
11-7

Utility
11-10x6-0

storage area

Living
19-11x15-5
vaulted

MBr
13-6x13-0
vaulted

Garage
21-8x27-4

Br 3
13-0x9-11

© Copyright by
designer/architect

Covered Porch
depth 6-0

PLAN FEATURES

1,400 total square feet of living area

Width: 72'-0" Depth: 34'-4"

Master bedroom is secluded for privacy

The large utility room has additional cabinet space

The covered porch provides an outdoor seating area

Roof dormers add great curb appeal

The living room and master bedroom feature vaulted ceilings

The oversized two-car garage has storage space

3 bedrooms, 2 baths, 2-car garage

Basement foundation, drawings also include crawl space foundation

Price Code B

Photo, below: Loaded with curb appeal, this family friendly plan is modest in size, yet includes all the features modern families are yearning for, including a vaulted open living area. Don't forget the enjoyable dining room with sliding glass doors onto a spacious patio.

houseplansandmore.com

PLAN FEATURES

6,360 total square feet of living area

Width: 94'-0" Depth: 82'-0"

Energy efficient home with 2" x 6" exterior walls

The striking turret and use of stone sets the stage for elegance that is seen throughout this entire home

A see-through fireplace warms the great room and the adjoining hearth room, dining room and kitchen that flow together for a comfortable living area with an octagon-shaped sunroom nearby

A curved staircase leads to the finished lower level that includes a family room, wet bar, recreation room, craft room and storage

4 bedrooms, 3 full baths, 2 half baths, 2-car side entry garage, 1-car garage

Walk-out basement foundation

Price Code S1

First Floor
3,394 sq. ft.

Lower Level
2,966 sq. ft.

Handy craft room!

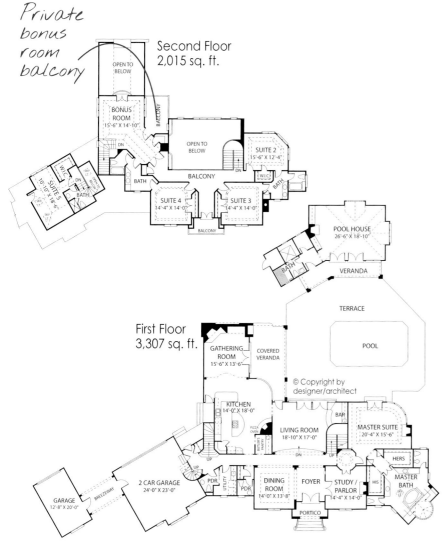

Private bonus room balcony

Second Floor
2,015 sq. ft.

OPEN TO BELOW

BONUS ROOM
15'-6" X 14'-10"

OPEN TO BELOW

BALCONY

SUITE 2
15'-6" X 12'-4"

W.I.C.

BATH

BALCONY

DN

BATH

W.I.C.

SUITE 5
10'-10" X 18'-6"

DN

BATH

SUITE 4
14'-4" X 14'-0"

SUITE 3
14'-4" X 14'-0"

BALCONY

POOL HOUSE
26'-6" X 18'-10"

VERANDA

BATH

TERRACE

POOL

First Floor
3,307 sq. ft.

GATHERING ROOM
15'-6" X 13'-6"

COVERED VERANDA

© Copyright by designer/architect

KITCHEN
14'-0" X 18'-0"

PIZZA OVEN

BUTLER'S PANTRY

LIVING ROOM
18'-10" X 17'-0"

BAR

MASTER SUITE
20'-4" X 15'-6"

DN

UP

HERS

UP

2 CAR GARAGE
24'-0" X 23'-0"

BREEZEWAY

UP

PDR.

UTILITY

PDR.

DINING ROOM
14'-0" X 13'-8"

FOYER

STUDY / PARLOR
14'-4" X 14'-0"

HIS

MASTER BATH

GARAGE
12'-8" X 20'-0"

PORTICO

PLANFEATURES

5,322 total square feet of living area

Width: 143'-3" Depth: 71'-2"

The kitchen enjoys space for a pizza oven, a large center island, and a spacious butler's pantry

Relaxing in luxury is a breeze in the master bath's whirlpool tub with a delightful view

Suite #5 is privately accessed by an additional staircase and has a private bath and walk-in closet

The bonus room on the second floor has an additional 761 square feet of living area

5 bedrooms, 5 full baths, 2 half baths, 3-car rear entry garage

Crawl space foundation

Price Code S2

CEDAR VISTA

PLAN #651-024D-0055

2,968 total square feet of living area

Width: 72'-0" Depth: 85'-6"

Energy efficient home with 2" x 6" exterior walls

The optional second floor has an additional 304 square feet of living area

4 bedrooms, 3 1/2 baths, 2-car side entry garage

Slab foundation

Price Code H

ENGLER

PLAN #651-065D-0013

2,041 total square feet of living area

Width: 67'-6" Depth: 63'-6"

The optional lower level has an additional 1,942 square feet of living area

3 bedrooms, 2 baths, 2-car side entry garage

Walk-out basement foundation

Price Code C

houseplansandmore.com

DAWNBREAK

PLAN #651-055D-0046

1,934 total square feet of living area

Width: 36'-8" Depth: 85'-0"

The master suite has access onto the grilling porch and enjoys a private bath with two walk-in closets

3 bedrooms, 2 baths, 2-car rear entry garage

Crawl space or slab foundation, please specify when ordering

Price Code C

BELLEZONA

PLAN #651-111D-0001

1,748 total square feet of living area

Width: 54'-0" Depth: 50'-0"

Large and open, the formal dining room maintains a spacious feeling with two walls open to the entry and living room beyond

4 bedrooms, 2 baths, 2-car garage

Basement, crawl space or slab foundation, please specify when ordering

Price Code B

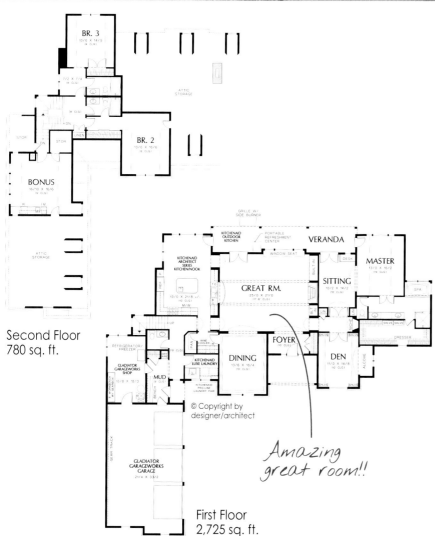

Second Floor
780 sq. ft.

© Copyright by
designer/architect

*Amazing
great room!!*

First Floor
2,725 sq. ft.

PLANFEATURES

3,505 total square feet of living area

Width: 90'-6" Depth: 84'-0"

The great room has a taste of everything, from a fireplace with flanking shelves to a sunny window seat viewing the veranda

The master bedroom has many amenities including a sitting room with access to the veranda, a private bath and a spacious walk-in closet

The bonus room on the second floor has an additional 387 square feet of living area and a large storage closet

3 bedrooms, 3 1/2 baths, 3-car side entry garage

Crawl space foundation

Price Code S1

PLANFEATURES

2,568 total square feet of living area

Width: 63'-0" Depth: 48'-0"

An impressive staircase in the foyer ascends to the second floor where all the bedrooms can be found

The formal living and dining rooms have tray ceilings and connect for great entertaining possibilities

Double doors off the foyer lead to a cozy den with a bay window

The bonus room on the second floor has an additional 303 square feet of living area

3 bedrooms, 2 1/2 baths, 3-car garage

Crawl space foundation

Price Code E

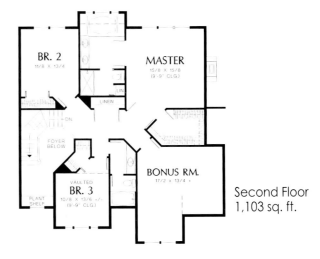

Second Floor
1,103 sq. ft.

Handy shop area in the garage

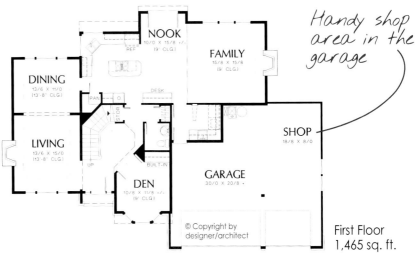

First Floor
1,465 sq. ft.

© Copyright by designer/architect

PLAN FEATURES

6,075 total square feet of living area

Width: 65'-0" Depth: 70'-0"

A curved wall of windows in the formal living room offers unbelievable views of the outdoor covered patio

A large media room with a tray ceiling also includes a wet bar

An elevator connects the two floors easily

The exceptional second floor master bedroom has a vestibule with a wet bar near the double walk-in closets and a private bath with spa tub, nearby fireplace and walk-in shower

Framing - only concrete block available

5 bedrooms, 6 1/2 baths, 3-car garage

Slab foundation

Price Code S1

Enchanting covered balconies!!

© Copyright by designer/architect

First Floor
3,149 sq. ft.

Second Floor
2,926 sq. ft.

houseplansandmore.com

Photo, above: The rear view at twilight illuminates the home as the abundant use of windows provides a breathtaking view. The proper use of interior lighting helps display the great architecture both inside and out. Plus, it accentuates the spaciousness of the vaulted ceilings and open floor plan.

Photo, right: The great room's open floor plan and expansive two-story ceiling are further accented by numerous windows and rustic beams. The honey-colored wood trim on the windows mimics the decorative beams of the vaulted ceiling for a dramatic style elevated to new heights.

houseplansandmore.com

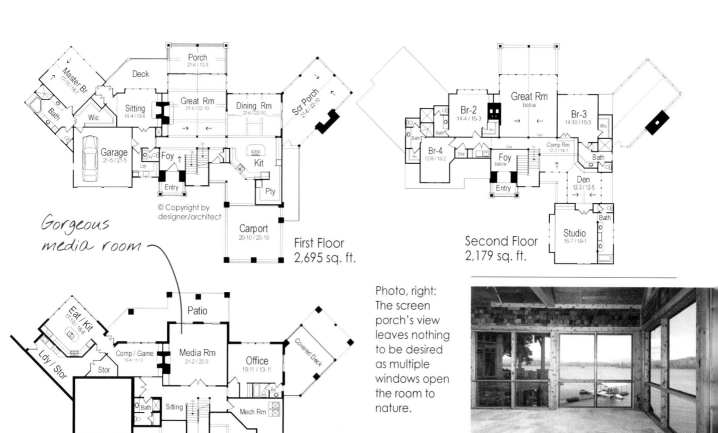

First Floor 2,695 sq. ft.

Master Br 17-10 / 16-7

Bath

Wic

Garage 21-5 / 21-5

Deck

Sitting 16-4 / 13-6

Great Rm 21-6 / 22-10

Porch 21-6 / 10-3

Dining Rm 21-6 / 22-10

Scr Porch 21-6 / 22-10

Foy

Kit

Entry

Pty

© Copyright by designer/architect

Gorgeous media room

Carport 20-10 / 20-10

Second Floor 2,179 sq. ft.

Br-2 14-4 / 15-3

Great Rm below

Br-3 14-10 / 15-3

Bath

Wic

Br-4 12-8 / 16-2

Comp Rm 12-2 / 14-1

Foy below

Bath

Den 12-3 / 12-5

Entry

Studio 15-7 / 19-1

Bath

Lower Level 1,896 sq. ft.

Eat / Kit 17-10 / 16-6

Ldy / Stor

Comp / Game 16-4 / 11-10

Stor

Patio

Media Rm 21-2 / 22-0

Office 19-11 / 13-11

Covered Deck

Bath

Sitting

Mech Rm

Photo, right: The screen porch's view leaves nothing to be desired as multiple windows open the room to nature.

Photo, below: From the kitchen's cooktop, the view into the dining room and beyond can make any kitchen chore an absolute treat.

PLAN FEATURES

6,770 total square feet of living area

Width: 121'-4" Depth: 78'-4"

The first floor features an abundance of amenities including a two-story great room, and an enchanting sun porch

Three additional bedroom suites and a studio for guests are offered on the second floor

The lower level includes an amazing media room, a computer/game room, an office and a second kitchen

4 bedrooms, 7 1/2 baths, 2-car garage and 2-car side entry carport

Basement or walk-out basement foundation, please specify when ordering

Price Code S6

houseplansandmore.com

BRADINGTON

PLANFEATURES

2,614 total square feet of living area

Width: 57'-4" Depth: 45'-4"

The grand two-story entry features a majestic palladian window, double French doors to the parlor and access to the powder room

The state-of-the-art kitchen has a corner sink with two large archtop windows, an island snack bar, a menu desk and a walk-in pantry

The master bath is vaulted and offers a luxurious step-up tub, a palladian window, built-in shelves, and columns with a plant shelf

4 bedrooms, 2 1/2 baths,
2-car garage

Basement foundation

Price Code E

Br 2
11-0x11-4

MBr
17-0x13-9
vaulted

plant shelf above

Hall

Dn   Dn

Br 3
11-0x11-0

Br 4
11-10x12-0

entry below

plant shelf

French doors open to a relaxing master bath

Second Floor
1,203 sq. ft.

Deck

Dn

Brk'ft
10-0x15-7

Kit
9-10x15-0

Family
19-0x19-3

P

First Floor
1,411 sq. ft.

Up

Laun.

Dn

shelves

Entry
2 story

Dining
14-0x12-0
tray clg

Garage
19-4x21-0

Parlor
11-0x13-4

vaulted

Porch

© Copyright by designer/architect

houseplansandmore.com

PLANFEATURES

3,940 total square feet of living area

Width: 120'-0" Depth: 88'-0"

A pass-thru bar connects the spacious great room and kitchen, further expanding the home's open floor space

The outdoor kitchen and grill is separated from the outdoor living space, allowing for multiple uses of either area

The bonus room above the garage is available for numerous uses, such as a play, media or game room and offers an additional 695 square feet of living area

3 bedrooms, 2 full baths, 2 half baths, 3-car side entry garage

Crawl space foundation

Price Code S1

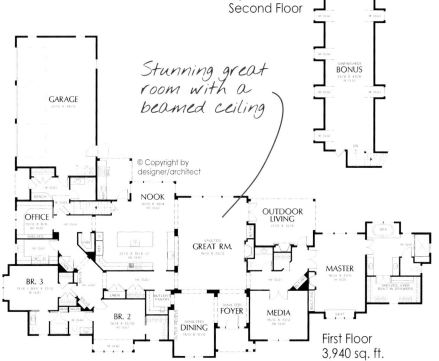

Optional
Second Floor

Stunning great room with a beamed ceiling

© Copyright by designer/architect

BONUS

GARAGE

OFFICE

NOOK

OUTDOOR LIVING

GREAT RM.

BR. 3

MASTER

BR. 2

FOYER

MEDIA

DINING

First Floor
3,940 sq. ft.

houseplansandmore.com

PLANFEATURES

4,160 total square feet of living area

Width: 62'-9" Depth: 61'-8"

The cozy sitting area off the breakfast room offers a comfortable space for relaxation

The master bedroom pleases with its private sitting alcove, entry to the rear deck and elegant dressing area

The lower level is an inviting space to spend fun times including an exercise room, two additional bedrooms, a wet bar, and space for a game table and media area

3 bedrooms, 2 1/2 baths, 2-car side entry garage

Walk-out basement foundation

Price Code G

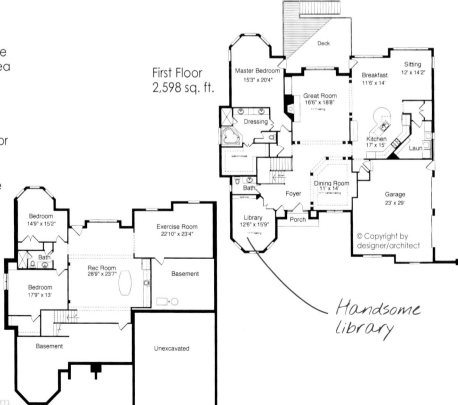

First Floor
2,598 sq. ft.

Master Bedroom 15'3" x 20'4"

Deck

Sitting 12' x 14'2"

Breakfast 11'6" x 14'

Great Room 16'6" x 18'8"
11'1" ceiling

Dressing

Kitchen 17' x 15'

Laun.

walk-in closet

Bath

Dining Room 11' x 14'
11'1" corner ceiling

Foyer

Garage 23' x 29'

Library 12'6" x 15'9"
11'1" ceiling

Porch

© Copyright by designer/architect

Handsome Library

Lower Level
1,562 sq. ft.

Bedroom 14'9" x 15'2"

Bath

Exercise Room 22'10" x 23'4"

Basement

Rec Room 28'9" x 23'7"

Bedroom 17'9" x 13'

Basement

Unexcavated

houseplansandmore.com

PLANFEATURES

1,325 total square feet of living area

Width: 33'-0" Depth: 26'-0"

Energy efficient home with 2" x 6" exterior walls

An amazing exterior continues to impress once you take a step inside

The first floor houses a grand open area with a stylish hot tub set into the turret

The second floor offers flexibility with a one or two bedroom design both with balcony access and a tub set into the turret

1 bedroom, 1 1/2 baths

Walk-out basement foundation

Price Code D

Second Floor
584 sq. ft.

Two Bedroom
Second Floor Option

Octagon-shaped sitting area with cheerful windows

© Copyright by
designer/architect

First Floor
741 sq. ft.

houseplansandmore.com

SAVOY HILL

3,394 total square feet of living area

Width: 94'-0" Depth: 79'-0"

A covered porch opens to a two-story foyer with a den on one side and a formal dining room on the other

The vaulted great room is perfect for gatherings of any type and connects to the nook and island kitchen

The first floor master suite has a walk-in closet and private bath with a see-through fireplace, dual sinks and a spa tub

The bonus room on the second floor has an additional 613 square feet of living area

4 bedrooms, 4 1/2 baths, 3-car garage

Crawl space foundation

Price Code S1

Second Floor
1,110 sq. ft.

First Floor
2,284 sq. ft.

© Copyright by designer/architect

Two-story foyer!!

DANNENBERG

2,389 total square feet of living area

Width: 48'-0" Depth: 44'-0"

The bayed breakfast room leads to a terrific patio/optional deck

Vaulted ceilings in the master bedroom and bath create an open feel

The second floor laundry closet is convenient to all bedrooms

4 bedrooms, 2 1/2 baths, 2-car side entry garage

Walk-out basement foundation

Price Code F

First Floor
1,067 sq. ft.

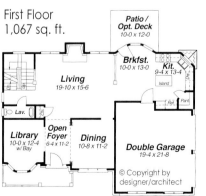

Second Floor
1,322 sq. ft.

© Copyright by designer/architect

Sizable walk-in closet

houseplansandmore.com

88

Amazing Kitchen!!

First Floor
2,624 sq. ft.

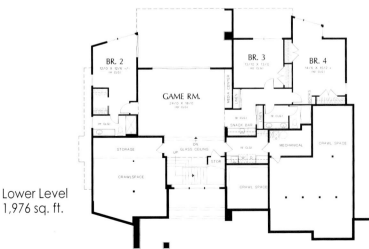

Lower Level
1,976 sq. ft.

PLANFEATURES

4,600 total square feet of living area

Width: 76'-6" Depth: 65'-0"

A unique glass floor leads to the staircase and allows one to look down to the lower level below

Plant shelves adorn this house in numerous places

The differently designed kitchen has most of its emphasis on a gracious center island

The master bedroom flows into an open bathroom with a spa tub and a double-bowl vanity

4 bedrooms, 3 1/2 baths, 3-car garage

Partial crawl space/walk-out basement foundation

Price Code S1

houseplansandmore.com

PLAN FEATURES

5,548 total square feet of living area

Width: 81'-6" Depth: 93'-2"

The kitchen, breakfast and hearth rooms are natural gathering places

Design extras include a corner computer room off the kitchen and a hobby/exercise room

A large laundry room is great for household chores and enjoys plenty of counterspace and a handy sink

The amazing master bedroom has a vaulted bath

5 bedrooms, 4 1/2 baths, 3-car side entry garage with two spacious walk-in closets

Basement, crawl space or slab foundation, please specify when ordering

Price Code S1

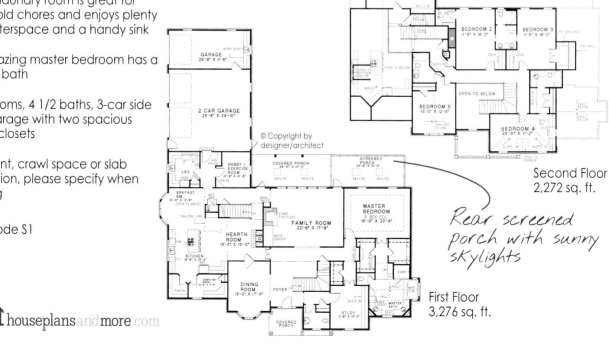

© Copyright by designer/architect

Rear screened porch with sunny skylights

Second Floor
2,272 sq. ft.

First Floor
3,276 sq. ft.

PLAN**FEATURES**

1,480 total square feet of living area

Width: 32'-0" Depth: 40'-0"

Energy efficient home with 2" x 6" exterior walls

Cathedral ceilings can be found in the family and dining rooms

The master bedroom has a walk-in closet and access to a bath

2 bedrooms, 2 baths

Walk-out basement foundation

Price Code C

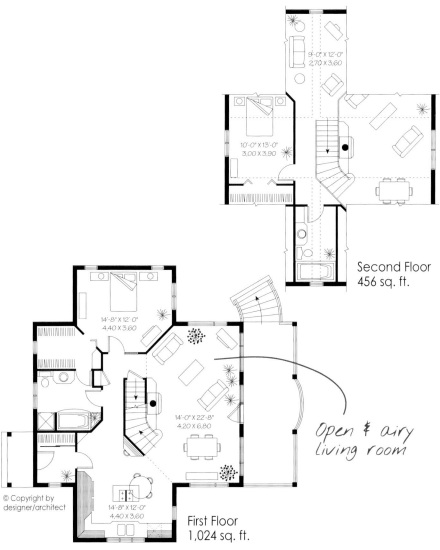

9'-0" X 12'-0"
2,70 X 3,60

10'-0" X 13'-0"
3,00 X 3,90

Second Floor
456 sq. ft.

14'-8" X 12'-0"
4,40 X 3,60

14'-0" X 22'-8"
4,20 X 6,80

Open & airy living room

14'-8" X 12'-0"
4,40 X 3,60

First Floor
1,024 sq. ft.

© Copyright by
designer/architect

houseplansandmore.com

KASSIDY MANOR

PLAN FEATURES

5,689 total square feet of living area

Width: 60'-2" Depth: 60'-2"

Wrap-around porches with boxed columns welcome family and friends into this Southern-style home

Access all floors by the elevator or take the beautiful spiral staircase from the second floor up to the spacious hobby room

Entertain with ease in the lower level game room that is complete with a kitchen and outdoor access

The optional third floor hobby room has an additional 1,744 square feet of living area

5 bedrooms, 4 1/2 baths, 3-car drive under side entry garage

Walk-out basement foundation

Price Code F

houseplansandmore.com

Spectacular wrap-around porches!!

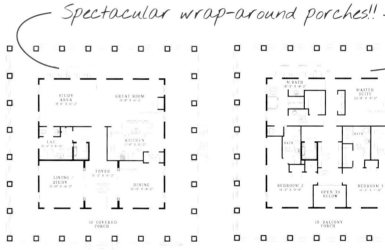

First Floor
1,600 sq. ft.

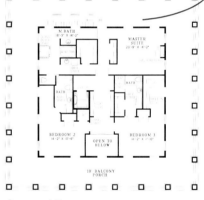

Second Floor
1,530 sq. ft.

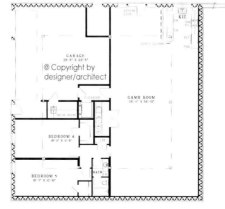

Lower Level
2,559 sq. ft.

© Copyright by designer/architect

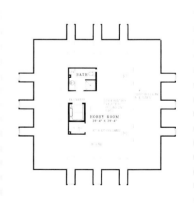

Optional
Third Floor

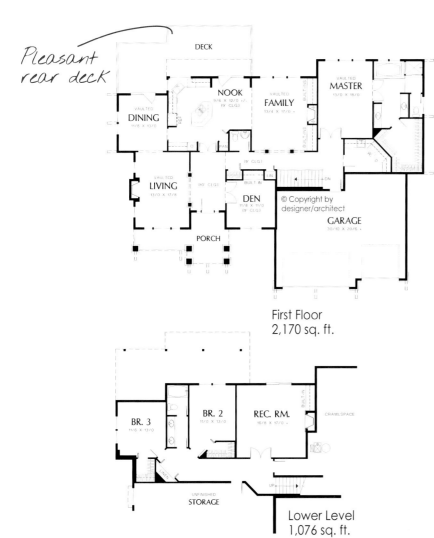

Pleasant rear deck

First Floor
2,170 sq. ft.

Lower Level
1,076 sq. ft.

PLANFEATURES

3,246 total square feet of living area

Width: 74'-0" Depth: 54'-0"

Energy efficient home with 2" x 6" exterior walls

The private master bedroom has a sumptuous bath and large walk-in closet

The lower level recreation room is a great casual family area

The L-shaped kitchen has a large center island with stove top and dining space

3 bedrooms, 2 1/2 baths, 3-car garage

Walk-out basement foundation

Price Code G

Photo, above: Intricate woodwork and beautiful countertops decorate the efficient kitchen of this luxury home plan. The wrap-around peninsula invites everyone for a casual visit.

Photo, right: The homeowners will love the rear outdoor living areas of this luxury house since they are as stunning as the indoor spaces. A grill and bar makes entertaining easy and a second floor balcony is great for relaxing away from the action.

houseplansandmore.com

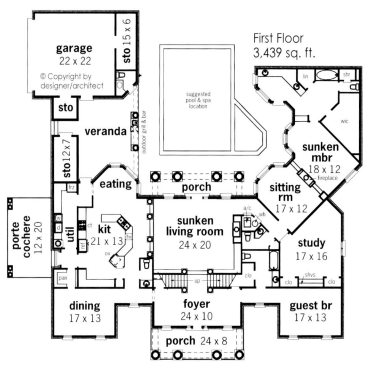

garage
22 x 22

sto 15 x 6

© Copyright by designer/architect

sto

veranda

sto 12 x 7

frz

eating

porte cochere 12 x 20

util

kit 21 x 13

pan

dining 17 x 13

First Floor
3,439 sq. ft.

suggested pool & spa location

outdoor grill & bar

porch

sunken living room
24 x 20

up

foyer
24 x 10

porch 24 x 8

lin

shr

wic

sunken mbr
18 x 12
fireplace

sitting rm
17 x 12

a/c

wh

study
17 x 16

clo

shvs

clo

guest br
17 x 13

Photo, right: This cheerful veranda is perfect for taking meals outdoors.

Unique library balcony!

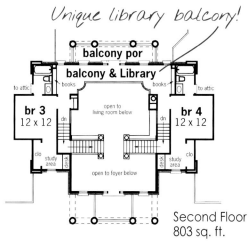

balcony por

balcony & Library

to attic

books

books

to attic

br 3
12 x 12

open to living room below

br 4
12 x 12

dn

dn

clo

study area

desk

desk

study area

clo

open to foyer below

Second Floor
803 sq. ft.

Photo, below: The bright foyer steps down to the lovely living room equipped with handy built-in shelves.

PLANFEATURES

4,242 total square feet of living area

Width: 95'-0" Depth: 90'-0"

The foyer and sunken living room feature breathtaking two-story ceilings adorned by stately columns

Twin stairwells ascend to the second floor balconies, that offer an amazing view of the rooms below

The living room and master bedroom are sunken to create an even more dramatic mood

4 bedrooms, 4 full baths, 3 half baths, 2-car side entry garage

Slab foundation, drawings also include basement foundation

Price Code S2

houseplansandmore.com

JULIANA

PLANFEATURES

3,424 total square feet of living area

Width: 82'-4" Depth: 83'-8"

The enormous master bath features double walk-in closets and a huge whirlpool tub under a bay window

Angled walls throughout this home add interest in every room

An open and airy kitchen looks into a cozy breakfast nook as well as the casual family room

Future space on the second floor has an additional 507 square feet of living area

Framing - only concrete block available

5 bedrooms, 4 baths, 3-car side entry garage

Slab foundation

Price Code F

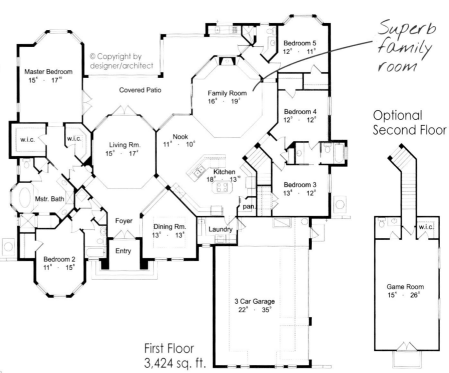

Superb family room

© Copyright by designer/architect

Master Bedroom
15⁴ · 17¹⁰

Covered Patio

Bedroom 5
12⁰ · 11⁰

Family Room
16⁹ · 19²

Bedroom 4
12⁰ · 12⁰

w.i.c.   w.i.c.

Living Rm.
15⁹ · 17²

Nook
11⁸ · 10⁰

Kitchen
18⁰ · 13¹⁰

Bedroom 3
13⁸ · 12⁰

Mstr. Bath

pan.

Foyer   Dining Rm.
13⁰ · 13⁸

Laundry

Entry

Bedroom 2
11⁸ · 15⁰

3 Car Garage
22⁸ · 35⁰

First Floor
3,424 sq. ft.

Optional Second Floor

w.i.c.

Game Room
15⁴ · 26⁰

houseplansandmore.com

PLANFEATURES

2,069 total square feet of living area

Width: 56'-4" Depth: 35'-4"

The lovely great room has a warming fireplace and direct access to the screen porch

There is extra room for storage in the garage

The master bath features many amenities including a whirlpool tub, a double-bowl vanity and a his/her walk-in wardrobe

The future recreation room on the second floor has an additional 382 square feet of living area

3 bedrooms, 2 1/2 baths, 2-car side entry garage

Partial basement/crawl space foundation

Price Code C

Second Floor
994 sq. ft.

Delightful fireplace!

First Floor
1,075 sq. ft.

houseplansandmore.com

PLANFEATURES

2,120 total square feet of living area

Width: 50'-0" Depth: 56'-0"

Energy efficient home with 2" x 6" exterior walls

The first floor vaulted master bedroom has a spacious and open feel

Built-in shelves adorn the dining room

The office has a double-door entry helping to maintain privacy

3 bedrooms, 2 1/2 baths, 3-car garage

Crawl space foundation

Price Code E

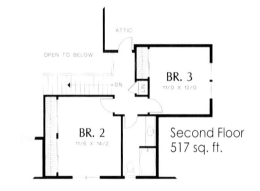

Second Floor
517 sq. ft.

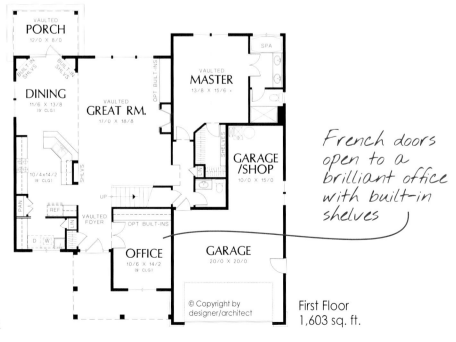

French doors open to a brilliant office with built-in shelves

First Floor
1,603 sq. ft.

© Copyright by designer/architect

Second Floor
1,429 sq. ft.

Lovely center Kitchen island

First Floor
1,571 sq. ft.

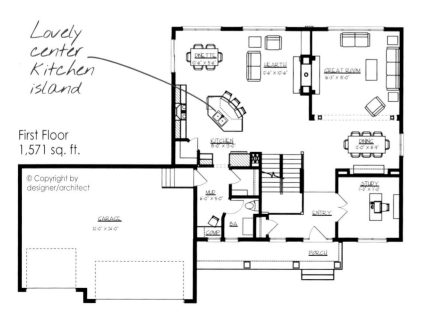

© Copyright by designer/architect

PLANFEATURES

3,000 total square feet of living area

Width: 70'-0" Depth: 49'-0"

The cheerful kitchen has a double-bowl sink in the island, a large pantry and opens up nicely to the dinette area

The centralized fireplace separates the hearth and great rooms, warming the home from both sides

The relaxing owner's bedroom offers a generous closet, and a bath with a double-bowl vanity, an amazing walk-in shower and a spa-style tub to soak your cares away

The lower level has an additional 1,544 square feet of optional living area

4 bedrooms, 2 1/2 baths, 3-car garage

Walk-out basement foundation

Price Code D

PLANFEATURES

8,930 total square feet of living area

Width: 145'-11" Depth: 126'-6"

An outdoor kitchen, covered porch with fireplace, and expansive covered terrace are perfect for enjoying the open air

The master suite boasts a sitting area surrounded with windows, a fireplace and a spacious bath with two walk-in closets

A private guest suite above the garage has a full bath and walk-in closet

5 bedrooms, 6 full baths, 2 half baths, 4-car side entry garage

Walk-out basement foundation

Price Code S3

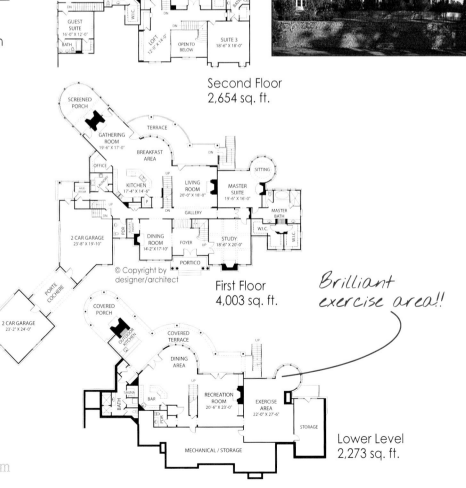

Second Floor
2,654 sq. ft.

© Copyright by designer/architect

First Floor
4,003 sq. ft.

Brilliant exercise area!!

Lower Level
2,273 sq. ft.

PLAN #651-028D-0022

KINSLEY

3,029 total square feet of living area

Width: 70'-0" Depth: 80'-0"

The master bedroom is isolated from the other bedrooms for privacy

Bedroom #4 would make an ideal home office with plenty of storage

The bonus room above garage has an additional 288 square feet of living area

4 bedrooms, 3 baths, 2-car side entry garage

Slab or crawl space foundation, please specify when ordering

Price Code F

Jack & Jill bath with walk-in closets

Optional Second Floor

First Floor
3,029 sq. ft.

PLAN #651-047D-0046

PALM AIRE

2,597 total square feet of living area

Width: 98'-6" Depth: 50'-0"

The angled design creates unlimited views and spaces that appear larger

The den/bedroom #4 makes a perfect home office or guest suite

The island kitchen enjoys views to the nook and family room and includes a walk-in pantry

A pool bath is shared by both outdoor and indoor areas

4 bedrooms, 3 baths, 3-car rear entry garage

Slab foundation

Price Code D

Luxurious master suite!

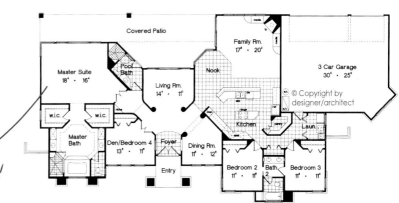

houseplansandmore.com

Photo, right: A pleasant L-shaped kitchen with large window above the sink creates a functional and pleasing workspace ideal for creating meals of all kinds.

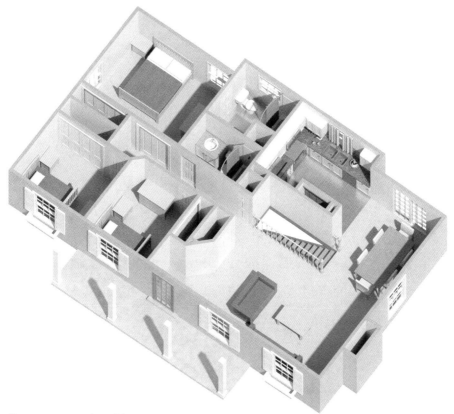

Friendly rear deck is great for entertaining family & friends!

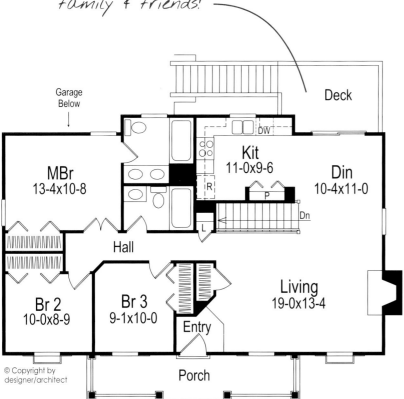

Garage Below

Deck

MBr
13-4x10-8

Kit
11-0x9-6

Din
10-4x11-0

Hall

Br 2
10-0x8-9

Br 3
9-1x10-0

Living
19-0x13-4

Entry

Porch

© Copyright by designer/architect

PLANFEATURES

1,140 total square feet of living area

Width: 46'-0" Depth: 32'-0"

Open and spacious living and dining areas are great for family gatherings

The well-organized kitchen has an abundance of cabinetry and a built-in pantry

A roomy master bath features a double-bowl vanity

3 bedrooms, 2 baths, 2-car drive under rear entry garage

Basement foundation

Price Code AA

houseplansandmore.com

PLANFEATURES

2,525 total square feet of living area

Width: 58'-4" Depth: 53'-0"

The living room has a 10' ceiling and a large fireplace

The parlor is a perfect place for entertaining guests

The bayed breakfast room is flooded with light and opens to the optional deck

3 bedrooms, 2 1/2 baths, 2-car garage

Basement, crawl space or slab foundation, please specify when ordering

Price Code F

Second Floor
1,116 sq. ft.

Cheerful breakfast area with beautiful windows

First Floor
1,409 sq. ft.

© Copyright by designer/architect

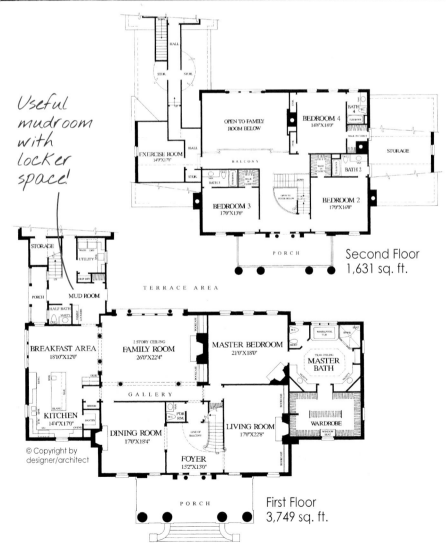

Useful mudroom with locker space!

Second Floor
1,631 sq. ft.

First Floor
3,749 sq. ft.

© Copyright by designer/architect

PLANFEATURES

5,380 total square feet of living area

Width: 92'-4" Depth: 112'-0"

The stately family room enjoys a two-story ceiling, built-in bookcases, a fireplace and access to the rear terrace area

Luxury abounds in the master bedroom featuring a corner fireplace, a spacious master bath with a tray ceiling and a wardrobe closet with windows to provide extra light

The second floor boasts three bedrooms each with their own bath and closet space, an exercise room and an additional 1,171 square feet of storage space

4 bedrooms, 4 full baths, 2 half baths

Crawl space or basement foundation, please specify when ordering

Price Code G

PLANFEATURES

1,728 total square feet of living area

Width: 72'-0" Depth: 54'-0"

Energy efficient home with 2" x 6" exterior walls

The second bedroom can easily be converted into an office with ample shelf space

You will love the master bath equipped with a large walk-in closet, a relaxing shower and a spa-style tub to pamper yourself

The charming kitchen includes a breakfast island perfect for family gatherings in the mornings

The lower level offers an additional 1,005 square feet of finished area

2 bedrooms, 2 baths, 3-car side entry garage

Walk-out basement foundation

Price Code A

houseplansandmore.com

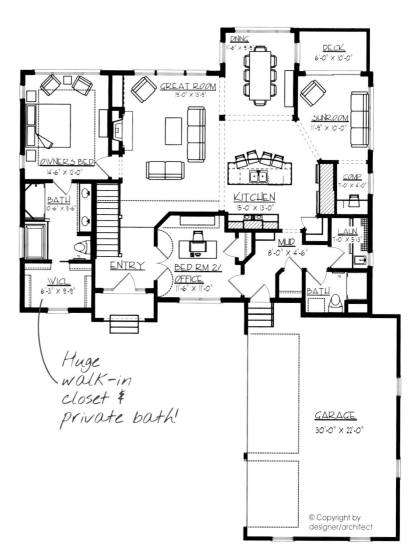

Huge walk-in closet & private bath!

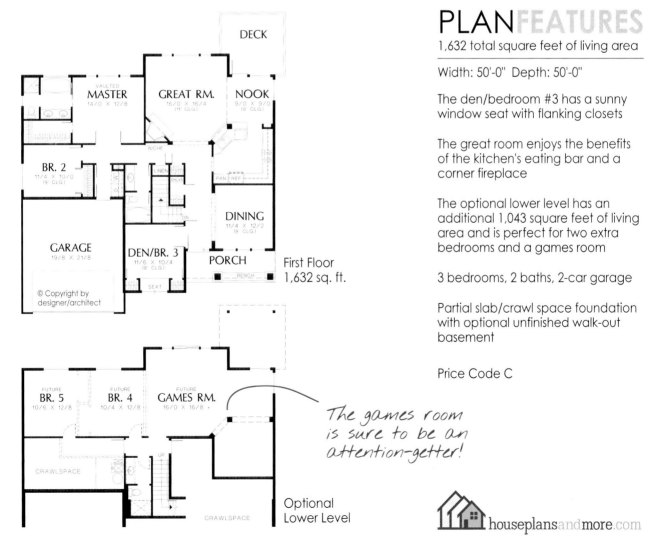

DECK

VAULTED
MASTER
14/0 X 12/8

GREAT RM.
16/0 X 16/4
(11' CLG.)

NOOK
9/0 X 9/0
(9' CLG.)

NICHE

BR. 2
11/4 X 10/0
(9' CLG.)

LINEN

PAN REF

DINING
11/4 X 12/2
(9' CLG.)

GARAGE
19/8 X 21/8

DEN/BR. 3
11/6 X 10/4
(9' CLG.)

DN

PORCH
BENCH

SEAT

© Copyright by
designer/architect

First Floor
1,632 sq. ft.

FUTURE
BR. 5
10/6 X 12/8

FUTURE
BR. 4
10/4 X 12/8

FUTURE
GAMES RM.
16/0 X 16/8 +

CRAWLSPACE

UP

CRAWLSPACE

*The games room
is sure to be an
attention-getter!*

Optional
Lower Level

PLANFEATURES

1,632 total square feet of living area

Width: 50'-0" Depth: 50'-0"

The den/bedroom #3 has a sunny
window seat with flanking closets

The great room enjoys the benefits
of the kitchen's eating bar and a
corner fireplace

The optional lower level has an
additional 1,043 square feet of living
area and is perfect for two extra
bedrooms and a games room

3 bedrooms, 2 baths, 2-car garage

Partial slab/crawl space foundation
with optional unfinished walk-out
basement

Price Code C

houseplansandmore.com

PLANFEATURES

1,978 total square feet of living area

Width: 43'-0" Depth: 53'-3"

Energy efficient home with 2" x 6" exterior walls

A cheerful breakfast nook is a great place to start the day

An enormous walk-in pantry permits easy organization

Large enough for entertaining, the dining room is a great gathering place

2 bedrooms, 2 baths, 1-car garage

Basement foundation

Price Code F

Second Floor
803 sq. ft.

16'-0" X 14'-0"
4,80 X 4,20

14'-4" X 11'-0"
4,30 X 3,30

First Floor
1,175 sq. ft.

14'-0" X 18'-0"
4,20 X 5,40

14'-4" X 17'-4"
4,30 X 5,20

13'-4" X 12'-0"
4,00 X 3,60

16'-8" X 20'-4"
5,00 X 6,10

Warming fireplace in the living room

© Copyright by
designer/architect

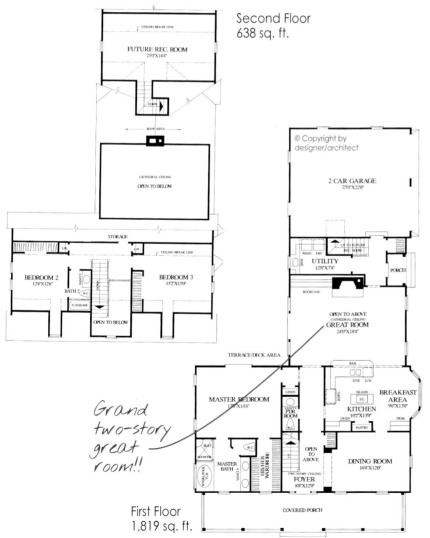

Second Floor
638 sq. ft.

CEILING BREAK LINE

FUTURE REC. ROOM
25'0"X14'4"

ROOF AREA

CATHEDRAL CEILING
OPEN TO BELOW

STORAGE

CEILING BREAK LINE

BEDROOM 2
12'4"X12'6"

BEDROOM 3
15'2"X15'0"

BATH 2

OPEN TO BELOW

© Copyright by
designer/architect

2 CAR GARAGE
25'0"X22'0"

UTILITY
12'8"X7'4"

PORCH

WASH DRY SINK

BOOKCASE

OPEN TO ABOVE
CATHEDRAL CEILING
GREAT ROOM
24'0"X18'4"

TERRACE/DECK AREA

BAR
SINK D/W

MASTER BEDROOM
17'0"X14'4"

LINEN

VANITY
PDR
ROOM
W.C.

REFRIG
ISLAND
S.U.

BREAKFAST
AREA
9'6"X13'0"

KITCHEN
10'2"X13'0"

DESK

OVEN

PANTRY

Grand two-story great room!!

SEAT
SHOWER

W.C.

MASTER
BATH
VANITY

HIS/HER
WARDROBE

OPEN
TO
ABOVE

DINING ROOM
16'4"X12'0"

WHIRLPOOL
TUB

TWO STORY CEILING
FOYER
8'8"X12'0"

COVERED PORCH

First Floor
1,819 sq. ft.

PLAN FEATURES

2,457 total square feet of living area

Width: 47'-4" Depth: 82'-8"

A brilliant cathedral ceiling and warming fireplace makes the great room the perfect place to enjoy company

The kitchen boasts a center island and adjoins the bayed breakfast area that includes a desk

The master bedroom is located on the first floor for added privacy and features a private bath complete with a whirlpool tub and double-bowl vanity

Future recreation room has an additional 385 square feet of living area

3 bedrooms, 2 1/2 baths, 2-car side entry garage

Partial basement/crawl space foundation

Price Code C

Photo, above: Amazing Country French charm is highlighted in this luxurious kitchen where an expansive eating bar/island topped with granite will no doubt be a popular hangout place.

Photo, right: The amazing beam work continues on the interior in the great room where views of the outdoors can be admired from anywhere in the room.

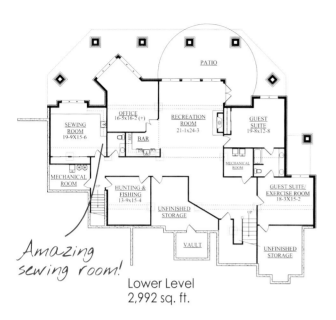

Lower Level
2,992 sq. ft.

Amazing sewing room!

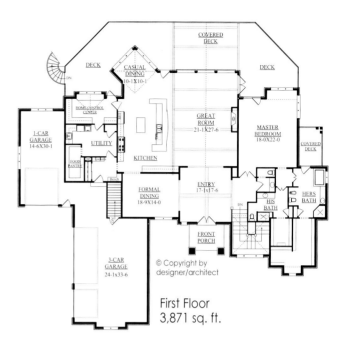

© Copyright by designer/architect

First Floor
3,871 sq. ft.

Photo, below: Cheerful and inviting, the casual dining area promises great meals in a relaxed setting perfect any time of the day.

PLAN FEATURES

6,863 total square feet of living area

Width: 102'-6" Depth: 99'-0"

Energy efficient home with 2" x 6" exterior walls

The amazing great room has a wall of windows, beautiful timber beams, access to the rear deck and a fireplace

A home control center room is located just off the kitchen that boasts two islands

The lower level is perfect for enjoying company with a large recreation room with fireplace and bar

3 bedrooms, 3 full baths, 2 half baths, 3-car side entry garage, 1-car garage

Walk-out basement foundation

Price Code S2

PLANFEATURES

2,211 total square feet of living area

Width: 53'-6" Depth: 76'-10"

The great room features a tray ceiling for added elegance and includes a fireplace for added warmth and charm

Bedroom #2/den is a versatile space that features a walk-in closet and direct access to a full bath

The kitchen features an angled center island with enough casual seating for four people

The bonus room above the garage has an additional 278 square feet of living area

3 bedrooms, 2 baths, 2-car garage

Crawl space or slab foundation, please specify when ordering

Price Code D

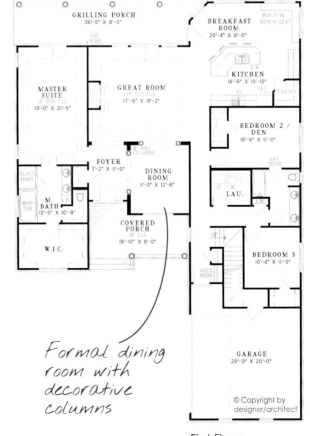

Formal dining room with decorative columns

First Floor
2,211 sq. ft.

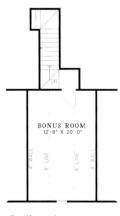

Optional
Second Floor

© Copyright by designer/architect

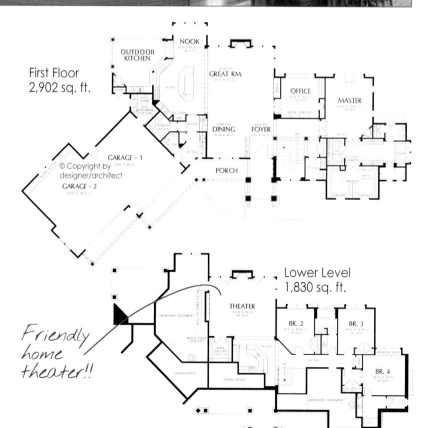

First Floor
2,902 sq. ft.

Lower Level
1,830 sq. ft.

Friendly home theater!!

PLANFEATURES

4,732 total square feet of living area

Width: 130'-3" Depth: 79'-3"

The luxurious master bedroom has abundant his and hers closet space with built-in dressers

The gourmet kitchen, accompanying nook and great room offer ample entertainment space, especially when utilized with the fully equipped outdoor kitchen

The adjoining theater room and wet bar with separate wine cellar complements three lower level bedrooms

4 bedrooms, 3 full baths, 2 half baths, 4-car garage

Walk-out basement foundation

Price Code S1

PLANFEATURES

1,783 total square feet of living area

Width: 49'-4" Depth: 45'-4"

The family room gives a warm welcome with its stone fireplace and open railing upon entering the room

The beautiful screened porch boasts a vaulted wood beam ceiling and fireplace

The master bath has a spacious glass shower, large garden tub, double-bowl vanities and a compartmentalized toilet

3 bedrooms, 3 1/2 baths

Crawl space foundation

Price Code E

Spectacular screened porch with fireplace!!

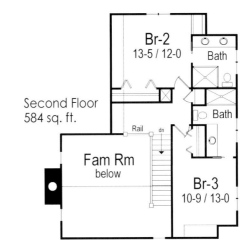

Second Floor
584 sq. ft.

Br-2
13-5 / 12-0
Bath

Bath

Fam Rm
below

Rail   dn

Br-3
10-9 / 13-0

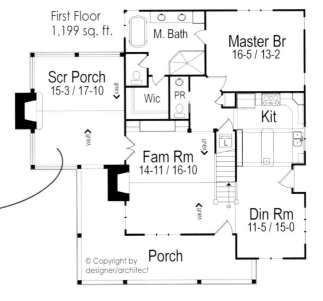

First Floor
1,199 sq. ft.

M. Bath

Master Br
16-5 / 13-2

Scr Porch
15-3 / 17-10

Wic   PR

Kit

Fam Rm
14-11 / 16-10

Din Rm
11-5 / 15-0

© Copyright by
designer/architect

Porch

PLANFEATURES

1,787 total square feet of living area

Width: 55'-8" Depth: 56'-6"

Skylights brighten the screen porch that connects to the family room and deck outdoors

The master bedroom features a comfortable sitting area, a large private bath and direct access to the screen porch

The kitchen has a serving bar that extends dining into the family room

The bonus room above the garage has an additional 263 square feet of living area

3 bedrooms, 2 baths, 2-car side entry garage

Basement, crawl space or slab foundation, please specify when ordering

Price Code B

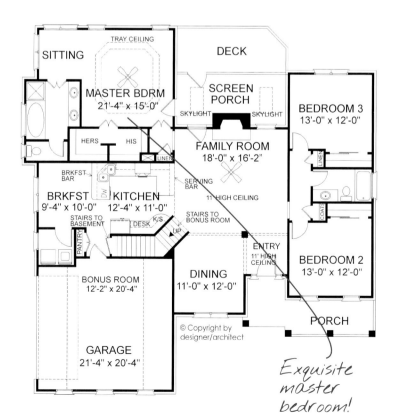

Exquisite master bedroom!

PLANFEATURES

4,725 total square feet of living area

Width: 71'-0" Depth: 70'-0"

Energy efficient home with 2" x 6" exterior walls

Step into the foyer and let it lead you to the stunning rotunda with an angled staircase to the second floor

The family room is full of warmth thanks to the corner fireplace

The kitchen is perfectly positioned between the formal dining room and the casual breakfast nook

4 bedrooms, 4 1/2 baths, 4-car side entry garage

Crawl space foundation

Price Code G

Second Floor
2,390 sq. ft.

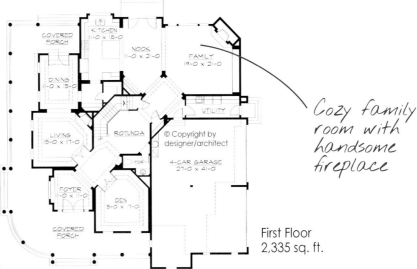

© Copyright by designer/architect

Cozy family room with handsome fireplace

First Floor
2,335 sq. ft.

PLANFEATURES

3,938 total square feet of living area

Width: 61'-0" Depth: 64'-6"

The spacious great room features a fireplace and open design

The master bedroom is vaulted and includes a large walk in closet and bath area

A large bonus room above the garage adds an additional 500 square feet of flexible space that families need

The family will love escaping downstairs to the theater room with built-in cabinetry that neighbors a recreation room and wet bar

5 bedrooms, 4 1/2 baths, 3-car side entry garage

Basement foundation

Price Code S2

Second Floor
1,446 sq. ft.

Wonderful lower level rec room & theater

Lower Level
942 sq. ft.

© Copyright by designer/architect

First Floor
1,550 sq. ft.

houseplansandmore.com

PLAN FEATURES

1,992 total square feet of living area

Width: 72'-0" Depth: 48'-0"

A 12' ceiling and wall of windows open up the great room creating an expansive feel

A sloped ceiling and prominent arched window add a touch of elegance to the interior of the formal dining room

Extra storage is definitely a plus in the garage creating the perfect place for garden equipment or hobby storage

The bonus room above the garage has an additional 428 square feet of living area

3 bedrooms, 2 1/2 baths, 2-car side entry garage

Slab or crawl space foundation, please specify when ordering

Price Code D

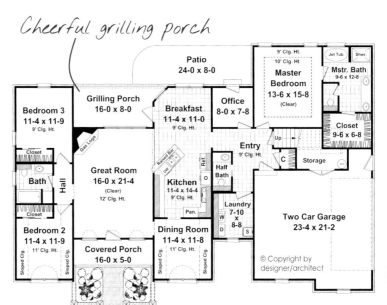

Cheerful grilling porch

Patio
24-0 x 8-0

Grilling Porch
16-0 x 8-0

Bedroom 3
11-4 x 11-9
9' Clg. Ht.

Breakfast
11-4 x 11-0
9' Clg. Ht.

Office
8-0 x 7-8

Master Bedroom
13-6 x 15-8
(Clear)

Mstr. Bath
9-6 x 12-8

Closet
9-6 x 6-8

Closet

Bath

Hall

Great Room
16-0 x 21-4
(Clear)
12' Clg. Ht.

Kitchen
11-4 x 14-4
9' Clg. Ht.

Entry
9' Clg. Ht.

Half Bath

Storage

Two Car Garage
23-4 x 21-2

Laundry
7-10 x 8-8

Bedroom 2
11-4 x 11-9
11' Clg. Ht.

Dining Room
11-4 x 11-8
11' Clg. Ht.

Covered Porch
16-0 x 5-0

© Copyright by
designer/architect

Brick Fence

First Floor
1,992 sq. ft.

Bonus Room
13-8 x 25-4
(Clear)
8' Clg. Ht.

Optional Bath

Down

Attic Access

Approx. 5' Wall Ht.

Optional Second Floor

houseplansandmore.com

Second Floor
1,260 sq. ft.

Two-story family room

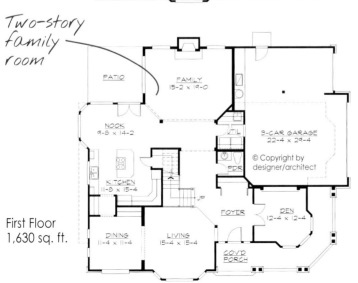

First Floor
1,630 sq. ft.

© Copyright by designer/architect

PLANFEATURES

2,890 total square feet of living area

Width: 59'-0" Depth: 50'-0"

Energy efficient home with 2" x 6" exterior walls

The formal dining and living rooms in the front of the home create a private place for entertaining

The kitchen is designed for efficiency including a large island with cooktop and extra counterspace in route to the dining room

A stunning oversized whirlpool tub is showcased in the private master bath

The bonus room on the second floor has an additional 240 square feet of living area

3 bedrooms, 2 1/2 baths, 3-car side entry garage

Crawl space foundation

Price Code E

PLANFEATURES

3,901 total square feet of living area

Width: 79'-6" Depth: 71'-4"

The column-lined entries add elegance to the formal dining room

The massive great room/hearth room enjoys an open atmosphere with a vaulted ceiling

An exquisite master suite offers a boxed ceiling, a sitting area and a private bath with a whirlpool tub flanked by columns

3 bedrooms, 4 baths, 2-car side entry garage

Slab or crawl space foundation, please specify when ordering

Price Code S1

Second Floor
716 sq. ft.

Delightful gallery

First Floor
3,185 sq. ft.

© Copyright by designer/architect

houseplansandmore.com

PLANFEATURES

5,155 total square feet of living area

Width: 121'-2" Depth: 104'-4"

The two-story grand room boasts a fireplace with flanking shelves and double-door access to the rear terrace

A unique center island in addition to an eating bar provides ample counterspace for the lovely kitchen

The spacious apartment above the garage has an additional 622 square feet, a full bath and kitchen, making it perfect for live-in relatives

5 bedrooms, 4 1/2 baths, 3-car detached side entry garage

Crawl space foundation

Price Code S2

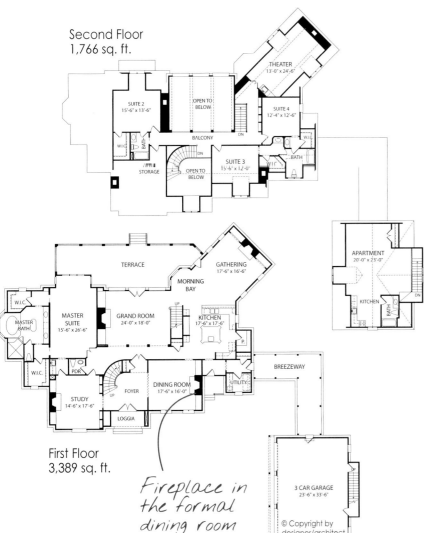

Second Floor
1,766 sq. ft.

THEATER
13'-0" x 24'-6"

SUITE 2
15'-6" x 13'-6"

OPEN TO BELOW

SUITE 4
12'-4" x 12'-6"

W.I.C. BATH BALCONY DN W.I.C.

DN BATH

STORAGE OPEN TO BELOW SUITE 3 W.I.C.
15'-6" x 12'-0"

APARTMENT
20'-0" x 23'-0"

KITCHEN BATH DN

TERRACE GATHERING
17'-6" x 16'-6"

MORNING BAY

W.I.C. MASTER SUITE GRAND ROOM KITCHEN
15'-6" x 26'-6" 24'-0" x 18'-0" 17'-6" x 17'-6"

MASTER BATH UP P.

W.I.C. PDR BREEZEWAY

STUDY FOYER DINING ROOM UTILITY
14'-6" x 17'-6" 17'-6" x 16'-0"

UP LOGGIA

First Floor
3,389 sq. ft.

Fireplace in the formal dining room

3 CAR GARAGE
23'-6" x 33'-6"

© Copyright by designer/architect

houseplansandmore.com

PLANFEATURES

3,368 total square feet of living area

Width: 71'-0" Depth: 57'-0"

The sunken great room features a cathedral ceiling, wooden beams, skylights and a masonry fireplace

The octagon-shaped breakfast room has a domed ceiling with beams, large windows and a door to the patio

The private master bedroom has a deluxe bath and dressing area

Oversized walk-in closets and storage areas are located in each bedroom

4 bedrooms, 3 full baths, 2 half baths, 2-car side entry garage

Basement foundation

Price Code F

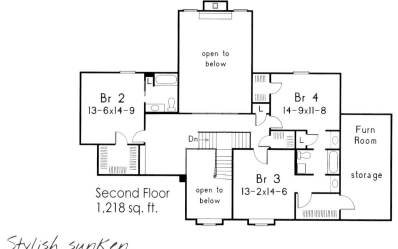

Second Floor
1,218 sq. ft.

Stylish sunken great room!

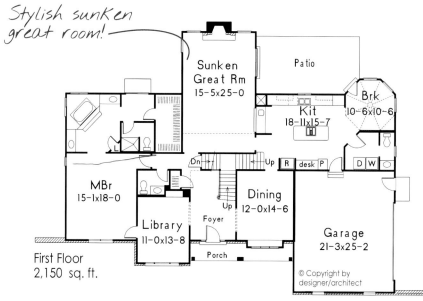

First Floor
2,150 sq. ft.

© Copyright by designer/architect

houseplansandmore.com

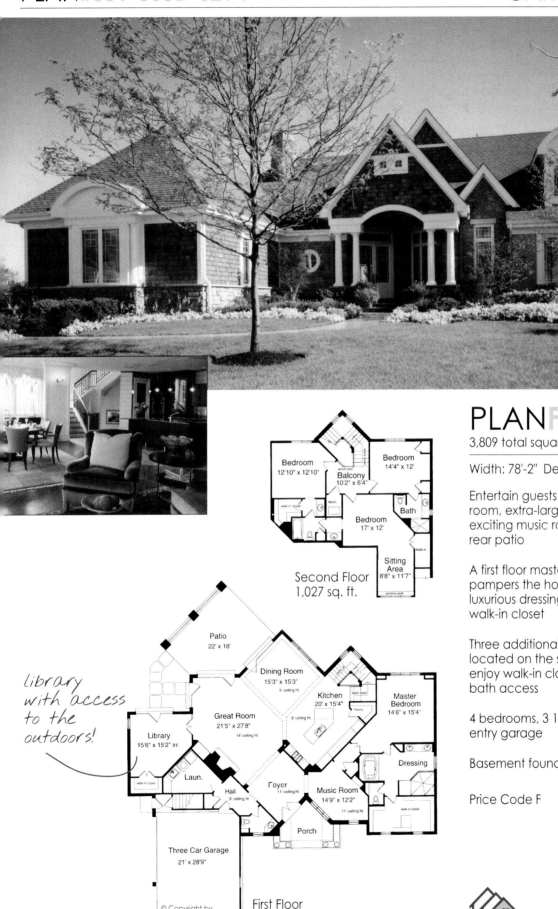

library with access to the outdoors!

Second Floor
1,027 sq. ft.

Bedroom
12'10" x 12'10"

Bedroom
14'4" x 12'

Balcony
10'2" x 6'4"

Bedroom
17' x 12'

Bath

Sitting
Area
8'8" x 11'7"

First Floor
2,782 sq. ft.

Patio
22' x 18'

Dining Room
15'3" x 15'3"

Kitchen
20' x 15'4"

Master
Bedroom
14'6" x 15'4"

Great Room
21'5" x 27'8"

Library
15'6" x 15'2" irr.

Laun.

Hail

Foyer

Music Room
14'9" x 12'2"

Dressing

Three Car Garage
21' x 28'9"

Porch

© Copyright by
designer/architect

PLANFEATURES

3,809 total square feet of living area

Width: 78'-2" Depth: 74'-6"

Entertain guests with a formal dining room, extra-large great room, exciting music room and enchanting rear patio

A first floor master bedroom pampers the homeowner with its luxurious dressing area and large walk-in closet

Three additional bedrooms are located on the second floor and enjoy walk-in closets and private bath access

4 bedrooms, 3 1/2 baths, 3-car side entry garage

Basement foundation

Price Code F

houseplansandmore.com

Photo, above: Stately columns and arches frame the plush outdoor living space and fireplace without restricting the open air atmosphere.

Photo, right: Located in the heart of this home, the sweeping stairwell and rotunda provide a dazzling view to a spectacular domed stained glass ceiling above.

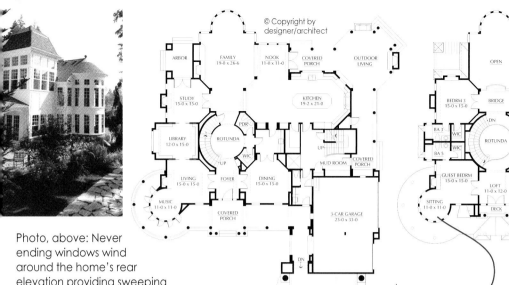

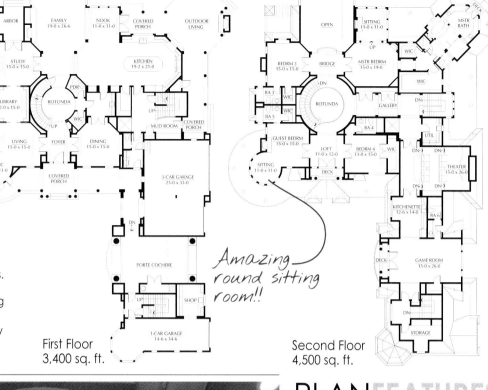

© Copyright by designer/architect

Photo, above: Never ending windows wind around the home's rear elevation providing sweeping views in all directions and bright, cheerful interior spaces.

Photo, below: Total pampering is sure to occur in the lavish private master bath with every amenity imaginable enclosed in a spa-like setting.

First Floor
3,400 sq. ft.

Amazing round sitting room!!

Second Floor
4,500 sq. ft.

PLAN FEATURES

7,900 total square feet of living area

Width: 96'-0" Depth: 145'-0"

Energy efficient home with 2" x 6" exterior walls

The grand, open kitchen has ample counter space and a center island

A circular music room sits just off the living room providing entertainment and relaxation

An impressive rotunda staircase leads you to the immense second floor that features all the bedrooms, a theater, a kitchenette and game room with double-door access to a lovely deck

4 bedrooms, 5 full baths, 2 half baths, 4-car side entry garage

Crawl space foundation

Price Code S1

houseplansandmore.com

PLAN FEATURES

3,268 total square feet of living area

Width: 53'-10" Depth: 71'-10"

Stucco and brick combine to create a beautiful facade

As you enter the home, a grand entrance greets you with an elegant staircase and formal dining room

The second floor includes three bedrooms, two of which open to the outdoor balcony and include their own sitting areas

The future gameroom has an additional 323 square feet of living space

4 bedrooms, 3 1/2 baths, 2-car side entry garage

Slab foundation

Price Code H

Bright breakfast area!

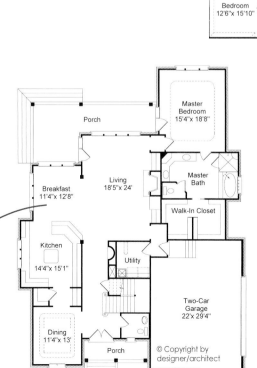

Second Floor
1,098 sq. ft.

Balcony 11'9"x 11'9"
Sitting 8'4"x 8'8"
Sitting 4'2"x 10'
Bedroom 11'x 14'11"
Bedroom 11'3"x 16'1"
Bath
Bath
Bedroom 12'6"x 15'10"
Open to Below
Gameroom 16'4"x 19'4"

Porch
Master Bedroom 15'4"x 18'8"
Living 18'5"x 24'
Master Bath
Breakfast 11'4"x 12'8"
Walk-In Closet
Kitchen 14'4"x 15'1"
Utility
Two-Car Garage 22'x 29'4"
Dining 11'4"x 13'
Porch

© Copyright by designer/architect

First Floor
2,170 sq. ft.

houseplansandmore.com

CASTLETON

Second Floor
2,207 sq. ft.

MASTER
17/0 X 16/6
(11' CLG.)

8/4 X 6/8
(9' CLG.)

SPA

LINEN

MEDIA/ PLAYRM
16/10 X 13/8
(11' CLG.)

OPEN TO BELOW

(9' CLG.)

NICHE

LINEN

UP

(10' CLG.)

DN

LINEN

SNACK BAR

BR. 3
12/10 X 12/0
(9' CLG.)

BR. 4
11/0 X 14/0
(9' CLG.)

BR. 2
13/0 X 13/8
(9' CLG.)

First Floor
1,634 sq. ft.

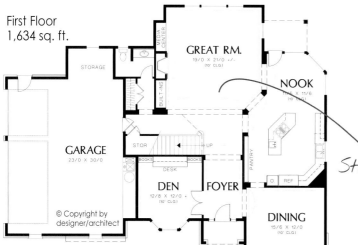

STORAGE

MEDIA CENTER

GREAT RM.
19/0 X 21/0 +/-
(10' CLG.)

BUILT-INS

NOOK
(10' CLG.)

GARAGE
23/0 X 30/0

STOR

UP

BOOKS

DESK

BOOKS

PANTRY

REF

DEN
12/8 X 12/0 +
(10' CLG.)

FOYER

DINING
15/6 X 12/0
(10' CLG.)

Stately great room

© Copyright by designer/architect

PLANFEATURES

3,841 total square feet of living area

Width: 64'-0" Depth: 50'-0"

The great room, equipped with a fireplace, built-in shelves and a media center, is a central gathering place for family members

Decorative columns define the kitchen and nook, while allowing seamless flow from one room to the next

The second floor media/playroom is equipped with a snack station, creating an ideal entertainment space

4 bedrooms, 3 1/2 baths, 3-car side entry garage

Crawl space foundation

Price Code S1

houseplansandmore.com

EUREKA

Photo, above: This view from above shows off the open feeling that this energy efficient home enjoys. The first floor's open floor plan makes everyday living easy and comfortable.

Photo, right: A handy raised breakfast bar extends off the kitchen counter making casual dining or watching the family chef easy and fun.

houseplansandmore.com

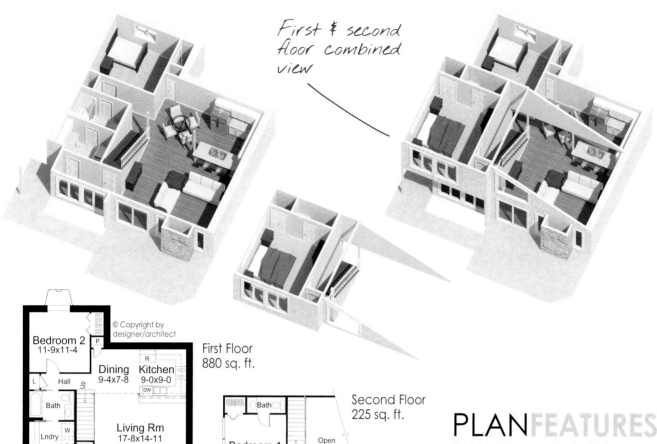

First & second floor combined view

© Copyright by designer/architect

Bedroom 2
11-9x11-4

Dining
9-4x7-8

Kitchen
9-0x9-0

Hall

Bath

Lndry

Foyer

Living Rm
17-8x14-11
Sloped Clg.

Patio

First Floor
880 sq. ft.

Bath

Bedroom 1
11-10x14-2

Open

Second Floor
225 sq. ft.

Photo, below: An immense amount of windows in the living room create a bright and open interior.

PLANFEATURES

1,105 total square feet of living area

Width: 33'-0" Depth: 35'-0"

Energy efficient home with 2" x 6" exterior walls

This fresh, modern design enjoys sleek window lines and a stucco exterior making it a truly one-of-a-kind living experience

The compact, yet efficient U-shaped kitchen offers a tremendous amount of counterspace within reach for all sorts of kitchen tasks at hand

A tall sloped ceiling in the two-story living room gives this home an open and spacious feel all those who enter will appreciate

2 bedrooms, 1 1/2 baths

Slab foundation

Price Code AAA

houseplansandmore.com

PLAN FEATURES

2,824 total square feet of living area

Width: 67'-0" Depth: 64'-2"

9' ceilings on the first floor

The second floor bedrooms feature private dressing areas and share a bath

The large great room includes a fireplace flanked by French doors leading to the rear patio

The kitchen conveniently serves the formal dining room and breakfast area which features a large bay window

4 bedrooms, 3 baths, 2-car side entry garage

Slab foundation, drawings also include crawl space foundation

Price Code E

Second Floor
704 sq. ft.

Br 2
12-10x15-5

Br 3
11-6x15-5

Dn

First Floor
2,120 sq. ft.

Garage
21-4x21-4

Patio

Covered Porch

© Copyright by designer/architect

MBr
14-0x17-0

Laun
12-6x7-6

Great Rm
19-4x17-0

Brk
14-0x9-0

Kit
12-0x12-0

Dining
11-3x15-10

up

Living
11-4x11-4

Guest Rm
12-0x12-0

Large walk-in closet in the master bedroom

Porch Depth 6-0

PLANFEATURES

2,982 total square feet of living area

Width: 80'-0" Depth: 49'-8"

French doors lead into a private study perfect for a home office

An extra-large kitchen island offers space for quick meals or buffet dinners and opens to the enchanting sun room

A double-door entry leads into the elegant master suite that features a vaulted ceiling and plush bath with walk-in closet

4 bedrooms, 2 1/2 baths, 3-car garage

Walk-out basement foundation

Price Code E

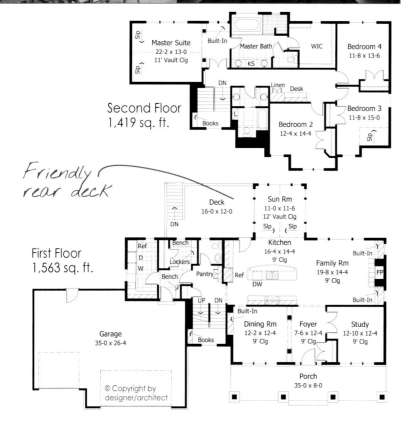

Second Floor 1,419 sq. ft.

Master Suite 22-2 x 13-0 11' Vault Clg

Built-In

Master Bath

KS

WIC

Bedroom 4 11-8 x 13-6

DN

Linen Desk

Books

Bedroom 2 12-4 x 14-4

Bedroom 3 11-8 x 15-0

Friendly rear deck

First Floor 1,563 sq. ft.

Deck 16-0 x 12-0

DN

Sun Rm 11-0 x 11-6 12' Vault Clg

Kitchen 16-4 x 14-4 9' Clg

Family Rm 19-8 x 14-4 9' Clg

Built-In

FP

Built-In

Ref
D
W

Bench

Lockers

Bench

Pantry

Ref

DW

UP DN

Books

Built-In

Dining Rm 12-2 x 12-4 9' Clg

Foyer 7-6 x 12-4 9' Clg

Study 12-10 x 12-4 9' Clg

Garage 35-0 x 26-4

Porch 35-0 x 8-0

© Copyright by designer/architect

houseplansandmore.com

PLAN FEATURES

1,504 total square feet of living area

Width: 39'-6" Depth: 72'-5"

A private master suite has its own luxury bath featuring an oversized tub and shower

A full bath is positioned between the two secondary bedrooms for convenience

Enjoy the outdoors on the covered porch directly off the breakfast room

3 bedrooms, 2 baths, 2-car garage

Crawl space or slab foundation, please specify when ordering

Price Code C

French doors open to a lovely master bath

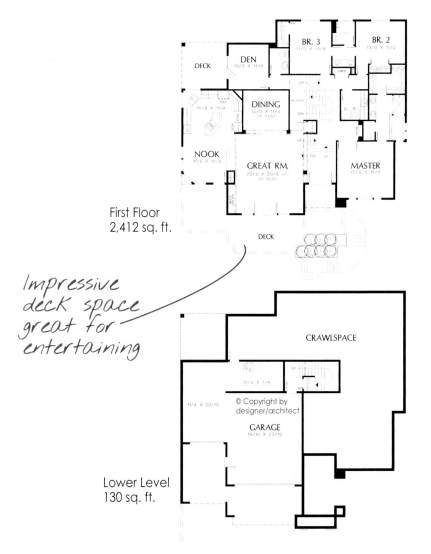

First Floor
2,412 sq. ft.

Impressive deck space great for entertaining

Lower Level
130 sq. ft.

© Copyright by designer/architect

PLANFEATURES

2,542 total square feet of living area

Width: 60'-0" Depth: 59'-0"

Energy efficient home with 2" x 6" exterior walls

A private den enjoys easy outdoor access directly onto the deck

A cheerful breakfast nook has windows on all sides for great views of the outdoors

The spacious great room steps out onto a large wrap-around front deck ideal for entertaining in style

3 bedrooms, 2 1/2 baths, 3-car drive under garage

Partial crawl space/slab foundation

Price Code F

Photo, above: This stately English inspired home enjoys a refreshing swimming pool in the backyard and has nearby arch entryways leading to a majestic outdoor dining space.

Photo, right: This spectacular master bedroom walk-in closet takes personal pampering to a whole new level with an immense amount of storage space as well as panache.

houseplansandmore.com

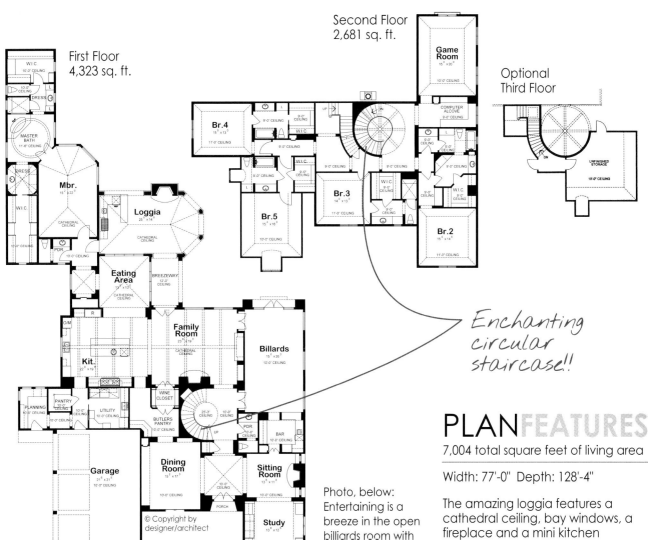

First Floor
4,323 sq. ft.

W.I.C.
10'-0" CEILING
DRESS

MASTER BATH
11'-6" CEILING

DRESS

Mbr.
15'² x 22'⁰

W.I.C.
10'-0" CEILING

PDR.
10'-0" CEILING

Loggia
25'⁶ x 14'

CATHEDRAL CEILING

CATHEDRAL CEILING

Eating Area
13'⁶ x 13'³
CATHEDRAL CEILING

BREEZEWAY
12'-0" CEILING

Family Room
23'⁶ x 19'⁶
CATHEDRAL CEILING

Billards
15'⁶ x 26'⁰
10'-0" CEILING

Kit.
22'⁰ x 19'⁶

O/M
R

PLANNING
10'-0" CEILING

PANTRY
10'-0" CEILING

UTILITY
10'-0" CEILING

WINE CLOSET
25'-3" CEILING

BUTLERS PANTRY
10'-0" CEILING

UP

PDR.

BAR
10'-0" CEILING

Garage
21'⁶ x 31'⁶
10'-0" CEILING

Dining Room
15'⁶ x 17'⁰
10'-0" CEILING

Sitting Room
13'⁶ x 11'⁰
10'-0" CEILING

PORCH

Study
13'⁶ x 12'⁰
10'-0" CEILING

© Copyright by designer/architect

Second Floor
2,681 sq. ft.

Game Room
15'⁶ x 20'⁰
10'-0" CEILING

COMPUTER ALCOVE
9'-0" CEILING

UP

Br.4
15'⁶ x 13'⁰
11'-0" CEILING

9'-0" CEILING

W.I.C.

W.I.C.

9'-0" CEILING

Br.5
15'⁶ x 16'⁰
10'-0" CEILING

Br.3
14'⁶ x 13'⁰
11'-0" CEILING

W.I.C.
9'-0" CEILING

W.I.C.
9'-0" CEILING

Br.2
15'⁶ x 14'⁶
11'-0" CEILING

Optional Third Floor

DN

UNFINISHED STORAGE
10'-0" CEILING

Enchanting circular staircase!!

Photo, below: Entertaining is a breeze in the open billiards room with double-doors to the outdoor patio and swimming pool.

PLAN FEATURES

7,004 total square feet of living area

Width: 77'-0" Depth: 128'-4"

The amazing loggia features a cathedral ceiling, bay windows, a fireplace and a mini kitchen

There are many amenities in the delightful master bedroom including a dressing room, two large walk-in closets, and a corner tub in the private bath

Entertaining is a breeze in the open billiards room with double-doors to the outdoors

The unfinished storage on the third floor has an additional 400 square feet of living area

5 bedrooms, 5 full baths, 2 half baths, 3-car side entry garage

Slab foundation

Price Code I

PLAN FEATURES

6,732 total square feet of living area

Width: 116'-0" Depth: 115'-4"

Energy efficient home with 2" x 6" exterior walls

An outdoor kitchen is found on the covered deck and has a fireplace

A massive center island in the kitchen is a bold element that adds great design, while providing workspace as well as dining space

The lower level is designed for memorable entertaining with an exercise room, a wet bar, a covered patio with hot tub space, a billiards and media area, and a wine cellar

4 bedrooms, 5 full baths, 2 half baths, 2-car side entry garage, 2-car garage

Walk-out basement or basement foundation, please specify when ordering

Price Code S3

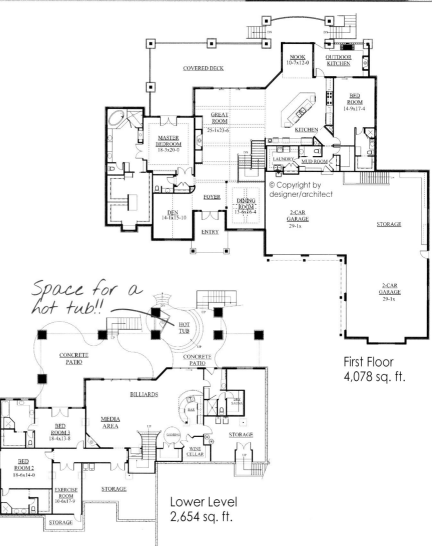

First Floor
4,078 sq. ft.

Lower Level
2,654 sq. ft.

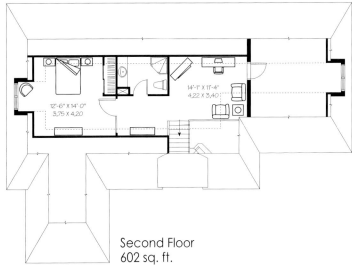

Second Floor
602 sq. ft.

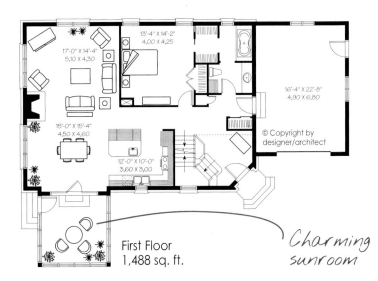

First Floor
1,488 sq. ft.

Charming sunroom

PLAN FEATURES

2,090 total square feet of living area

Width: 60'-0" Depth: 44'-0"

Energy efficient home with 2" x 6" exterior walls

Two bedrooms share a full bath on the second floor

A prominent fireplace is the focal point of the combined living and dining rooms

An oversized kitchen island includes a vegetable sink and has enough space for dining

2 bedrooms, 2 baths, 1-car garage

Basement foundation

Price Code H

© Copyright by designer/architect

houseplansandmore.com

Photo, right: A gable duo along with a brick arched entry into the covered front porch offers a tremendous amount of curb appeal.

houseplansandmore.com

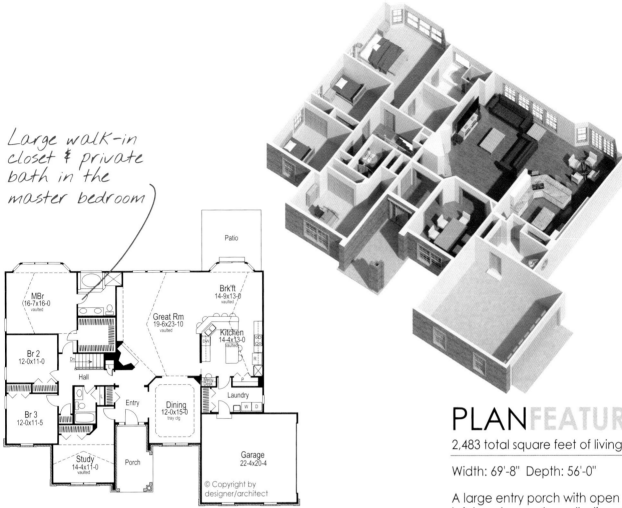

Large walk-in closet & private bath in the master bedroom

Photo, below: It is easy to see how functional the kitchen layout will be. From the center work island, to the wrap-around counter with seating for up to five people, this is bound to be the spot where everyone ends up no matter what time of day.

PLANFEATURES

2,483 total square feet of living area

Width: 69'-8" Depth: 56'-0"

A large entry porch with open brick arches and a palladian door welcomes guests

The vaulted great room features an entertainment center alcove and the ideal layout for furniture placement

The dining room is extra large with a stylish tray ceiling

A convenient kitchen with wrap-around counter, menu desk and pantry opens to the cozy breakfast area

2" x 6" exterior walls available, please order plan #651-007E-0062

3 bedrooms, 2 baths, 2-car side entry garage

Basement foundation

Price Code D

houseplansandmore.com

PLAN FEATURES

3,157 total square feet of living area

Width: 70'-0" Depth: 50'-0"

A grand circular staircase can be found in the two-story foyer

Double doors off the foyer lead to a private den ideal as a home office

An oversized island in the kitchen offers extra dining and preparation space

4 bedrooms, 2 1/2 baths, 3-car garage

Crawl space foundation

Price Code F

Second Floor
1,393 sq. ft.

Open & comfortable family room

First Floor
1,764 sq. ft.

© Copyright by designer/architect

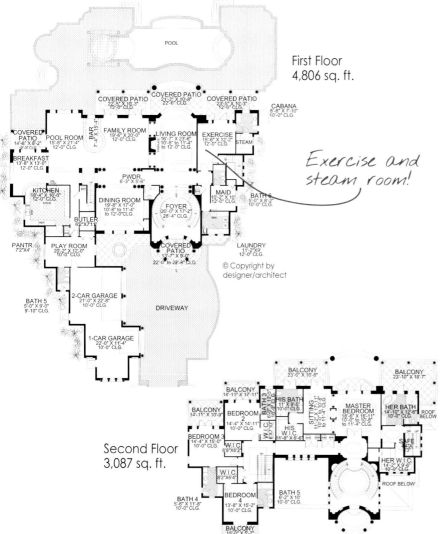

First Floor
4,806 sq. ft.

Exercise and steam room!

© Copyright by
designer/architect

Second Floor
3,087 sq. ft.

PLANFEATURES

7,893 total square feet of living area

Width: 102'-6" Depth: 120'-2"

This home offers multiple spaces for entertainment; from the playroom to the exercise room and steam room, as well as a full bar that separates the pool room from the family room

The master suite is completely divided into his and hers spaces, with each even having their own private balcony

Numerous covered patios and bedroom balconies offer outdoor retreats from the busier rooms

Framing - only concrete block available

5 bedrooms, 7 full baths, 2 half baths, 3-car side entry garage

Slab foundation

Price Code S1

houseplansandmore.com

Photo, above: The center island of this refined kitchen is definitely the focal point with its strong contrast against the dark-stained cabinetry, decorative details and lighting, this spot is great for preparing meals and enjoying casual snacks or appetizers. This enormous granite-topped kitchen island is sure to be the hub of activity with casual seating for dining and an oversized sink.

Photo, right: Sunlight streams into the great room through an amazing two-story window design. With the addition of the fireplace and dark wood bookcases, this room has a handsome feel. A towering window wall offers sweeping views of the outdoors while also filling the interior of the great room with natural sunlight.

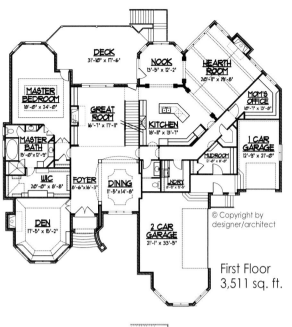

DECK
31'-10" x 11'-6"

NOOK
13'-5" x 12'-2"

HEARTH ROOM
20'-11" x 19'-8"

MOM'S OFFICE
10'-1" x 13'-0"

MASTER BEDROOM
18'-0" x 24'-0"

GREAT ROOM
16'-1" x 17'-11"

KITCHEN
18'-11" x 13'-1"

1 CAR GARAGE
12'-9" x 21'-0"

MASTER BATH
15'-0" x 12'-9"

WIC
20'-0" x 8'-8"

FOYER

DINING
11'-5" x 14'-8"

MUDROOM
12'-0" x 8'-0"

LNDRY
8'-9" x 9'-5"

DEN
17'-5" x 15'-2"

2 CAR GARAGE
21'-1" x 33'-5"

© Copyright by designer/architect

First Floor
3,511 sq. ft.

BED #3
13'-3" x 18'-8"

O.T.B.

BED #4
21'-7" x 12'-1"

BED #2
12'-1" x 15'-4"

ACTIVITY ROOM
12'-0" x 31'-4"

Second Floor
1,719 sq. ft.

Photo, below: A highly functional "mom's office" enjoys expansive counterspace for all types of home, school or work projects.

Desirable theater, game area & pub!!

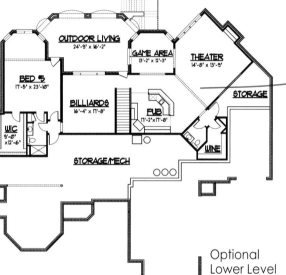

OUTDOOR LIVING
24'-9" x 16'-2"

GAME AREA
13'-2" x 12'-2"

THEATER
14'-8" x 13'-9"

BED #5
17'-5" x 23'-10"

BILLIARDS
16'-4" x 11'-8"

PUB
11'-2" x 17'-8"

STORAGE

WIC
9'-0" x 12'-6"

STORAGE/MECH

WINE

Optional Lower Level

Photo, below: Specialty ceiling beams tower over the hearth room adding a rustic Old World touch in addition to the stone fireplace. Oversized arched windows frame the cozy stone fireplace in the hearth room.

PLAN FEATURES

5,230 total square feet of living area

Width: 86'-1" Depth: 86'-3"

A stunning bay-shaped den with fireplace is the perfect spot for cozy relaxation, or as a home office

Mom's office offers an organized place for planning all the family activities

The second floor activity room could easily be converted to a home theater

The optional lower level has an additional 2,126 square feet of living area

4 bedrooms, 3 1/2 baths, 2-car side entry garage, 1-car garage

Walk-out basement foundation

Price Code S1

houseplansandmore.com

PLANFEATURES

5,102 total square feet of living area

Width: 67'-6" Depth: 85'-0"

The star attraction of the Spanish Mediterranean home is its multi-purpose cabana

This home enjoys a unique covered patio/courtyard combination with a summer kitchen

Unique glass blocks around the spa-style tub brighten the interior of the private master bath

5 bedrooms, 5 1/2 baths, 3-car garage

Slab foundation

Price Code S1

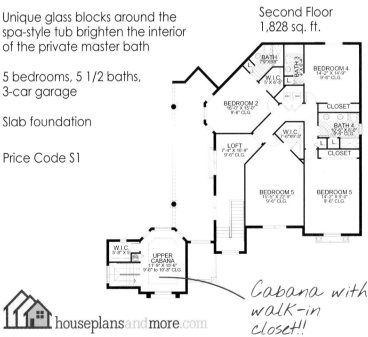

Second Floor
1,828 sq. ft.

Cabana with walk-in closet!!

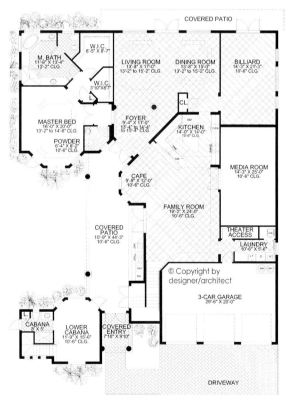

First Floor
3,274 sq. ft.

houseplansandmore.com

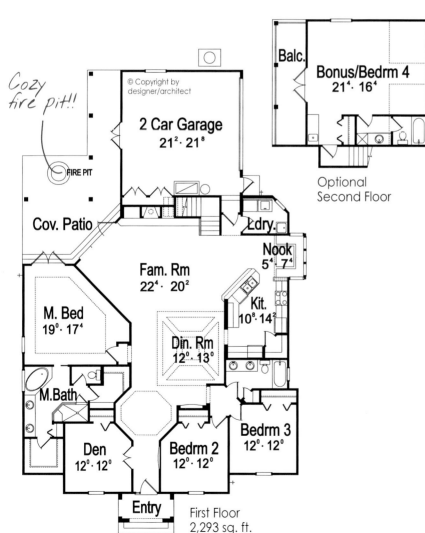

Cozy fire pit!!

FIRE PIT

© Copyright by designer/architect

2 Car Garage
21² · 21⁸

Cov. Patio

Ldry.

Fam. Rm
22⁴ · 20²

Nook
5⁴ · 7⁴

Kit.
10⁸ · 14²

M. Bed
19⁰ · 17⁴

Din. Rm
12⁰ · 13⁰

M. Bath

Den
12⁰ · 12⁰

Bedrm 2
12⁰ · 12⁰

Bedrm 3
12⁰ · 12⁰

Entry

First Floor
2,293 sq. ft.

Balc.

Bonus/Bedrm 4
21⁴ · 16⁴

Optional
Second Floor

PLANFEATURES

2,293 total square feet of living area

Width: 51'-0" Depth: 74'-4"

The family and dining rooms feature 12' ceilings for added openness

The cozy nook area brings in an abundance of warm natural light

The master bedroom enjoys private access onto the covered patio and a deluxe bath

The optional second floor has an additional 509 square feet of living area with space for a bedroom and bath

3 bedrooms, 2 baths, 2-car side entry garage

Slab foundation

Price Code E

houseplansandmore.com

SALINA

2,333 total square feet of living area

Width: 77'-0" Depth: 50'-10"

9' ceilings on the first floor

The master bedroom features a large walk-in closet and an inviting double-door entry into a spacious bath

The convenient laundry room is located near the kitchen

4 bedrooms, 3 baths, 2-car side entry garage

Slab foundation, drawings also include crawl space and partial crawl space/basement foundations

Price Code D

Charming dormers!

Second Floor
648 sq. ft.

© Copyright by designer/architect

First Floor
1,685 sq. ft.

PESCADO

2,698 total square feet of living area

Width: 70'-2" Depth: 51'-4"

The great room feels spacious with a vaulted ceiling and windows overlooking the covered porch

The master bath has a glass shower and whirlpool tub

The laundry area includes counterspace and a sink

5 bedrooms, 3 baths, 2-car side entry garage

Slab or crawl space foundation, please specify when ordering

Price Code E

First Floor
1,813 sq. ft.

Second Floor
885 sq. ft.

© Copyright by designer/architect

Welcoming covered front porch

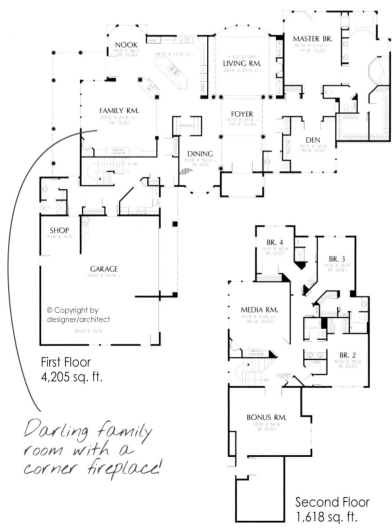

First Floor
4,205 sq. ft.

© Copyright by
designer/architect

Darling family room with a corner fireplace!

Second Floor
1,618 sq. ft.

PLANFEATURES

5,823 total square feet of living area

Width: 104'-0" Depth: 97'-0"

Upon entering this home, you will be greeted by a stunning 14' foyer that leads to a sun-filled living room

The second floor media room is sure to be a favorite gathering spot near the secondary bedrooms

The open casual family room is only partially separated from the kitchen and nook by a freestanding wet bar

The bonus room on the second floor has an additional 504 square feet of living area

4 bedrooms, 5 1/2 baths, 3-car side entry garage

Crawl space foundation

Price Code S1

houseplansandmore.com

PLANFEATURES

5,183 total square feet of living area

Width: 90'-0" Depth: 73'-6"

The double-door entry opens to a spacious foyer and an arched passageway into the great room

Built-in cabinets, a corner fireplace and a 12' ceiling are featured in the expansive great room

A media center is conveniently located adjacent to the breakfast room allowing easy computer access

4 bedrooms, 5 1/2 baths, 2-car side entry garage

Basement foundation, drawings also include crawl space and slab foundations

Price Code S2

Second Floor
1,780 sq. ft.

First Floor
3,403 sq. ft.

Walk-in closets galore!!

houseplansandmore.com

© Copyright by designer/architect

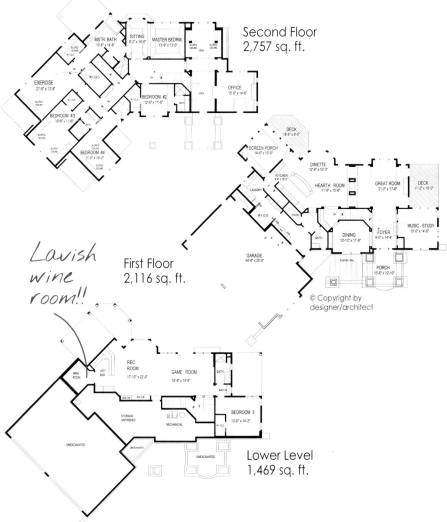

Second Floor
2,757 sq. ft.

First Floor
2,116 sq. ft.

Lavish wine room!!

Lower Level
1,469 sq. ft.

© Copyright by designer/architect

PLANFEATURES

6,342 total square feet of living area

Width: 97'-0" Depth: 78'-9"

The eloquent pergola covered entry welcomes guests and leads them to a spacious covered porch

Once inside, this lovely home expands to include an open great room and hearth room that share a double-sided fireplace

The kitchen includes a pantry, in addition to a passageway and serving area into the formal dining room

The screen porch with fireplace will make for cozy family gatherings all year round

5 bedrooms, 4 1/2 baths, 4-car side entry garage

Walk-out basement foundation

Price Code S1

houseplansandmore.com

PLAN FEATURES

3,118 total square feet of living area

Width: 60'-0" Depth: 52'-0"

Energy efficient home with 2" x 6" exterior walls

The secluded den has a double-door entry and a built-in bookcase perfect for a home office

The spacious master bedroom has a lovely bath with an enormous whirlpool tub and walk-in closet

An oversized island in the kitchen has enough room for dining

The bonus room on the second floor is included in the square footage

3 bedrooms, 2 1/2 baths, 3-car garage

Crawl space foundation

Price Code G

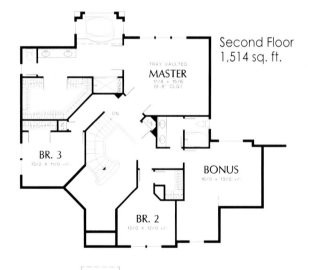

Second Floor
1,514 sq. ft.

MASTER
TRAY VAULTED
17/8 x 15/6
(9'-8" CLG)

BR. 3
13/2 X 11/0 +/-

BONUS
16/0 x 13/0 +/-

BR. 2
12/0 x 12/0 +/-

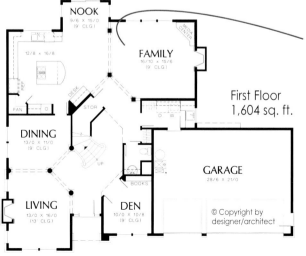

NOOK
9/6 x 15/0
(9' CLG)

FAMILY
16/10 x 15/6
(9' CLG)

Open family room, nook & Kitchen!

DINING
13/0 x 11/0
(9' CLG)

First Floor
1,604 sq. ft.

GARAGE
28/6 X 21/0

LIVING
13/0 x 16/0
(13' CLG)

DEN
10/0 x 10/8
(9' CLG)

BOOKS

© Copyright by designer/architect

houseplansandmore.com

PLANFEATURES

1,833 total square feet of living area

Width: 49'-5" Depth: 40'-10"

The family room enjoys a warming stone fireplace and is brightened by a wall of windows

The eating room, that is adjacent to the kitchen and family room, is surrounded by casement windows and has a sloped ceiling that adds volume

The master bedroom has a unique sloped tray ceiling, a wall of windows, and a walk-in closet

The optional lower level has an additional 1,009 square feet of living area and would be perfect as an apartment

3 bedrooms, 3 baths

Walk-out basement foundation

Price Code E

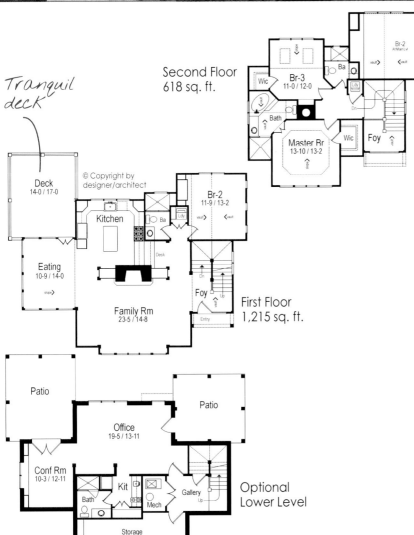

Tranquil deck

Second Floor
618 sq. ft.

Br-2
At Main Lvl

Ba

Wic

Br-3
11-0 / 12-0

Ldy

Bath

Dn

Master Br
13-10 / 13-2

Wic

Foy

© Copyright by designer/architect

Deck
14-0 / 17-0

Kitchen

Ba

Br-2
11-9 / 13-2

Ldy

Eating
10-9 / 14-0

Desk

Dn

Foy

Up

First Floor
1,215 sq. ft.

Family Rm
23-5 / 14-8

Entry

Patio

Patio

Office
19-5 / 13-11

Conf Rm
10-3 / 12-11

Kit

Gallery

Up

Optional
Lower Level

Bath

Mech

Storage

houseplansandmore.com

PLANFEATURES

5,794 total square feet of living area

Width: 71'-6" Depth: 84'-0"

This two-story plan has a spacious kitchen that is open to the great room wrapped by two large decks and a four season room

The second floor has a loft area and four bedrooms, including a private master bedroom and bedrooms #2 and #3 sharing a Jack and Jill bath

A full lower level provides a wet bar, recreation/media, game, exercise, and guest rooms

The bonus room on the second floor has an additional 425 square feet of living area

5 bedrooms, 4 1/2 baths, 3-car side entry garage

Walk-out basement foundation

Price Code S4

Second Floor
1,884 sq. ft.

FUTURE STORAGE
15'-0" x 22'-4"

© Copyright by designer/architect

Soothing music room or study!

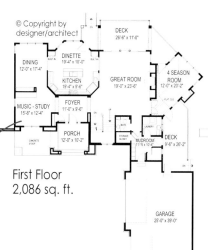

First Floor
2,086 sq. ft.

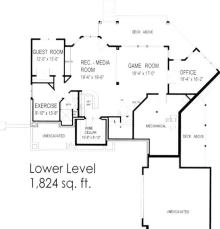

Lower Level
1,824 sq. ft.

PLANFEATURES

2,525 total square feet of living area

Width: 67'-2" Depth: 55'-10"

Stunning columns frame the foyer that leads into the open great room with fireplace, as well as the home theater/living room

The formal dining room, casual breakfast room and grilling porch with fireplace provide an abundance of dining opportunities

Three bedrooms and two baths occupy one side of this home, while the master suite is secluded on the other

4 bedrooms, 3 baths, 2-car garage

Crawl space or slab foundation, please specify when ordering

Price Code E

Pampering master bath!!

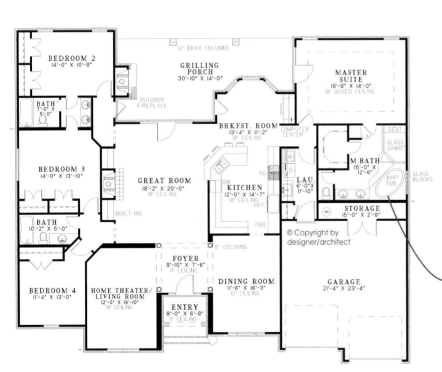

PLAN FEATURES

5,387 total square feet of living area

Width: 88'-6" Depth: 98'-0"

Elegance and comfort surround all aspects of this refined home starting with the two-story living room with three sets of double-doors accessing the rear terrace

Convenience is a priority with two separate sets of stairs to access the lavish second floor

An enchanting lounge area on the second floor overlooks the open and bright living room below

The future recreation room on the second floor has an additional 489 square feet of living area

4 bedrooms, 5 1/2 baths, 3-car side entry garage

Crawl space or basement foundation, please specify when ordering

Price Code G

Second Floor
1,924 sq. ft.

Triple French doors!

First Floor
3,463 sq. ft.

© Copyright by designer/architect

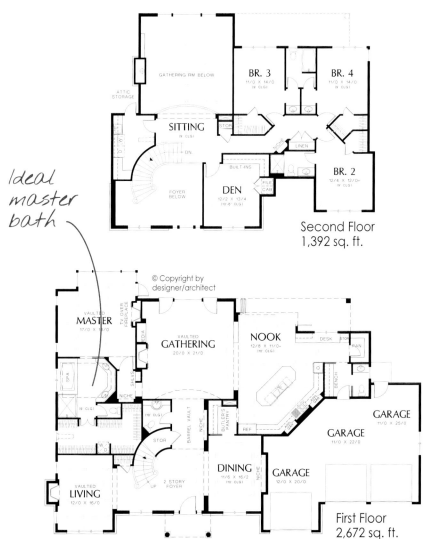

Ideal master bath

Second Floor
1,392 sq. ft.

© Copyright by designer/architect

First Floor
2,672 sq. ft.

PLANFEATURES

4,064 total square feet of living area

Width: 80'-0" Depth: 57'-0"

A wonderful second floor sitting balcony overlooks the spacious gathering room below

The cozy vaulted living room with fireplace would make a great reading room

A convenient butler's pantry connects the formal dining room and kitchen perfectly for ease when entertaining

4 bedrooms, 3 full baths, 2 half baths, 3-car garage

Crawl space foundation

Price Code S1

PLAN FEATURES

5,282 total square feet of living area

Width: 95'-0" Depth: 62'-0"

Energy efficient home with 2" x 6" exterior walls

Decorative columns, arch soffits and a curved staircase create a breathtaking first impression

Live in luxury with this amazing master bedroom suite complete with a private deck, bath with whirlpool tub and walk-in closet with built-ins

The lower level allows you to entertain in style with the family room and bar, and stay fit with your very own exercise room

4 bedrooms, 3 1/2 baths, 3-car side entry garage

Walk-out basement foundation

Price Code H

houseplansandmore.com

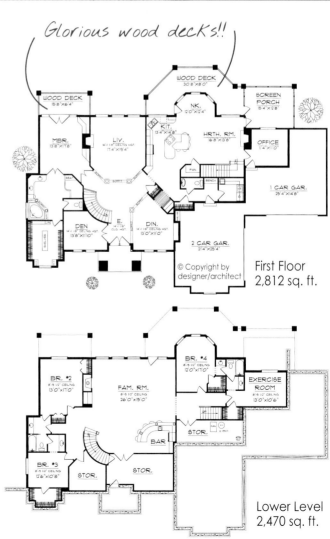

Glorious wood decks!!

First Floor
2,812 sq. ft.

© Copyright by
designer/architect

Lower Level
2,470 sq. ft.

PLANFEATURES

5,800 total square feet of living area

Width: 81'-9" Depth: 69'-7"

The nook and hearth room are completely open to one another and offer an immense amount of casual living space near the kitchen

The bayed master bedroom has a cozy fireplace creating the perfect homeowner's retreat

Double doors off the foyer lead into a quiet library perfectly suited for a home office

The optional lower level has an additional 2,030 square feet of living area

6 bedrooms, 5 1/2 baths, 2-car side entry garage, 1-car garage

Basement foundation

Price Code S1

Second Floor
2,892 sq. ft.

Awesome game room & pub

© Copyright by designer/architect

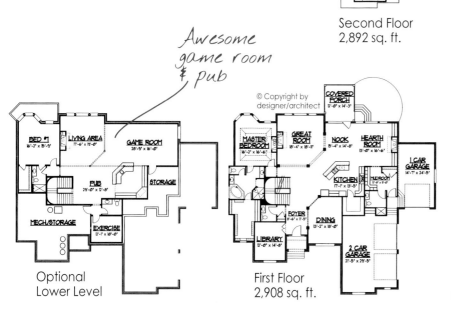

Optional
Lower Level

First Floor
2,908 sq. ft.

housand**more**.com

157

PLANFEATURES

1,428 total square feet of living area

Width: 46'-0" Depth: 42'-6"

Energy efficient home with 2" x 6" exterior walls

The large vaulted family room opens to the dining area and kitchen with breakfast bar

The first floor master bedroom offers a large bath, walk-in closet and nearby laundry facilities

A spacious loft/bedroom #3 overlooking the family room and an additional bedroom and bath complement the second floor

3 bedrooms, 2 baths

Basement foundation

Price Code A

Delightful wrap-around porch!!

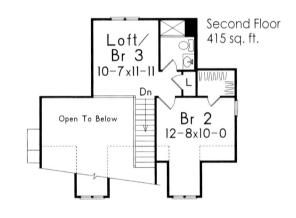

Second Floor
415 sq. ft.

Loft/
Br 3
10-7x11-11

Open To Below

Dn

Br 2
12-8x10-0

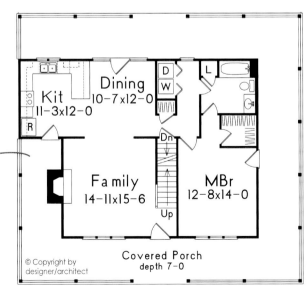

First Floor
1,013 sq. ft.

Dining
10-7x12-0

Kit
11-3x12-0

Family
14-11x15-6

MBr
12-8x14-0

Dn

Up

Covered Porch
depth 7-0

© Copyright by
designer/architect

OAKBURY

PLAN #651-007D-0146

1,929 total square feet of living area

Width: 68'-0" Depth: 49'-8"

A classic traditional exterior for timeless elegance

4 bedrooms, 3 baths, 3-car side entry garage

Crawl space foundation, drawings also include slab and basement foundations

Price Code C

STRICKLAND

PLAN #651-010D-0006

1,170 total square feet of living area

Width: 47'-4" Depth: 52'-0"

The kitchen has an angled bar that overlooks the great room and breakfast area

3 bedrooms, 2 baths, 2-car garage

Slab foundation

Price Code AA

JOLLY CREEK

PLAN #651-013D-0032

2,275 total square feet of living area

Width: 62'-0" Depth: 60'-0"

Spacious double walk-in closets flank the hallway that leads to the master bath

The living room features a cathedral ceiling while an angled tray ceiling highlights the dining room

3 bedrooms, 2 baths, 2-car side entry garage

Basement or crawl space foundation, please specify when ordering

Price Code D

ANABEL

PLAN #651-121D-0002

2,025 total square feet of living area

Width: 69'-8" Depth: 42'-8"

2" x 6" exterior walls available, please order plan #651-121E-0002

3 bedrooms, 2 1/2 baths, 2-car side entry garage

Basement foundation

Price Code B

houseplansandmore.com

PLANFEATURES

3,462 total square feet of living area

Width: 113'-7" Depth: 57'-5"

A beautiful rear covered terrace is perfect for entertaining outdoors and can be accessed from the grand room and the master suite

The turret-style stairwell is brightened by windows

A corner fireplace, two walk-in closets and a private bath are some of the features of the master suite

The bonus room on the second floor has an additional 609 square feet of living area

3 bedrooms, 3 1/2 baths, 3-car side entry garage

Crawl space foundation

Price Code S1

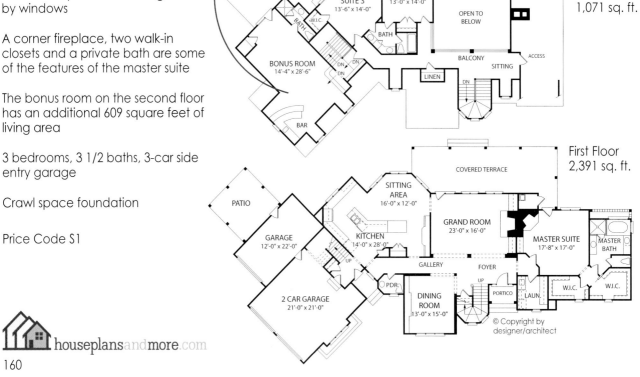

Bonus room with a bar!

Second Floor
1,071 sq. ft.

First Floor
2,391 sq. ft.

© Copyright by designer/architect

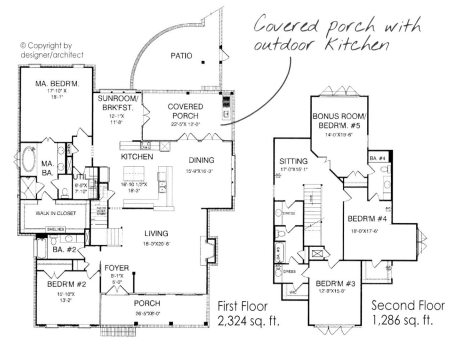

© Copyright by
designer/architect

PATIO

MA. BEDR'M.
17'-10" X
18'-1"

SUNROOM/
BRK'FST.
12'-1"X
11'-8"

COVERED
PORCH
22'-5"X 12'-0"

Covered porch with outdoor Kitchen

MA.
BA.

KITCHEN
16'-10 1/2"X
16'-3"

DINING
15'-9"X16'-3"

UTIL
6'-5"X
7'-10"

WALK IN CLOSET

SHELVES

LIVING
18'-0"X20'-6"

BA. #2

FOYER
8'-1"X
5'-0"

BEDR'M #2
15'-10"X
13'-2"

PORCH
26'-5"X8'-0"

First Floor
2,324 sq. ft.

BONUS ROOM/
BEDR'M. #5
14'-0"X19'-6"

BA. #4

SITTING
17'-0"X15'-1"

DRESS

BEDR'M #4
18'-0"X17'-6"

BA. #3

DRESS

BEDR'M #3
12'-8"X15'-8"

WIC

Second Floor
1,286 sq. ft.

PLAN FEATURES

3,610 total square feet of living area

Width: 52'-0" Depth: 62'-0"

This home uses perimeter insulation called icynene spray foam insulation that reduces heating and cooling bills

Dimmer switches are used on all the lighting fixtures to conserve energy

The oversized covered porch enjoys a built-in sink and grill space for cooking outdoors

The second floor sitting room makes a great spot for a computer area

Two sets of double doors lead from the dining area to the covered porch creating a great set-up when entertaining

5 bedrooms, 4 baths,
2-car detached garage

Slab foundation

Price Code S1

PLANFEATURES

1,763 total square feet of living area

Width: 48'-0" Depth: 44'-0"

The dining room has a large box-bay window and a recessed ceiling

The living room includes a large fireplace

The kitchen has plenty of workspace, a pantry and a double sink overlooking the deck

The master bedroom features a large bath with walk-in closet

3 bedrooms, 2 1/2 baths, 2-car garage

Basement foundation

Price Code C

Line of Floor Below

Master Br
14-3 x 17-5

Br 3
12-2 x 10-1

Railing

DN

Flue

Second Floor
854 sq. ft.

Br 2
13-11 x 11-9

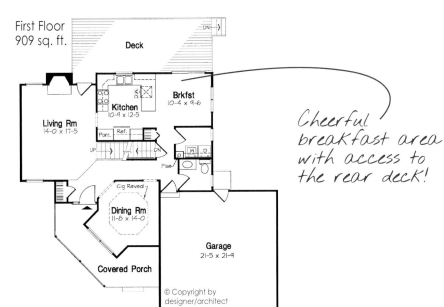

First Floor
909 sq. ft.

Deck

DN

Kitchen
10-9 x 12-5

Brkfst
10-4 x 9-6

Living Rm
14-0 x 17-5

Pant.

Ref.

UP

DN

Flue

Cheerful breakfast area with access to the rear deck!

Clg Reveal

Dining Rm
11-8 x 14-0

Garage
21-5 x 21-9

Covered Porch

houseplansandmore.com

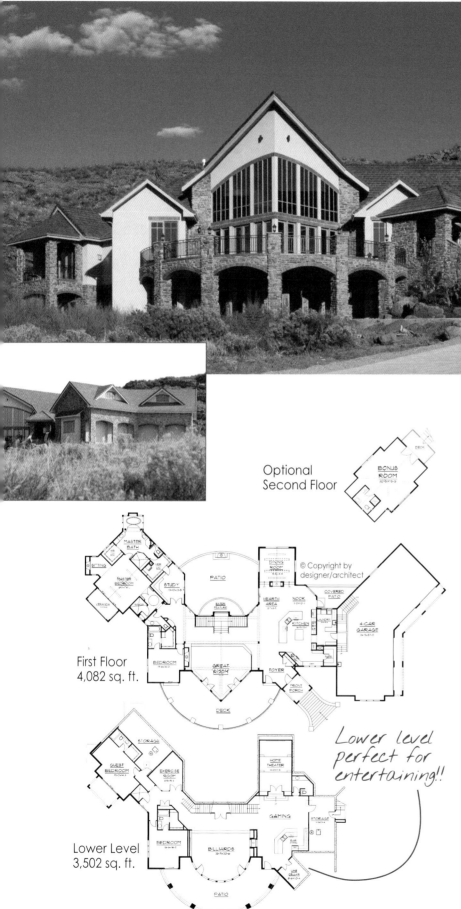

Optional
Second Floor

First Floor
4,082 sq. ft.

Lower Level
3,502 sq. ft.

Lower level perfect for entertaining!!

PLANFEATURES

7,584 total square feet of living area

Width: 156'-9" Depth: 91'-6"

Energy efficient home with 2" x 6" exterior walls

Relax in the master bedroom retreat that features a sitting area with fireplace, a private veranda, and a deluxe bath complete with a whirlpool tub surrounded by windows

Enjoy the lower level equipped with a gaming center, bar, wine cellar, home theater, billiards area, exercise room, and two bedrooms and baths

The second floor bonus room has an additional 511 square feet of future living area

4 bedrooms, 4 full baths, 2 half baths, 4-car side entry garage

Walk-out basement foundation

Price Code S4

BRIGHTMOORE

PLAN #651-001D-0024

1,360 total square feet of living area

Width: 68'-0" Depth: 38'-0"

The kitchen/dining room features an island workspace and plenty of dining area

3 bedrooms, 2 baths, 2-car side entry garage

Basement foundation, drawings also include crawl space and slab foundations

Price Code A

HALIFAX LAKE

PLAN #651-028D-0018

2,614 total square feet of living area

Width: 80'-0" Depth: 63'-0"

The snack bar overlooks into the great room

4 bedrooms, 2 1/2 baths, 2-car side entry garage

Slab or crawl space foundation, please specify when ordering

Price Code E

houseplansandmore.com

SPRINGDALE

PLAN #651-007D-0105

1,084 total square feet of living area

Width: 35'-0" Depth: 40'-8"

The U-shaped kitchen features lots of cabinets and a bayed breakfast room with built-in pantry

2 bedrooms, 2 baths

Basement foundation

Price Code AA

CASSANDRA

PLAN #651-121D-0010

1,281 total square feet of living area

Width: 37'-6" Depth: 52'-0"

The vaulted great room and dining area combine, maximizing the interior for an open, airy feel

The vaulted master bedroom enjoys a sizable walk-in closet and its own private bath

3 bedrooms, 2 baths, 2-car garage

Basement foundation

Price Code AA

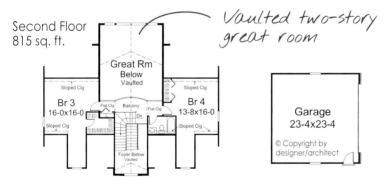

PLANFEATURES

3,782 total square feet of living area

Width: 76'-8" Depth: 50'-0"

An enchanting second floor balcony overlooks the vaulted great room with warming fireplace

The beautiful country kitchen has a walk-in pantry, ample counterspace and an eating bar for easy meals

The spacious master bedroom enjoys a sitting area, walk-in closet and private bath with corner whirlpool tub

4 bedrooms, 3 1/2 baths, 2-car detached garage

Basement foundation

Price Code E

Second Floor
815 sq. ft.

Vaulted two-story great room

Great Rm Below Vaulted

Sloped Clg · Sloped Clg

Br 3
16-0x16-0

Flat Clg Balcony Flat Clg

Br 4
13-8x16-0

Sloped Clg · Sloped Clg · On

Foyer Below Vaulted

Garage
23-4x23-4

© Copyright by designer/architect

First Floor
2,571 sq. ft.

Patio

MBr
16-0x23-0

Great Rm
18-4x25-0
Vaulted

Balcony Above

Bookshelves

Sitting Area

Hall

Br 2/Study
16-2x11-8

Foyer

Porch

Country Kitchen
21-0x19-9

Laun/ Mud Rm

P

Dining Rm
15-6x16-11
Tray Clg

Lower Level
396 sq. ft.

Component Shelving

Media/Theater Rm
18-8x21-3

Bookshelves

Up

houseplansandmore.com

Photo, above: As striking as the front, this home's rear view reveals abundant outdoor living space and additional unseen curb appeal. Multiple windows line the rear of this home filling the interior spaces with sunlight, while providing the exterior with unrivaled style.

Photo, right: Become "one" with nature the minute you step out onto the covered area just beyond the family room. With its corner stone fireplace for added warmth in fall and winter or a ceiling fan to stir up breezes in the spring and summer, this spot will be a favorite family hangout all year long.

Photo, above: Elegant details combine in this stunning family room, creating a place of rest for families or guests to gather.

Photo, below: Defined by an open archway, this dining room is warm without being stuffy.

Comfortable media room

Second Floor 1,189 sq. ft.

BONUS AREA

First Floor 2,800 sq. ft.

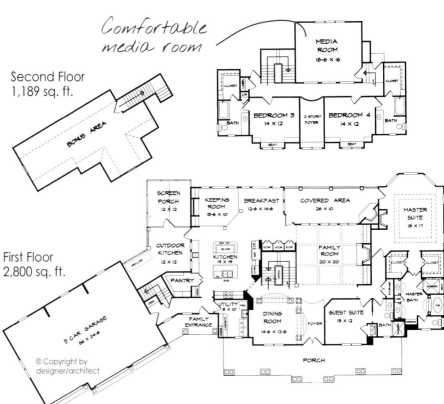

MEDIA ROOM 18-6 x 16

BEDROOM 3 14 x 12

2 STORY FOYER

BEDROOM 4 14 x 12

CLOSET

CLOSET

BATH

BATH

SCREEN PORCH 12 x 12

KEEPING ROOM 18-6 x 10

BREAKFAST 12-6 x 14-6

COVERED AREA 26 x 10

MASTER SUITE 18 x 17

OUTDOOR KITCHEN 12 x 12

KITCHEN 14 x 14

FAMILY ROOM 20 x 20

PANTRY

UTILITY 8 x 10

DINING ROOM 14-6 x 12-6

FOYER

GUEST SUITE 18 x 12

MASTER BATH

FAMILY ENTRANCE

3 CAR GARAGE 36 x 24-6

BATH

PORCH

© Copyright by designer/architect

PLANFEATURES

3,989 total square feet of living area

Width: 122'-6" Depth: 64'-0"

This enormous home enjoys large living spaces and a popular outdoor kitchen that connects to a screen porch

A keeping room is attached to the breakfast area creating a spacious and casual area near the kitchen

A guest suite offers a nice place for visitors with direct access to a full bath

The bonus room above the garage has an additional 675 square feet of living area

4 bedrooms, 4 baths, 3-car garage

Walk-out basement, slab or crawl space foundation, please specify when ordering

Price Code G

houseplansandmore.com

PLANFEATURES

1,381 total square feet of living area

Width: 28'-0" Depth: 28'-0"

Energy efficient home with 2" x 6" exterior walls

This home has an inviting screened porch that is simply beautiful and creates an ideal outdoor living space

The beautiful living room has many bright windows and an open design that flows easily into the dining room

The attractive master suite has a large walk-in closet and the other two bedrooms have ample closet space as well

3 bedrooms, 1 1/2 baths

Basement foundation

Price Code D

9'-0" X 10'-0"
2,70 X 3,00

9'-0" X 10'-0"
2,70 X 3,00

15'-0" X 11'-0"
4,50 X 3,30

Second Floor
597 sq. ft.

10'-0" X 13'-8"
3,00 X 4,10

26'-8" X 13'-0"
8,00 X 3,90

Spacious storage closet!

© Copyright by designer/architect

First Floor
784 sq. ft.

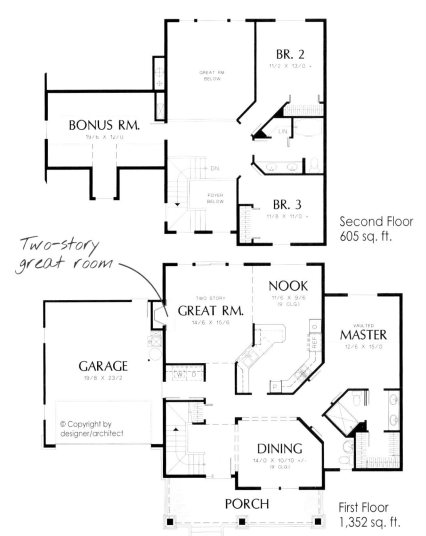

BR. 2
11/2 X 13/0 •

GREAT RM
BELOW

BONUS RM.
19/6 X 12/0

LIN.

DN

FOYER
BELOW

BR. 3
11/8 X 11/0 •

Second Floor
605 sq. ft.

Two-story great room

TWO STORY
GREAT RM.
14/6 X 15/6

NOOK
11/6 X 9/6
(9' CLG.)

REF.O

VAULTED
MASTER
12/6 X 15/0

GARAGE
19/8 X 23/2

W D

P

© Copyright by
designer/architect

DINING
14/0 X 10/10 +/-
(9' CLG.)

PORCH

First Floor
1,352 sq. ft.

PLANFEATURES

1,957 total square feet of living area

Width: 60'-0" Depth: 43'-0"

The vaulted master bedroom has its own private bath with walk-in closet for great luxury

The two-story great room creates a feeling of openness that can't be denied

Two second floor bedrooms skillfully share a full bath

The bonus room on the second floor has an additional 285 square feet of living area

3 bedrooms, 2 1/2 baths, 2-car garage

Crawl space foundation

Price Code C

houseplansandmore.com

PLANFEATURES

3,286 total square feet of living area

Width: 63'-0" Depth: 45'-0"

The cozy family room enjoys a fireplace and flows into the nook with access to the outdoors

A spacious games room on the first floor is perfect for entertaining guests

Double-doors open to the master bedroom with private bath, whirlpool tub surrounded with windows and a large walk-in closet

4 bedrooms, 2 1/2 baths, 3-car drive under garage

Partial crawl space/walk-out basement foundation

Price Code S1

Unique master bedroom with a private bath & walk-in closet!

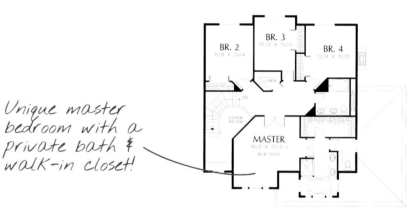

Second Floor
1,330 sq. ft.

Lower Level
163 sq. ft.

First Floor
1,793 sq. ft.

houseplansandmore.com

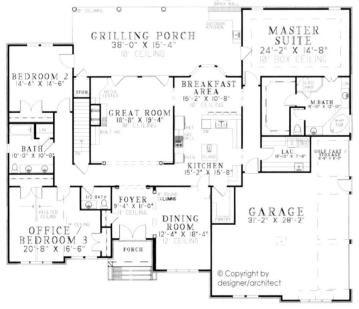

GRILLING PORCH
38'-0" X 15'-4"
10' CEILING

MASTER SUITE
24'-2" X 14'-8"
10' BOX CEILING

BEDROOM 2
14'-4" X 14'-6"

BREAKFAST AREA
15'-2" X 10'-8"
10' CEILING

M.BATH
19'-10" X 12'-10"

GREAT ROOM
18'-8" X 19'-4"
10' CEILING

KITCHEN
15'-2" X 15'-8"

LAU.
18'-10" X 7'-8"

GOLF CART / STORAGE
8'-8" X 8'-0"

BATH
10'-0" X 10'-0"

1/2 BATH

FOYER
9'-4" X 11'-0"
11' CEILING

DINING ROOM
12'-4" X 18'-4"
12' CEILING

GARAGE
31'-2" X 28'-2"

OFFICE BEDROOM 3
20'-8" X 16'-6"

PORCH

© Copyright by designer/architect

First Floor
3,009 sq. ft.

WORKOUT AREA
13'-8" X 10'-0"

WINE CELLAR BY OWNER
9'-6" X 6'8"

GAME ROOM / HOME THEATER
22'-2" X 23'-4"

Awesome game room or home theater!

BATH
9'-8" X 10'-6"

MECH.

10' X 10' PATIO

GUEST BEDROOM 4
20'-2" X 16'-6"

Lower Level
1,501 sq. ft.

PLANFEATURES

4,510 total square feet of living area

Width: 77'-10" Depth: 65'-0"

The elegant double-door entry opens to many excellent entertaining spaces including the formal dining room and the oversized great room

The master suite, great room and bedroom #2 all enjoy access to the rear grilling porch that offers a handy outdoor kitchen

The lower level is full of excitement with a game room/home theater as well as a workout area, wine cellar and guest suite with private patio

4 bedrooms, 4 1/2 baths, 2-car side entry garage

Walk-out basement foundation

Price Code S1

houseplansandmore.com

CHAPPELLE

PLAN FEATURES

3,335 total square feet of living area

Width: 59'-4" Depth: 51'-0"

This home features the comfort of a Country cottage with modern amenities providing convenience and luxury

The dining room and study have two sets of French doors brightening each area

The unfinished areas on the second floor have an additional 422 square feet of living space

The lower level gameroom has an additional 435 square feet of living space

4 bedrooms, 4 baths, 2-car drive under side entry garage

Basement foundation

Price Code H

Superb rear wood deck

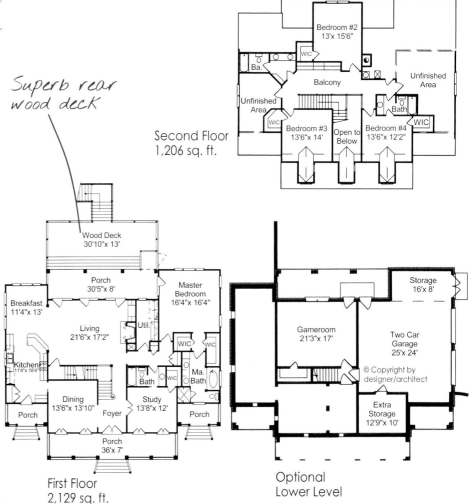

Second Floor
1,206 sq. ft.

First Floor
2,129 sq. ft.

Optional
Lower Level

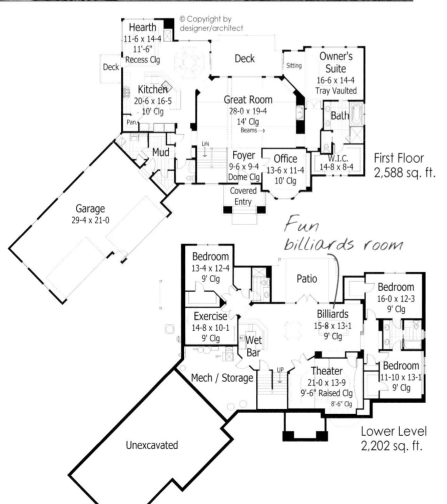

© Copyright by designer/architect

Hearth
11-6 x 14-4
11'-6"
Recess Clg

Deck

Owner's Suite
16-6 x 14-4
Tray Vaulted

Deck

Sitting

Kitchen
20-6 x 16-5
10' Clg

Bath

Great Room
28-0 x 19-4
14' Clg
Beams →

Pan.

Mud

DN

Foyer
9-6 x 9-4
Dome Clg

Office
13-6 x 11-4
10' Clg

W.I.C.
14-8 x 8-4

First Floor
2,588 sq. ft.

Covered Entry

Garage
29-4 x 21-0

Fun billiards room

Bedroom
13-4 x 12-4
9' Clg

Patio

Bedroom
16-0 x 12-3
9' Clg

Exercise
14-8 x 10-1
9' Clg

Wet Bar

Billiards
15-8 x 13-1
9' Clg

Mech / Storage

UP

Theater
21-0 x 13-9
9'-6" Raised Clg
8'-6" Clg

Bedroom
11-10 x 13-1
9' Clg

Unexcavated

Lower Level
2,202 sq. ft.

PLANFEATURES

4,790 total square feet of living area

Width: 101'-3" Depth: 79'-3"

Energy efficient home with 2" x 6" exterior walls

A cozy hearth room and dinette surround the kitchen with functional casual living and dining space

The lower level enjoys the fun and excitement of its own home theater with a raised ceiling

Other special amenities throughout this home include a billiards room, a wet bar and an exercise room

4 bedrooms, 3 1/2 baths, 4-car garage

Walk-out basement foundation

Price Code S3

PLANFEATURES

1,800 total square feet of living area

Width: 65'-0" Depth: 56'-8"

Double doors open into the foyer crowned with a 10' ceiling

The vaulted great room opens into the kitchen and bayed breakfast area with decorative columns

The unfinished bonus room has an additional 302 square feet of living area

3 bedrooms, 2 baths, 2-car side entry garage

Slab, basement or crawl space foundation, please specify when ordering

Price Code D

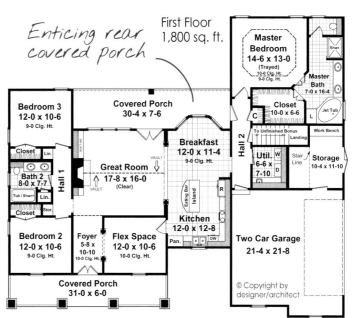

Enticing rear covered porch

First Floor
1,800 sq. ft.

Optional Second Floor

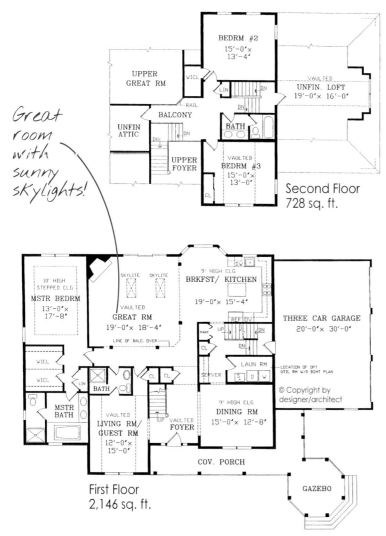

Great room with sunny skylights!

Second Floor
728 sq. ft.

BEDRM #2
15'-0" x 13'-4"

UPPER GREAT RM

WICL

LIN

VAULTED
UNFIN. LOFT
19'-0" x 16'-0"

BALCONY

RAIL

UNFIN ATTIC

BATH

DN

UPPER FOYER

VAULTED
BEDRM #3
15'-0" x 13'-0"

CL

First Floor
2,146 sq. ft.

10' HIGH STEPPED CLG
MSTR BEDRM
13'-0" x 17'-8"

SKYLITE SKYLITE

VAULTED
GREAT RM
19'-0" x 18'-4"

LINE OF BALC. OVER

9' HIGH CLG
BRKFST/ KITCHEN
19'-0" x 15'-4"

THREE CAR GARAGE
20'-0" x 30'-0"

WICL

WICL

LIN

BATH

CL CL

PANT

UP

REF DV

DN

CL

SERVER

LAUN RM

W D S

LOCATION OF OPT
UTIL RM W/O BSHT PLAN

© Copyright by designer/architect

MSTR BATH

VAULTED
LIVING RM/ GUEST RM
12'-0" x 15'-0"

UP

VAULTED
FOYER

9' HIGH CLG
DINING RM
15'-0" x 12'-8"

COV. PORCH

GAZEBO

PLANFEATURES

2,874 total square feet of living area

Width: 72'-0" Depth: 47'-0"

Energy efficient home with 2" x 6" exterior walls

Openness characterizes the casual areas

The kitchen is separated from the bayed breakfast nook by an island workspace

The stunning great room has a dramatic vaulted ceiling and a corner fireplace

The unfinished loft on the second floor has an additional 300 square feet of living area

4 bedrooms, 3 baths, 3-car side entry garage

Basement, crawl space or slab foundation, please specify when ordering

Price Code G

houseplansandmore.com

PLANFEATURES

3,688 total square feet of living area

Width: 75'-0" Depth: 64'-11"

Formal and informal spaces are provided throughout this home for various social events and comfortable family living

A gourmet kitchen with breakfast bar and island serves the dining room and breakfast area with equal ease

A secluded hall creates an orderly transition from the kitchen to the laundry room and garage

A wonderful master bedroom is decorated by a stepped ceiling, crown molding, boxed window and lavish bath with a platform whirlpool tub

4 bedrooms, 3 1/2 baths, 3-car side entry garage

Basement foundation

Price Code F

Second Floor
986 sq. ft.

First Floor
2,702 sq. ft.

Striking dining room!

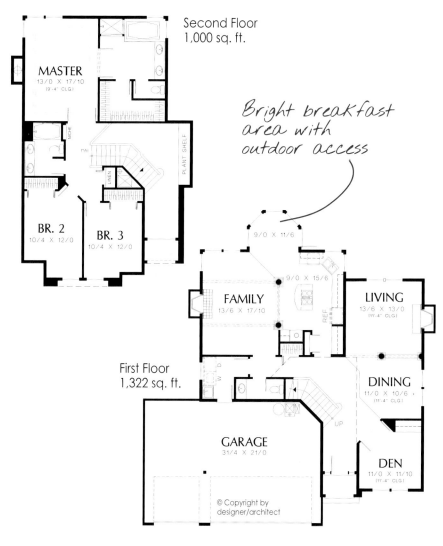

Second Floor
1,000 sq. ft.

MASTER
13/0 X 17/10
(9'-4" CLG)

BR. 2
10/4 X 12/0

BR. 3
10/4 X 12/0

First Floor
1,322 sq. ft.

FAMILY
13/6 X 17/10

LIVING
13/6 X 13/0
(11'-4" CLG)

9/0 X 11/6

9/0 X 15/6

DINING
11/0 X 10/6
(11'-4" CLG)

GARAGE
31/4 X 21/0

DEN
11/0 X 11/10
(11'-4" CLG)

UP

Bright breakfast area with outdoor access

© Copyright by designer/architect

PLAN FEATURES

2,322 total square feet of living area

Width: 50'-0" Depth: 54'-10"

The vaulted family room has a centered fireplace and a bayed dining area nearby

Double doors off the foyer lead to a cozy den with a built-in desk

Decorative columns in the dining and family rooms maintain an open atmosphere

3 bedrooms, 2 1/2 baths, 3-car garage

Crawl space foundation

Price Code D

houseplansandmore.com

PLANFEATURES

4,808 total square feet of living area

Width: 81'-0" Depth: 66'-0"

The sunken great room boasts a built-in media center, a corner fireplace and access to the rear deck

All of the bedrooms feature a private bath and a walk-in closet

The amazing master bedroom has a corner media center, access to the rear deck and a large bath with the spa tub as the focal point

4 bedrooms, 4 1/2 baths, 3-car garage

Partial slab/walk-out basement foundation

Price Code S1

Games room with handsome corner fireplace!

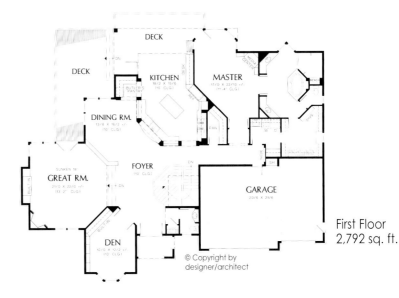

First Floor
2,792 sq. ft.

© Copyright by designer/architect

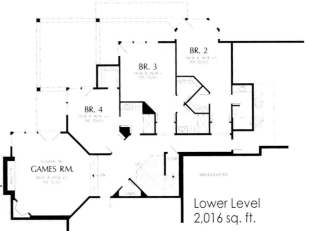

Lower Level
2,016 sq. ft.

PLANFEATURES

2,713 total square feet of living area

Width: 66'-4" Depth: 80'-8"

The corner fireplace in the family room can be seen from the kitchen and breakfast nook creating a cozy atmosphere

Double walk-in closets flank the entrance into the master bedroom's private bath

The optional second floor has an additional 440 square feet of living area

Framing - only concrete block available

3 bedrooms, 3 baths, 3-car side entry garage

Slab foundation

Price Code G

© Copyright by designer/architect

Family 20⁴ · 15⁵

Nook

Covered Porch

Bedroom 2 11⁰ · 12⁵

Kitchen

Living 16⁴ · 12⁰

Bath

Master Bedroom 14⁴ · 19⁰

Bath

Bedroom 3 11⁰ · 12²

Utility

Dining 11⁰ · 12⁵

Foyer

Den / Study 11⁰ · 11⁰

W.I.C. **W.I.C.**

Entry

Master Bath

3 Car Garage

Amazing master bath!

First Floor 2,713 sq. ft.

Optional Second Floor

Bath

Bonus Room 14⁰ · 21⁰

houseplansandmore.com

PLAN FEATURES

2,742 total square feet of living area

Width: 76'-8" Depth: 77'-7"

The luxurious master suite includes a wall of built-ins along with a private entrance to the rear porch

A fireplace nicely settled between built-ins punctuates the enormous great room

The oversized laundry/hobby room offers an abundance of space for do-it-yourself home projects

The optional second floor has an additional 352 square feet of living space

3 bedrooms, 2 1/2 baths, 2-car side entry garage

Slab or crawl space foundation, please specify when ordering

Price Code E

Optional
Second Floor

Plenty of storage!!

First Floor
2,742 sq. ft.

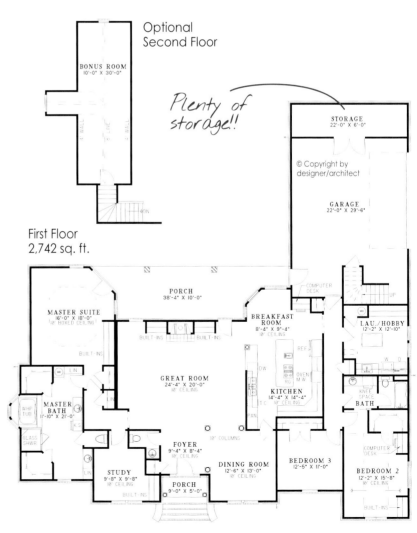

houseplansandmore.com

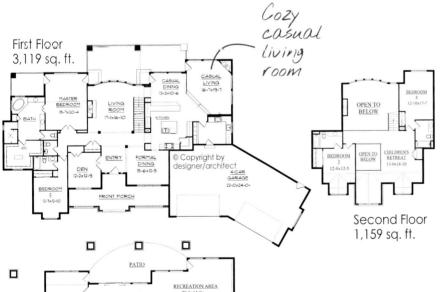

PLANFEATURES

6,336 total square feet of living area

Width: 115'-0" Depth: 74'-0"

Energy efficient home with 2" x 6" exterior walls

The lower level is filled with extras such as a home office, a library and a recreation area that includes a lounge and massive wet bar

The casual living area located just off the kitchen has a cozy corner fireplace

The second floor features a children's retreat perfect for a playroom

5 bedrooms, 5 full baths, 2 half baths, 4-car garage

Walk-out basement or basement foundation, please specify when ordering

Price Code S1

First Floor
3,119 sq. ft.

Cozy casual living room

MASTER BEDROOM
15-7x20-4

BATH

LIVING ROOM
17-1x16-10

KITCHEN

CASUAL DINING
13-3x10-6

CASUAL LIVING
16-7x19-7

DEN
12-2x12-9

ENTRY

FORMAL DINING
15-6x12-5

© Copyright by designer/architect

4-CAR GARAGE
22-0x24-0+

BEDROOM 2
12-7x12-10

FRONT PORCH

Second Floor
1,159 sq. ft.

OPEN TO BELOW

BEDROOM 4
12-10x17-7

BEDROOM 3
12-0x12-5

OPEN TO BELOW

CHILDREN'S RETREAT
13-0x18-10

Lower Level
2,058 sq. ft.

PATIO

BEDROOM 5
13-7x13-1

HOME OFFICE
21-7x13-6

LIBRARY
16-10x21-6

RECREATION AREA
29-6x14-0+

BAR

LOUNGE
10-0x10-0

UNFINISHED STORAGE

houseplansandmore.com

LILLIAN

2,487 total square feet of living area

Width: 96'-6" Depth: 66'-0"

An amazing see-through fireplace warms the kitchen, breakfast and hearth/dining areas

The rear covered patio is perfect for enjoying the outdoors and can be enjoyed by many different views

The garage boasts storage space and access to a convenient laundry/mud room

3 bedrooms, 2 1/2 baths, 2-car garage

Basement foundation

Price Code C

Handsome office!

HAILEY

2,037 total square feet of living area

Width: 70'-8" Depth: 47'-0"

The vaulted kitchen/breakfast area enjoys a walk-in pantry and a sunny bay window with access to the rear patio

There is extra storage space in the garage that has access to the outdoors

Two spacious walk-in closets and a private bath are some of the amenities of the master bedroom

3 bedrooms, 2 1/2 baths, 2-car garage

Basement foundation

Price Code B

Two walk-in closets!!

houseplansandmore.com

First Floor
2,700 sq. ft.

Lower Level
3,132 sq. ft.

Exquisite home theater!!

PLANFEATURES

5,832 total square feet of living area

Width: 70'-10" Depth: 102'-7"

Energy efficient home with 2" x 6" exterior walls

Vaulted ceilings in the dining area and great room make the space feel more open

This home gives the homeowner lots of opportunity to enjoy the outdoors with a deck, sunroom and a screen porch

The lower level is best for entertaining or occupying your own time; it includes an exercise area, meditation room, theater, a billiards area and a recreation room

4 bedrooms, 3 1/2 baths, 4-car side entry garage

Walk-out basement foundation

Price Code S3

houseplansandmore.com

PLANFEATURES

3,990 total square feet of living area

Width: 64'-4" Depth: 65'-4"

Just steps away from the breakfast room is the hearth room with a handsome corner fireplace, a bay window and access to the grilling porch

Elegant French doors open to the second floor home theater with an isolated window seat

The master suite has a bath with an amazing whirlpool tub, two large walk-in closets, and a delightful bay window

The bonus room on the second floor has an additional 334 square feet of living area

4 bedrooms, 3 baths, 2-car garage

Crawl space or slab foundation, please specify when ordering

Price Code S1

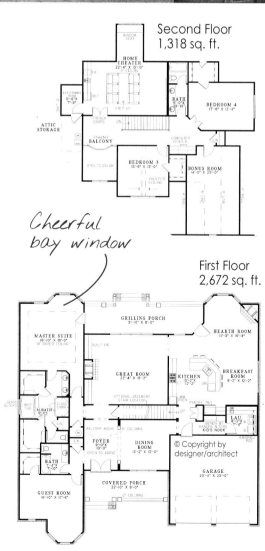

Second Floor
1,318 sq. ft.

Cheerful bay window

First Floor
2,672 sq. ft.

© Copyright by designer/architect

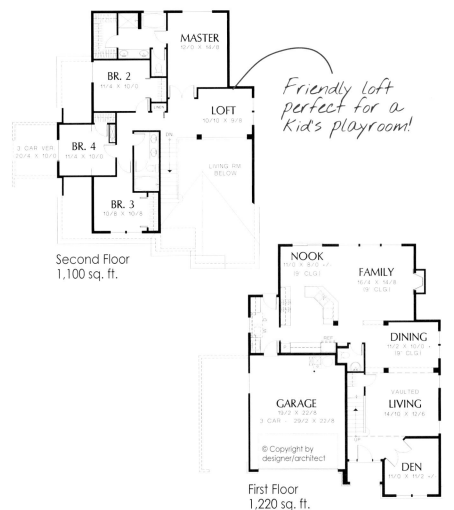

Second Floor
1,100 sq. ft.

Friendly loft perfect for a kid's playroom!

MASTER
12/0 X 14/8

BR. 2
11/4 X 10/0

LOFT
10/10 X 9/8

3 CAR VER.
20/4 X 10/0

BR. 4
11/4 X 10/0

BR. 3
10/8 X 10/8

LIVING RM
BELOW

DN

LINEN

NOOK
11/0 X 8/0 +/-
(9' CLG)

FAMILY
16/4 X 14/8
(9' CLG)

DINING
11/2 X 10/0 -
(9' CLG)

GARAGE
19/2 X 22/8
3 CAR - 29/2 X 22/8

VAULTED
LIVING
14/10 X 12/6

DEN
11/0 X 11/2 +/-

© Copyright by
designer/architect

UP

First Floor
1,220 sq. ft.

PLANFEATURES

2,320 total square feet of living area

Width: 40'-0" Depth: 50'-0"

Energy efficient home with 2" x 6" exterior walls

The family room is flooded with sunlight from wall of windows

Decorative columns help separate the dining area from the living area

The breakfast nook has sliding glass doors leading to the outdoors

4 bedrooms, 2 1/2 baths, 2-car garage

Crawl space foundation

Price Code E

houseplansandmore.com

PLAN FEATURES

4,100 total square feet of living area

Width: 90'-0" Depth: 66'-6"

Energy efficient home with 2" x 6" exterior walls

The family room connects to other casual living areas for convenience

French doors keep the den cozy and private from the rest of the first floor

A beautiful sitting area extends off the master bedroom

The bonus room on the second floor is included in the total square footage

4 bedrooms, 3 1/2 baths, 3-car side entry garage

Crawl space foundation

Price Code G

Second Floor
2,090 sq. ft.

Useful bonus room

First Floor
2,010 sq. ft.

© Copyright by designer/architect

houseplansandmore.com

PLANFEATURES

2,887 total square feet of living area

Width: 70'-0" Depth: 74'-1"

The home was designed perfectly to feature an in-ground swimming pool that hugs the perimeter of the rear of this home for a dramatic effect

A striking wet bar area overlooks the outdoors and is perfect when entertaining

The second floor enjoys a unique observatory for viewing the surroundings

4 bedrooms, 3 baths, 2-car garage

Slab foundation

Price Code E

Beautiful balcony deck!!

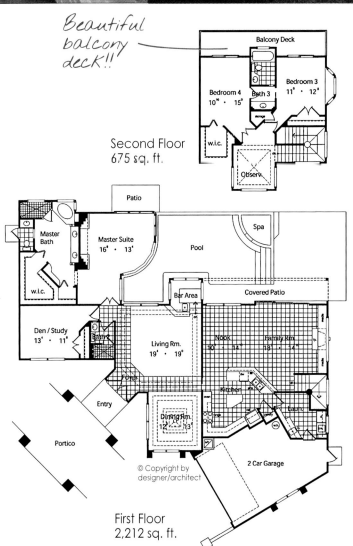

Second Floor
675 sq. ft.

First Floor
2,212 sq. ft.

© Copyright by designer/architect

houseplansandmore.com

Photo, above: The lower level steps directly out to the backyard making celebrations that are enjoyed in both an indoor and outdoor setting within reach.

Photo, right: This unexpected sun room has a drastically sloped ceiling for a unique interior design and a rear stone wall lined with windows. With access from many rooms in the home, this surprisingly private vaulted sun room maintains an exotic feel perfect for quiet moments reading or resting.

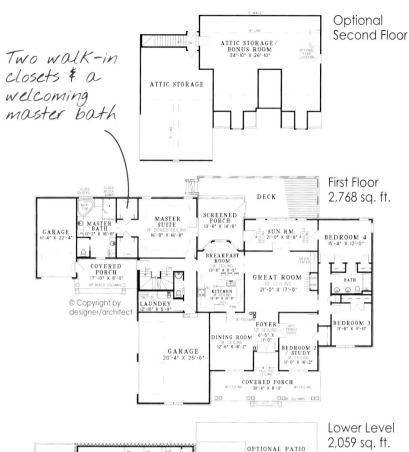

Two walk-in closets & a welcoming master bath

Optional Second Floor

First Floor
2,768 sq. ft.

© Copyright by designer/architect

Photo, above: The natural stone fireplace is the main focal point of the great room creating a bold design statement.

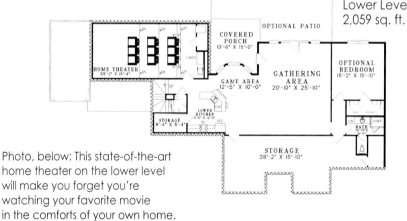

Lower Level
2,059 sq. ft.

Photo, below: This state-of-the-art home theater on the lower level will make you forget you're watching your favorite movie in the comforts of your own home.

PLANFEATURES

4,827 total square feet of living area

Width: 97'-8" Depth: 64'-6"

A vaulted covered porch and amazing double-door entry to the foyer invite guests into this home

The breakfast room with a bay window has access to the screened porch

A home theater, extra kitchen and large gathering area are some of the features of the lower level

The bonus room on the second floor has an additional 913 square feet of living area

4 bedrooms, 3 1/2 baths, 2-car side entry garage, 1-car garage

Walk-out basement foundation

Price Code S1

houseplansandmore.com

PLANFEATURES

6,060 total square feet of living area

Width: 139'-6" Depth: 92'-0"

Enter this home and be greeted by an amazing rotunda that branches off into many different rooms including the den, dining and living rooms

A spacious guest suite provides the utmost in privacy and luxury including a massive bath and a walk-in closet

A unique barrel vaulted ceiling tops the ultimate kitchen floor plan

4 bedrooms, 4 1/2 baths, 4-car side entry garage

Crawl space foundation

Price Code S1

Fabulous master suite!

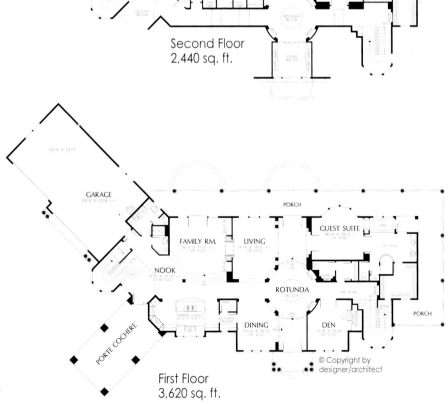

Second Floor
2,440 sq. ft.

First Floor
3,620 sq. ft.

houseplansandmore.com

PLANFEATURES

3,320 total square feet of living area

Width: 69'-0" Depth: 56'-0"

Energy efficient home with 2" x 6" exterior walls

The sunny octagon-shaped dining room has access to the rear deck

The double-sided fireplace warms the great room and the hearth room providing a bold statement that homeowners will enjoy

The lower level boasts a corner fireplace in the expansive family room and access to a large storage area, which is highly convenient

3 bedrooms, 2 1/2 baths, 3-car garage

Walk-out basement foundation

Price Code G

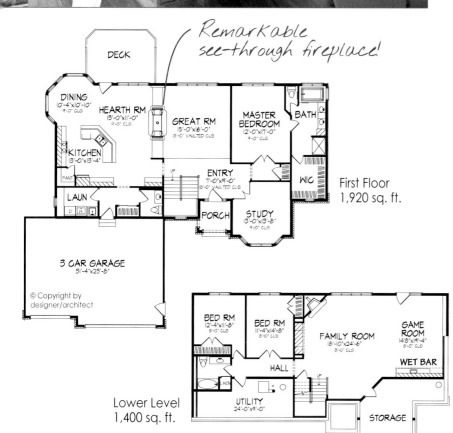

Remarkable see-through fireplace!

First Floor
1,920 sq. ft.

Lower Level
1,400 sq. ft.

© Copyright by designer/architect

Photo, right: The charming breakfast room feels like an easy extension right off the kitchen that features a wonderful center island workspace.

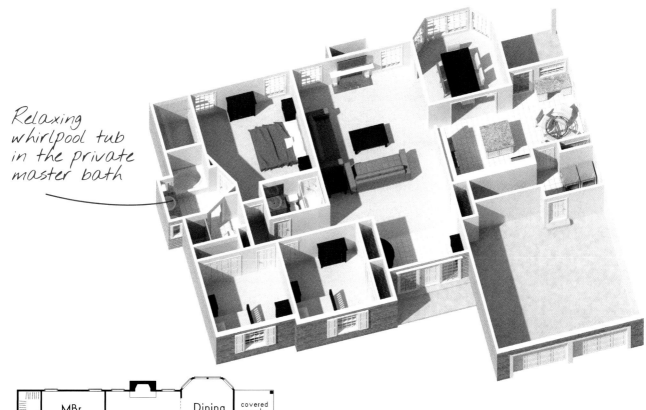

Relaxing whirlpool tub in the private master bath

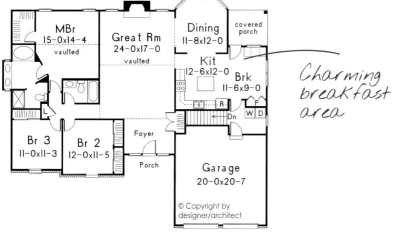

MBr
15-0x14-4
vaulted

Great Rm
24-0x17-0
vaulted

Dining
11-8x12-0

covered porch

Kit
12-6x12-0

Brk
11-6x9-0

Br 3
11-0x11-3

Br 2
12-0x11-5

Foyer

Porch

Garage
20-0x20-7

W D P R Dn L

© Copyright by designer/architect

Charming breakfast area

Photo, below: This homeowner used a different color brick than the previous page, another style of shutter and added a cupola on the roof of the garage to make this home design feel a bit more country.

PLANFEATURES

1,882 total square feet of living area

Width: 60'-10" Depth: 51'-2"

A wide, handsome entrance opens to the vaulted great room with a fireplace

The great room and dining area are conveniently joined but still allow privacy

A private covered porch extends the breakfast area

A practical passageway runs through the laundry room from the garage to the kitchen

There is a vaulted ceiling in the master bedroom

3 bedrooms, 2 baths, 2-car garage

Basement foundation

Price Code D

houseplansandmore.com

PLANFEATURES

3,888 total square feet of living area

Width: 82'-0" Depth: 72'-6"

Detailed brickwork surrounding the arched windows and quoined corners create a timeless exterior

The two-story great room has a large fireplace, flanking bookshelves, a massive window wall and a balcony overlook

The state-of-the-art kitchen has an island cooktop, built-in oven/microwave, a large pantry, a menu desk and opens to the breakfast and hearth rooms

A coffered ceiling, bay window, two walk-in closets and a huge bath adorn the master bedroom

4 bedrooms, 3 1/2 baths, 3-car side entry garage

Walk-out basement foundation

Price Code F

Second Floor
1,095 sq. ft.

Splendid vaulted parlor

First Floor
2,793 sq. ft.

Second Floor
617 sq. ft.

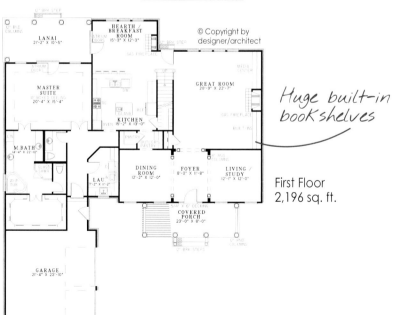

Huge built-in bookshelves

First Floor
2,196 sq. ft.

© Copyright by designer/architect

PLANFEATURES

2,843 total square feet of living area

Width: 61'-5" Depth: 73'-3"

Step inside to view the elegant formal living and dining rooms flanking the foyer

The massive great room is excellent for parties and large gatherings

The master bedroom and hearth/breakfast room enjoy direct access onto the rear lanai

The bonus area on the second floor has an additional 215 square feet of living area

4 bedrooms, 2 1/2 baths, 2-car side entry garage

Slab or crawl space foundation, please specify when ordering

Price Code E

houseplansandmore.com

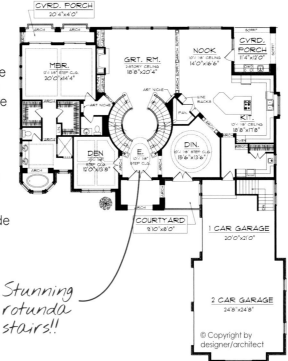

PLANFEATURES

3,687 total square feet of living area

Width: 71'-0" Depth: 87'-4"

Energy efficient home with 2" x 6" exterior walls

A magnificent circular staircase winds down to greet you as you enter this Tuscan style home

The two-story ceiling and fireplace flanked by built-in cabinets in the great room create an atmosphere that's perfect for entertaining

The spacious kitchen features a large eat-in island and direct access to the formal dining room and laundry area

4 bedrooms, 3 1/2 baths, 3-car side entry garage

Walk-out basement foundation

Price Code K

Stunning rotunda stairs!!

First Floor
2,567 sq. ft.

Second Floor
1,120 sq. ft.

Vaulted master bedroom with private bath!

VAULTED MASTER
12/2 X 14/10

BONUS / BR.4
17/6 X 12/8 +/-

BR. 2
12/0 X 10/0 +

OPEN TO FOYER

DN

LIN

PLANT SHELF

Second Floor
747 sq. ft.

DINING
11/6 X 11/6

DEN/BR. 3
10/8 X 10/0

GARAGE
11/0 X 17/0

VAULTED GREAT RM.
17/2 X 15/0
(TO ISLAND)

11/0 X 12/8

© Copyright by designer/architect

GARAGE
22/6 X 22/0

REF

2 STORY **FOYER**

UP

STOR

First Floor
951 sq. ft.

PLANFEATURES

1,698 total square feet of living area

Width: 50'-0" Depth: 44'-6"

Energy efficient home with 2" x 6" exterior walls

The vaulted master suite has a private bath and a spacious closet

The den/bedroom #3 has access to its own bath and is located on the first floor ideal for an in-law suite

The bonus room on the second floor has an additional 254 square feet of living area

3 bedrooms, 3 baths, 3-car garage

Crawl space foundation

Price Code D

houseplansandmore.com

PLANFEATURES

3,382 total square feet of living area

Width: 50'-0" Depth: 63'-0"

The great room features a corner built-in perfect as a media center plus a fireplace for coziness

All of the bedrooms are located on the second floor for privacy

Double doors in the breakfast nook lead to a covered patio perfect for grilling

3 bedrooms, 2 1/2 baths, 3-car garage

Crawl space foundation

Price Code S1

Perfect great room layout with entertainment center!

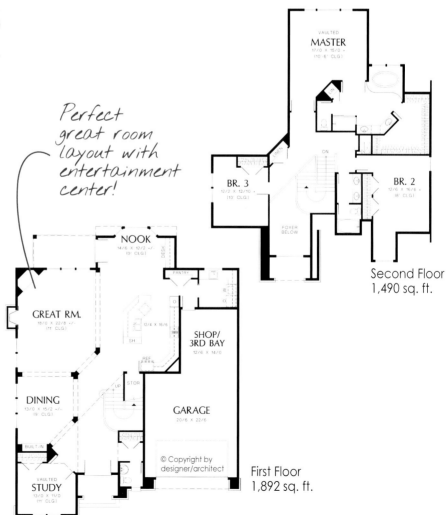

Second Floor
1,490 sq. ft.

First Floor
1,892 sq. ft.

© Copyright by designer/architect

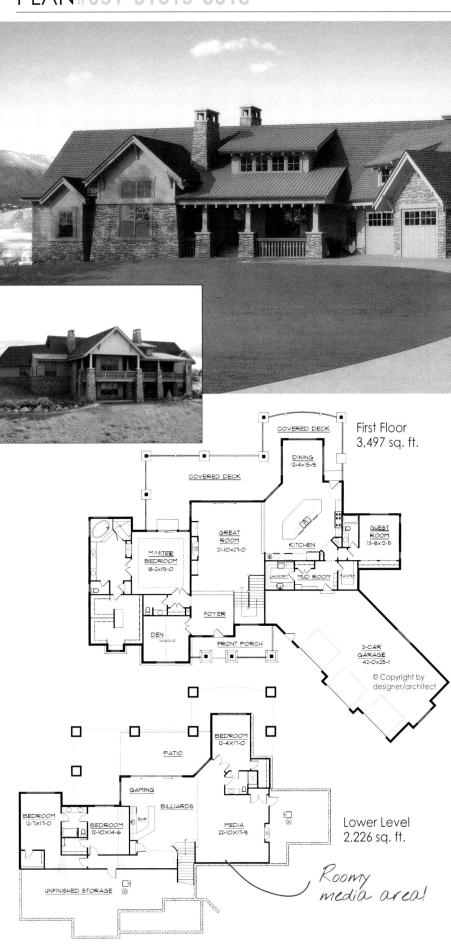

First Floor
3,497 sq. ft.

COVERED DECK

DINING
12-4x15-9

COVERED DECK

GREAT
ROOM
21-10x27-0

KITCHEN

GUEST
ROOM
13-8x12-5

MASTER
BEDROOM
18-2x19-0

LAUNDRY   MUD ROOM   PANTRY

FOYER

DEN
14-1x13-10

FRONT PORCH

3-CAR
GARAGE
42-0x25-1

© Copyright by
designer/architect

BEDROOM
12-4x17-0

PATIO

GAMING

BILLIARDS

BAR

BEDROOM
12-7x17-0

BEDROOM
12-10x14-6

MEDIA
22-10x17-8

Lower Level
2,226 sq. ft.

UNFINISHED STORAGE

Roomy media area!

PLANFEATURES

5,723 total square feet of living area

Width: 113'-8" Depth: 100'-6"

Energy efficient home with 2" x 6" exterior walls

This home features a lavish master bedroom that boasts a bath with a double-bowl vanity, an oversized corner tub, separate shower, see-through fireplace and a walk-in closet that is very generous in size

The kitchen, great and dining rooms are all combined and access the large covered deck

A media room, a billiards area, a wet bar, three bedrooms and two baths compose the extensive lower level

5 bedrooms, 4 1/2 baths, 3-car side entry garage

Walk-out basement foundation

Price Code S1

houseplansandmore.com

PLAN FEATURES

1,760 total square feet of living area

Width: 50'-0" Depth: 44'-6"

The open kitchen overlooks the vaulted great room and has an island with plenty of casual seating

The dining room enjoys outdoor access making it ideal for grilling

The oversized garage has space in the rear for an extra car

The bonus room on the second floor has an additional 251 square feet of living area

4 bedrooms, 3 baths, 3-car garage

Crawl space foundation

Price Code C

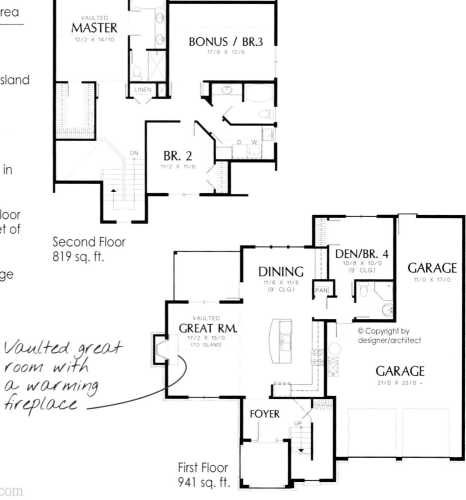

Second Floor
819 sq. ft.

Vaulted great room with a warming fireplace

First Floor
941 sq. ft.

SOLOMON

PLAN #651-011D-0012

2,755 total square feet of living area

Width: 84'-0" Depth: 73'-0"

Energy efficient home with 2" x 6" exterior walls

The master suite has its own wing

3 bedrooms, 2 1/2 baths, 3-car side entry garage

Crawl space foundation

Price Code F

MARYLBONE

PLAN #651-051D-0439

1,735 total square feet of living area

Width: 49'-4" Depth: 63'-8"

Energy efficient home with 2" x 6" exterior walls

Both a shower and an oversized garden tub add great efficiency to the private master bath

3 bedrooms, 2 baths, 2-car garage

Basement foundation

Price Code E

PLEASANT HILL

PLAN #651-020D-0295

2,366 total square feet of living area

Width: 50'-0" Depth: 86'-0"

This unique facade features a stunning courtyard leading to the main entrance

4 bedrooms, 3 baths, 2-car side entry garage

Slab foundation

Price Code F

SAHARA

PLAN #651-065D-0128

2,283 total square feet of living area

Width: 72'-0" Depth: 55'-10"

A corner fireplace and triple French doors highlight the great room

3 bedrooms, 2 baths, 2-car garage

Basement foundation

Price Code D

houseplansandmore.com

SUMMERVIEW

PLAN#651-007D-0068

1,922 total square feet of living area

Width: 55'-8" Depth: 46'-4"

The wrap-around country porch is perfect for peaceful evenings

2 bedrooms, 2 baths, 1-car side entry garage

Walk-out basement foundation

Price Code B

ALYSSA

PLAN#651-121D-0028

1,433 total square feet of living area

Width: 36'-0" Depth: 54'-0"

The kitchen boasts a corner island and flows into the vaulted great room

2 bedrooms, 2 baths, 2-car garage

Basement foundation

Price Code AA

PEYTON

PLAN#651-121D-0034

2,392 total square feet of living area

Width: 68'-10" Depth: 74'-0"

The master bedroom is separated for privacy and features a large bath and double walk-in closets

4 bedrooms, 2 1/2 baths, 2-car side entry garage

Basement foundation

Price Code C

houseplansandmore.com

CLAIRE

PLAN#651-121D-0036

1,820 total square feet of living area

Width: 60'-4" Depth: 52'-0"

The functional kitchen with a walk-in pantry features a breakfast bar with enough seating for three to comfortably dine

All of the bedrooms are located near each other for convenience

3 bedrooms, 2 baths, 2-car garage

Basement foundation

Price Code B

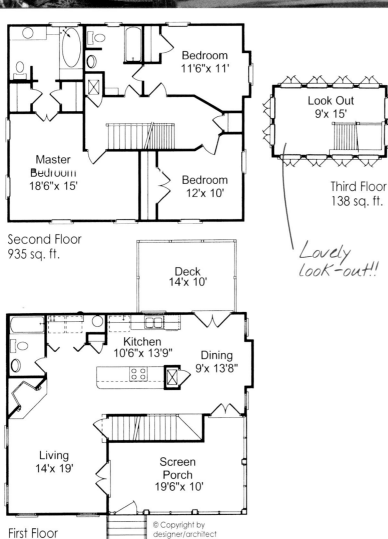

Bedroom
11'6"x 11'

Look Out
9'x 15'

Master Bedroom
18'6"x 15'

Bedroom
12'x 10'

Third Floor
138 sq. ft.

Second Floor
935 sq. ft.

Lovely look-out!!

Deck
14'x 10'

Kitchen
10'6"x 13'9"

Dining
9'x 13'8"

Living
14'x 19'

Screen Porch
19'6"x 10'

First Floor
731 sq. ft.

© Copyright by designer/architect

PLANFEATURES

1,804 total square feet of living area

Width: 38'-0" Depth: 35'-0"

Enter this home through the large screen porch and then you are invited into the home via French doors into the living room

The spacious kitchen boasts a cooktop island, a generous pantry, and a flowing design into the dining room

The second floor offers two additional bedrooms with a full bath to share as well as a luxurious master bedroom with a private bath featuring a whirlpool tub

3 bedrooms, 3 baths, 2-car drive under garage

Pier foundation

Price Code C

houseplansandmore.com

Photo, above: Just steps away from the interior is a lovely covered patio that creates year-round outdoor enjoyment. Add a refreshing pool just beyond like these homeowners did and this will become everyone's favorite place for relaxing.

Photo, right: A two-story ceiling, built-in nooks and the stunning fireplace join forces in creating an overly plush family room.

houseplansandmore.com

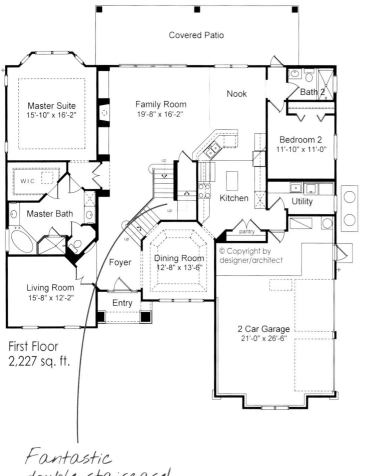

Covered Patio

Master Suite
15'-10" x 16'-2"

Family Room
19'-8" x 16'-2"

Nook

Bath 2

W.I.C.

Master Bath

Bedroom 2
11'-10" x 11'-0"

Kitchen

Utility

Foyer

Dining Room
12'-8" x 13'-6"

© Copyright by
designer/architect

pantry

Living Room
15'-8" x 12'-2"

Entry

2 Car Garage
21'-0" x 26'-6"

First Floor
2,227 sq. ft.

Fantastic double staircase!

Open Below

Bedroom 4
11'-10" x 9'-4"

Loft
24'-3" x 12'-10"

Bedroom 3
12'-8" x 11'-2"

Bath 3

Second Floor
771 sq. ft.

PLAN FEATURES

2,998 total square feet of living area

Width: 58'-8" Depth: 68'-0"

A split stairwell guides residents from the foyer or family room to the second floor loft and bedrooms

The kitchen peninsula overlooks the family room and neighboring nook, revealing the view beyond the rear patio

The living room opens beyond double doors, just off the foyer, and can be used in a variety of ways from private work to family game night

4 bedrooms, 4 baths, 2-car side entry garage

Slab foundation

Price Code E

Photo, below: Neat trim, distinctive windows, and an ambiance of peaceful luxury cover every aspect of this lavish home, even a space as simple as the master bedroom.

houseplansandmore.com

PLANFEATURES

2,555 total square feet of living area

Width: 72'-0" Depth: 36'-0"

A fireplace with flanking built-in shelves is the focal point of the great room

The kitchen enjoys an eating bar that is just steps away from the breakfast area with rear patio access

The loft area on the second floor overlooks the two-story foyer and has a closet for extra storage

3 bedrooms, 2 1/2 baths, 2-car garage

Basement foundation

Price Code C

Vaulted master bedroom

Br 2
12-6x10-9

MBr
16-2x15-4
Vault Clg
Opt Coffer

Dn

Br 3
13-6x10-5

Open to Below

Loft Area
11-5x13-8

Second Floor
1,236 sq. ft.

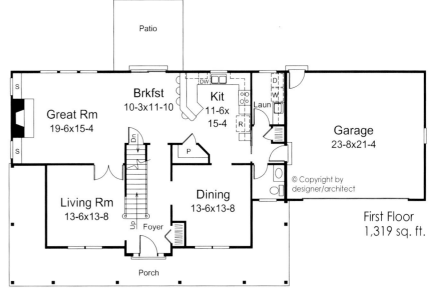

Patio

Great Rm
19-6x15-4

Brkfst
10-3x11-10

Kit
11-6x
15-4

DW

D W

Laun

Garage
23-8x21-4

Dn

P

Living Rm
13-6x13-8

Dining
13-6x13-8

© Copyright by designer/architect

Up   Foyer

Porch

First Floor
1,319 sq. ft.

BRIDGETON

PLAN #651-053D-0052

2,513 total square feet of living area

Width: 79'-4" Depth: 72'-4"

The kitchen has an island cooktop and built-in desk

The covered entry leads into the spacious foyer

4 bedrooms, 2 full baths, 2 half baths, 2-car side entry garage

Walk-out basement foundation

Price Code B

SANDRA

PLAN #651-121D-0008

2,487 total square feet of living area

Width: 96'-2" Depth: 65'-8"

The beautiful vaulted master bedroom features a spacious bath and direct access to a private patio

A trio of windows, 10' ceiling height and a corner fireplace create a pleasant atmosphere in the great room

3 bedrooms, 2 1/2 baths, 2-car garage

Basement foundation

Price Code C

PEDERSON

PLAN #651-077D-0098

2,000 total square feet of living area

Width: 67'-0" Depth: 56'-0"

Entertain in style with an outdoor kitchen located on the rear covered porch

3 bedrooms, 2 1/2 baths, 2-car side entry garage

Basement, crawl space or slab foundation, please specify when ordering

Price Code E

AUDREY

PLAN #651-121D-0035

1,759 total square feet of living area

Width: 45'-8" Depth: 72'-4"

The formal dining room is separated from the vaulted great room by decorative columns

3 bedrooms, 2 baths, 2-car garage

Basement foundation

Price Code A

LAWTON PLACE

PLAN#651-047D-0058

PLAN FEATURES

2,816 total square feet of living area

Width: 94'-0" Depth: 113'-6"

Unique angled rooms create an exciting feel

The well-organized kitchen with island is adjacent to the family room

The second floor bonus room with sun deck has an additional 290 square feet of living area

The guest house provides an additional 330 square feet of living area with 1 bedroom, 1 bath and a 1-car garage

Framing - only concrete block available

3 bedrooms, 3 full baths, 2 half baths, 2-car garage

Slab foundation

Price Code E

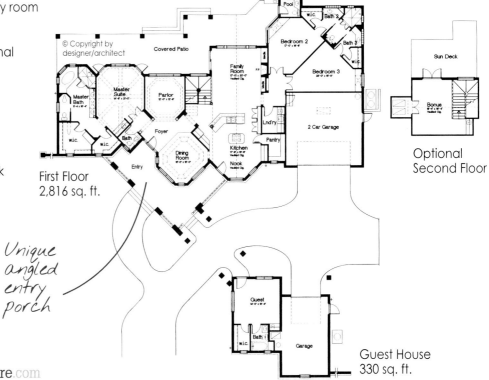

First Floor
2,816 sq. ft.

Unique angled entry porch

Optional Second Floor

Guest House
330 sq. ft.

© Copyright by designer/architect

houseplansandmore.com

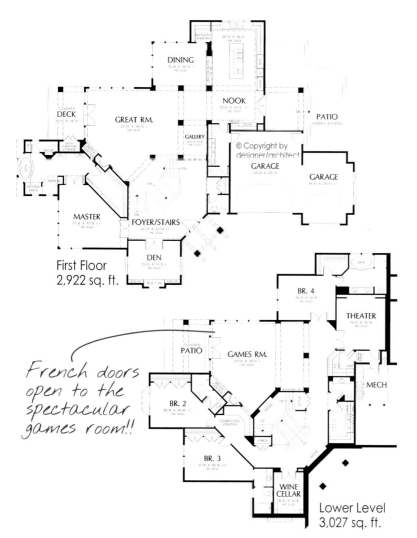

First Floor
2,922 sq. ft.

French doors open to the spectacular games room!!

Lower Level
3,027 sq. ft.

PLANFEATURES

5,949 total square feet of living area

Width: 98'-0" Depth: 76'-0"

A beautifully designed staircase greets guests as they enter this luxurious home

The enormous great room features a fireplace, a built-in media center and double-door access to the covered deck

The delightful lower level boasts a theater room, large wine cellar and many other lovely amenities

4 bedrooms, 4 full baths, 3 half baths, 3-car garage

Partial slab/walk-out basement foundation

Price Code S1

houseplansandmore.com

Open up and say "Ahh!"
our love for open floor plans

When visiting friends, do you ever feel cut off from the hosts as they flitter between rooms? You know they are attempting to take care of their duties while maintaining a connection with their guests, but it's a struggle to do so. Or perhaps there are times when work in the kitchen is begging your attention, but so are the children playing in the family room. Too many homeowners can relate with the desire to be in more than one place at one time within their own home.

These steps below allow homeowners to make the most of an open floor plan, allowing their home to accommodate them perfectly:

SPREAD OUT – Even homes with modest square footage can be transformed into airy and open space. Wherever possible, eliminate doorways, widen passages, and remove boundaries. Allowing traffic to flow easily from one "room" to another is important in spreading out.

LIGHTEN UP – Natural light can make any space inviting and warm. Use large windows and long views to connect with the outdoors and make an open room appear even larger. If window walls are not appropriate, consider skylights and strategically placed mirrors to make the most of some natural light and space.

FAMILY FUNCTIONALITY – Open floor plans in kitchens, dining, and living rooms are imperative for busy families. When open, these spaces transition easily into one another, allowing family members to take on various tasks without being entirely separated or tripping over one another. A great addition to an open kitchen is the snack bar/preparation island. Kids can keep busy and close while still allowing mom and dad enough room to visit and get meals underway.

USE IT OR LOSE IT – It's important to make the most of the space you have, using every corner and nook. The formal dining room is a space of the past, typically unused by today's busy families. Eliminating the extra walls can turn this formal space into usable dining space, allowing an easy transition from the kitchen to the table, while still maintaining a lovely dining spot. Most often windows, deck access, fireplaces, and bay windows can be incorporated into these new open spaces.

GET TOGETHER, OPEN UP – Like the dining room and kitchen, opening the great room presents many benefits to families. This once formally enclosed space can be a spacious area ideal for accommodating family members on game night or can transition seamlessly into the center of the party when having house guests.

By incorporating and creating open floor plans, there is no longer any reason to limit your spaces or banish particular tasks to designated rooms. Your home can become a seamless space where guests and hosts, parents and children can all interact without limitation.

$\mathcal{C}$apturing Curb $\mathcal{A}$ppeal

While driving down a street on a beautiful sunny afternoon your thoughts are halted as you glance at the house on the corner. You can't help slowing down, briefly stopping, giving it a second look. You drive away wondering why the attraction. Why did it turn your head? Two words...CURB APPEAL!

Adding curb appeal to your home is easy and you can begin with a simple exercise.

Take a good look at your home and answer these 3 questions:

1. What is your first impression of the house and yard?

2. What are the best exterior features of your home and yard?

3. What are the worst exterior features of your home and yard?

The first impression you have of your home and yard may be the fact that it needs a good, old-fashion cleaning up. This is the best project to begin with when adding curb appeal to your home. Is your yard cluttered with junk? While most find it necessary to add to improve curb appeal, there are times when removing is more effective. Remove all extras, like garden tools, toys, trash, or anything that gives your home a cluttered appearance.

Once you have the extra debris removed, mow the lawn and get rid of weeds. Rake and dispose of leaves. Trim shrubs and trees that are overgrown and blocking the view of your home. Does your house seem dirty or dingy? Give it a scrub down. You can pressure wash your home's exterior eliminating dirt, mold, and mildew. Give the driveway, patio, porch, and deck a good cleaning with the power sprayer. Grab a ladder and clean those windows and gutters. By completing these simple tasks, your home will just sparkle.

Now that you have cleaned up, what else can you do to add curb appeal to your home? Your next projects will depend on how you answered the above questions. However, here are a few things to consider.

Welcoming guests into your home begins at the entry. Start by freshening up your front door with a coat of paint or stain. Depending on the condition of the existing door, paint may not be the answer. If so, consider installing a new door perhaps with a glass insert or symmetrical sidelights. Polish the existing door knob and lock set or remove the old and update with new hardware. Create warmth and eye pleasing symmetry by adding light fixtures to each side of your entry. Compliment your lighting with matching front-door accents such as flower urns. With more time and a larger budget, you can create a grand entry by adding molding around your door. In addition, you may add a permanent welcome mat to your entry by tiling your front step or porch area. House numbers and a wall mounted mailbox also add flair to your home's exterior. Be sure the exterior features coordinate in style and color.

Another major feature of your home's exterior is landscaping. Once you have completed the simple task of cleaning the yard and trimming shrubs, step back and take in what you have to work with. Revisit your answers to the three questions on the previous page.

Try doing a couple of small projects that can be completed easily and in a little amount of time. Container gardens of various sizes strategically placed in your current landscaping add color and welcome others to take note of your home. Garden beds can be weeded and pruned to welcome new growth. If your garden beds are bare, plant flowers in varieties of annuals and perennials. Add new mulch to restore color. Replace old, worn out edging and consider a new look with stone.

If your landscaping is in need of more TLC than these small projects offer, set your sites on a larger project for the season. These types of projects may require more investment, but will pay great dividends in the future. Frame your home by creating new planting beds along the front and on the corners of your house. Enhance walkways and driveways with colorful plants or rock. Include a nice variety of plants with a mix of color, size, and texture but remember that plants do grow and many will require maintenance. Outdoor lighting along walkways or in plant beds will add warmth to your landscaping and security to your home. Personalize with outdoor art, such as water fountains or sculptures. Be sure to complement your home's natural exterior and charm. Additional larger projects may include adding arbors or fence panels with garden gates. Whatever additions or changes you make, keep in mind that you want to enhance the best features of your home.

Most of these curb appeal projects may be planned in phases and easily completed in a day or a weekend. With each project, or phase, step back and reevaluate the first impression of your home. Has your impression changed? Hopefully, yes. And in the future, the person driving down the street on a beautiful sunny afternoon, slowing down and briefly stopping to give that home a second look will not be you. You will be the person waving to them from your front yard knowing the attraction was... CURB APPEAL!

Other Ways to Capture the Appeal

Create symmetry and balance at your front entrance.

Be creative with your color scheme; create contrast.

Keep your roof in check - if your shingles are in shambles, then get a professional to install new roofing.

Find the right style of window because it can make or break the overall look and feel of your home.

Continually repair your driveway instead of having to replace it altogether in the future.

Your mailbox is the first impression of your home so match it with the style of your home.

Make sure your house numbers are visible so that guests and potential buyers can find your home without difficulty.

Step back and look at your home from across the street to see your home from a buyer's perspective.

Stylish Outdoor Design Ideas

Outdoor spaces are a "given" with any home being built today. Home-owners now insist their homes include an outdoor retreat. As seen with current outdoor living trends, many patio spaces have gone luxury. But, even if you desire something less extravagant; a simple place to relax and unwind after a long workday, here are some great ideas that can make your outdoor space a place of enjoyment no matter what the size.

Do you yearn for an intimate outdoor dining space?
Crave a comfortable reading nook?
Or, desire a place to tend to your own bountiful garden?

Let Me Entertain You

If you desire an intimate outdoor dining place, then select a casual table, or even long, flat benches that can be used for seating or can convert to low table space. To keep from overcrowding the area, hang planters above or off the edge. Lights give even more ambiance when hung in surrounding trees.

The Tranquil Retreat

Start with a comfortable chair and foot stool. Obviously, you must experience comfort in order to feel relaxed. So, fill a basket with maga-zines or books so you, as well as your guests, can find something to read with little effort. Remember, you want this area to be inviting! Then, place trellises with climbing plants around the patio with honeysuckle, wisteria and other fragrant plants. Not only will they be visually appealing, but the scent will relax you. Also, try placing a trickling water fountain on a nearby table. These small touches will transport you to a place of relaxation in your own backyard.

Grow A Garden

If gardening is your passion, or you want organic vegetables readily available for all your favorite recipes, then container gardening is the perfect idea for your patio. Many plants and vegetables can be grown in containers quite effectively. Also, many varieties of herbs can be grown in one single pot, perfect for conserving space. Or, think vertical and attach lattice to a wall creating a spot for tomato plants. Pots placed on plant stands of different heights are also beautiful.

Looking for some ways to add overall style and personality to your patio?

Patio spaces take on a life of their own when you add a little personality. If you love bold colors, plant vibrant flowers to liven up the area with color and interest. This is an inexpensive way to add a colorful focal point.

Outdoor Furniture

Select comfortable and durable outdoor furniture that can withstand the harsh weather elements. Include bold patterned pillows, or cushions to add even more style.

Accessories

Wind chimes, fountains and hammocks are accessories that add little expense. Who wouldn't enjoy falling into a hammock on a summer's day on the patio? This will be the perfect place to relax after mowing the grass or when playing on your ipad. Add in the trickle of water from a fountain or the sweet sound of wind chimes blowing in the breeze and you'll be in a place of complete relaxation.

Outdoor Lighting

Outdoor lighting is now a staple for many homeowners and solar lighting is a wonderful economical option that adds subtle ambiance homeowners crave when the sun sets.

Whether you are drawn to an expansive luxurious patio space with every amenity, or you yearn for something that requires much less maintenance, create an outdoor area that is full of personality and function. Use some or all of the ideas here and your patio oasis will be your favorite spot at home.

OLIVAIRE

PLANFEATURES

2,830 total square feet of living area

Width: 84'-11" Depth: 77'-9"

A bayed dinette offers a stunning atmosphere and opens to the relaxing screen porch with a corner fireplace

A large work area near the garage includes a laundry and mud room, walk-in closet for storage, lockers and a built-in desk

The owner's suite located on the second floor is an amazing retreat that includes a massive walk-in closet and extra-large private bath

2 bedrooms, 2 1/2 baths, 3-car garage

Walk-out basement foundation

Price Code F

Enormous mud room with walk-in closet & laundry room!!

Second Floor
1,157 sq. ft.

First Floor
1,673 sq. ft.

© Copyright by designer/architect

houseplansandmore.com

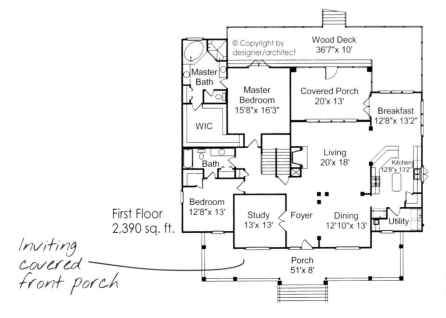

Multimedia Room
16' x 19'

WIC

Bath

WIC

Open To Below

WIC

Balcony

Bedroom
13 x 13

Open to Below

Bedroom
13 x 13

Second Floor
1,200 sq. ft.

© Copyright by designer/architect

Wood Deck
36'7"x 10'

Master Bath

Master Bedroom
15'8"x 16'3"

WIC

Covered Porch
20'x 13'

Breakfast
12'8"x 13'2"

Bath

Living
20'x 18'

Kitchen
12'8"x 13'2"

Bedroom
12'8"x 13'

Study
13'x 13'

Foyer

Dining
12'10"x 13'

Utility

First Floor
2,390 sq. ft.

Inviting covered front porch

Porch
51'x 8'

PLANFEATURES

3,590 total square feet of living area

Width: 61'-0" Depth: 64'-0"

The living room's crackling fireplace is enjoyed from numerous vantage points, including from the kitchen peninsula

The second floor multimedia room is a casual place to gather the family on game night or host the kids' sleepovers with plenty of space to spare

Double doors throughout the home create dramatic entryways

4 bedrooms, 3 baths, 3-car side entry drive under garage

Basement foundation

Price Code S1

houseplansandmore.com

FLORA PARK

PLAN#651-119D-0007

PLANFEATURES

4,390 total square feet of living area

Width: 55'-10" Depth: 84'-10"

The grand foyer enjoys a curved staircase descending to a plush lower level

A cheerful morning room extends off the luxury kitchen and has direct access to the outdoors

The lower level includes plenty of space for entertaining including a living/theater space, a large wet bar and game area

The unfinished storage and exercise area on the lower level has an additional 879 square feet of living area

3 bedrooms, 3 1/2 baths, 3-car side entry garage

Basement foundation

Price Code F

houseplansandmore.com

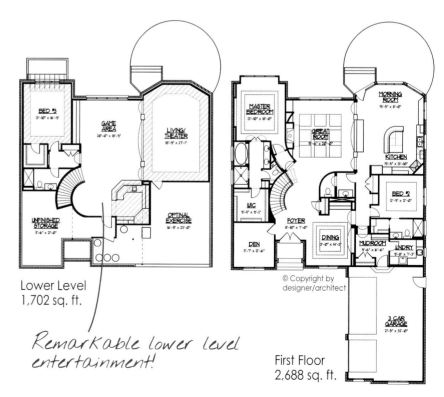

Lower Level
1,702 sq. ft.

Remarkable lower level entertainment!

© Copyright by designer/architect

First Floor
2,688 sq. ft.

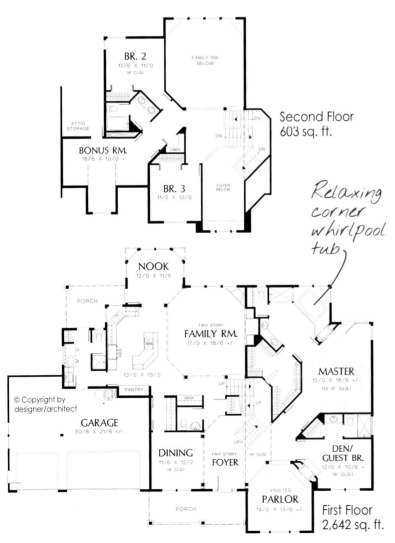

BR. 2
12/6 X 11/0
(9' CLG)

FAMILY RM.
BELOW

ATTIC
STORAGE

BONUS RM.
18/6 X 10/0 +/-

LINEN

DN

DN

DN

Second Floor
603 sq. ft.

BR. 3
11/2 X 12/0

FOYER
BELOW

Relaxing corner whirlpool tub

NOOK
12/0 X 11/6

PORCH

TWO STORY
FAMILY RM.
17/0 X 18/6 +/-

13/0 X 19/0

REF.

W D

PANTRY

UP

UP

MASTER
15/0 X 18/6 +/-
(10'-0" CLG)

DESK

UP

© Copyright by
designer/architect

GARAGE
30/8 X 21/8 +/-

UP

DINING
11/6 X 12/2
(9' CLG)

TWO STORY
FOYER
(11' CLG)

DEN/
GUEST BR.
12/0 X 10/6 +/-
(9' CLG)

VAULTED
PARLOR
14/0 X 14/6 +/-

PORCH

First Floor
2,642 sq. ft.

PLANFEATURES

3,245 total square feet of living area

Width: 80'-0" Depth: 61'-0"

The kitchen enjoys direct access onto a covered porch perfect for grilling

Off the formal dining room is a hallway with a built-in counterspace perfect for buffet style serving

The den/guest bedroom offers a full bath and shares a see-through fireplace with the parlor

The bonus room on the second floor has an additional 255 square feet of living area

4 bedrooms, 4 1/2 baths,
3-car garage

Crawl space foundation

Price Code F

houseplansandmore.com

Photo, above: The great room's immensity is artfully showcased by elegant columns defining the kitchen.

Photo, right: The gallery's barrel ceiling and crown moulding cannot help but draw the eye to this dramatic combination.

houseplansandmore.com

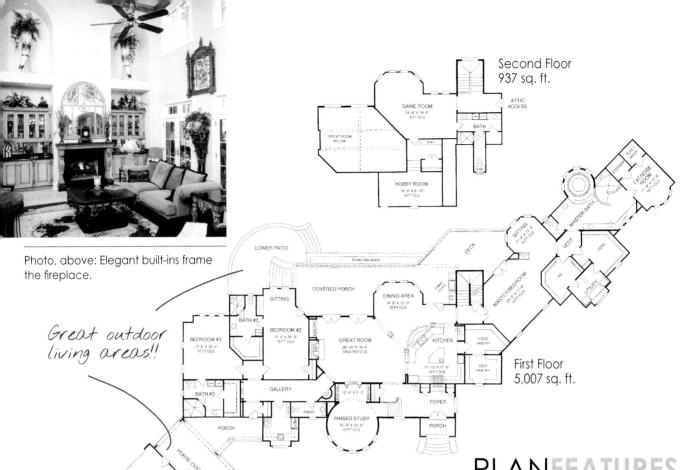

Second Floor
937 sq. ft.

GAME ROOM
24'-8" X 19'-6"
8 FT CLG

ATTIC ACCESS

BATH

GREAT ROOM BELOW

BENCH

HOBBY ROOM
19'-0" X 9'-10"
8 FT CLG

Photo, above: Elegant built-ins frame the fireplace.

Great outdoor living areas!!

LOWER PATIO

PLANTING AREA

DECK

COVERED PORCH

SITTING
11'-6" X 11'-2"
10 FT CLG

MASTER BATH

VEST

EXERCISE ROOM
11'-8" X 17'-6"
10 FT CLG

ELEC/MECH

STORAGE

SITTING

DINING AREA
14'-6" X 12'-0"
10 FT CLG

MASTER BEDROOM
22'-6" X 17'-6"
10 FT CLG

UTILITY

HERS

BATH #2

BEDROOM #3
17'-8" X 18'-5"
10 FT CLG

BEDROOM #2
13'-4" X 26'-6"
10 FT CLG

FP

GREAT ROOM
26'-10" X 19'-0"
VAULTED CLG

KITCHEN
17'-10" X 17'-6"
10 FT CLG

FOOD PANTRY

DISH PANTRY

First Floor
5,007 sq. ft.

BATH #3

GALLERY

PWDR

RAISED STUDY
15'-0" X 15'-0"
12 FT CLG

FOYER

PORCH

PORCH

PORCH

PORTE-COCHERE

4 CAR GARAGE

© Copyright by designer/architect

Photo, below: Whether admiring the contrasting tray ceiling treatment, the sunken whirlpool tub, or the glass block partitioned shower, this master bath is brimming with spa-like amenities. Such luxury can be enjoyed on a daily basis in this home.

PLANFEATURES

5,944 total square feet of living area

Width: 195'-7" Depth: 146'-10"

The raised study is illuminated by many windows in the turret-styled room

Two sets of double-doors in the great room lead to a magnificent covered porch

The second floor offers a game and hobby room as well as attic storage

The master suite incorporates the entire right wing of the home and includes two walk-in closets, unique shower, tub in a bay window and an exercise room

3 bedrooms, 4 1/2 baths, 4-car rear entry garage

Slab foundation

Price Code S7

houseplansandmore.com

SUNLAND PARK

PLAN FEATURES

3,261 total square feet of living area

Width: 87'-11" Depth: 75'-2"

Double-doors open to the cozy study with a warming fireplace

The master suite is brightened by windows and features a private bath and walk-in closet

A unique library loft on the second floor overlooks the open and airy gathering room

The bonus room above the garage has an additional 524 square feet of living area

3 bedrooms, 2 1/2 baths, 2-car garage

Crawl space foundation

Price Code S1

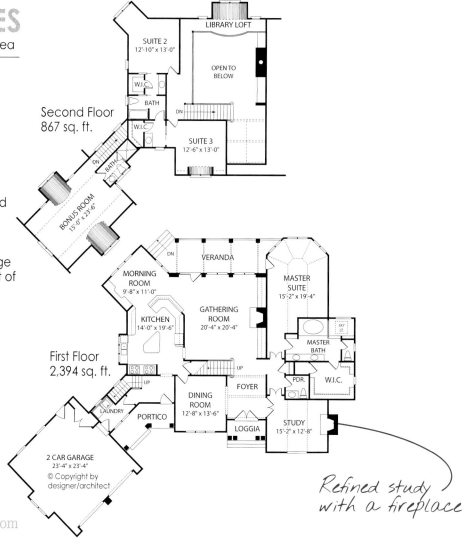

Second Floor 867 sq. ft.

- LIBRARY LOFT
- SUITE 2 — 12'-10" x 13'-0"
- OPEN TO BELOW
- W.I.C.
- BATH
- DN
- W.I.C.
- SUITE 3 — 12'-6" x 13'-0"
- DN
- BATH
- BONUS ROOM — 15'-0" x 23'-6"

First Floor 2,394 sq. ft.

- VERANDA
- DN
- MORNING ROOM — 9'-8" x 11'-0"
- MASTER SUITE — 15'-2" x 19'-4"
- GATHERING ROOM — 20'-4" x 20'-4"
- KITCHEN — 14'-0" x 19'-6"
- SKY LT.
- MASTER BATH
- UP
- LAUNDRY
- UP
- FOYER
- PDR.
- W.I.C.
- DINING ROOM — 12'-8" x 13'-6"
- PORTICO
- LOGGIA
- STUDY — 15'-2" x 12'-8"
- 2 CAR GARAGE — 23'-4" x 23'-4"

© Copyright by designer/architect

Refined study with a fireplace

PLANFEATURES

3,489 total square feet of living area

Width: 74'-8" Depth: 64'-8"

Energy efficient home with 2" x 6" exterior walls

Dramatic two-story ceilings enhance the entry and great room

The nook is flooded with sunlight from the large windows and skylights above

A stovetop island and walk-in pantry add convenience to the large kitchen

4 bedrooms, 3 1/2 baths, 3-car side entry garage

Basement foundation

Price Code S1

Second Floor
975 sq. ft.

Extraordinary great room!!

First Floor
2,514 sq. ft.

CRANE GROVE

PLAN FEATURES

5,884 total square feet of living area

Width: 165'-0" Depth: 116'-0"

This home's unique layout provides optimal privacy to the master suite as well as the other bedrooms

A shared vaulted play area, in addition to the laundry facilities, connects three secondary bedrooms

The garage entrance is outfitted with a mud room, complete with a half bath, a sizeable closet and bench seating ideal for combatting dirt tracked into the home

5 bedrooms, 5 1/2 baths, 3-car side entry garage

Crawl space foundation

Price Code S1

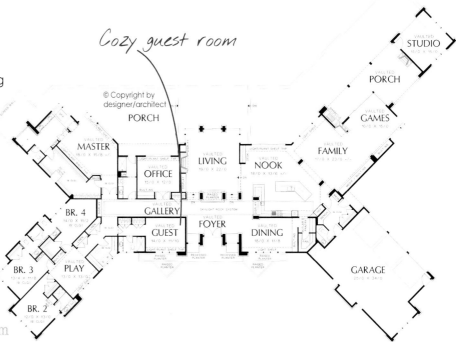

Cozy guest room

houseplansandmore.com

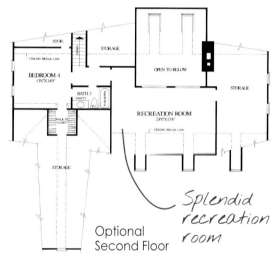

Optional
Second Floor

Splendid recreation room

First Floor
2,151 sq. ft.

© Copyright by
designer/architect

PLANFEATURES

2,151 total square feet of living area

Width: 61'-0" Depth: 59'-0"

An exceptional vaulted great room boasts a fireplace, a built-in entertainment center and access to the rear terrace/deck area

The bayed breakfast area is perfect for enjoying meals

A walk-in shower, double-bowl vanity and whirlpool tub give the master bath tantalizing appeal as well as access to a spacious walk-in closet

The optional second floor has an additional 814 square feet of living area

3 bedrooms, 2 baths, 2-car side entry garage

Partial basement/crawl space foundation

Price Code C

PLANFEATURES

5,283 total square feet of living area

Width: 120'-4" Depth: 98'-9"

Energy efficient home with 2" x 6" exterior walls

The large covered deck is a great way to enjoy the outdoors rain or shine

The lower level provides entertainment with its gaming and recreation rooms, home theater and casino

The master bedroom is located on the first floor with a private bath and walk-in closet

3 bedrooms, 2 full baths, 2 half baths, 3-car garage, RV garage

Basement or walk-out basement foundation, please specify when ordering

Price Code I

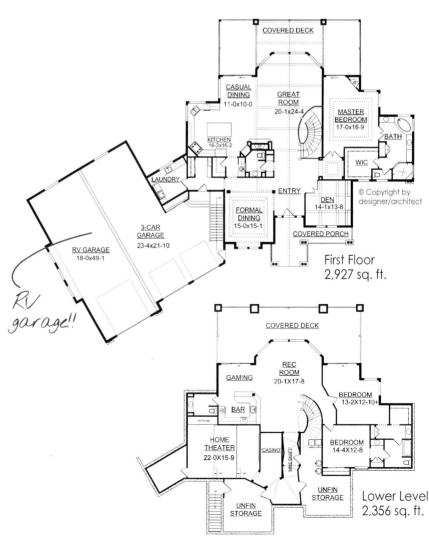

First Floor
2,927 sq. ft.

© Copyright by designer/architect

Lower Level
2,356 sq. ft.

PLAN FEATURES

5,003 total square feet of living area

Width: 87'-6" Depth: 74'-8"

A sunny breakfast room has access to two different covered porches on opposite sides

The second floor features a very large recreation room, adjacent computer room and a bonus area

The amazing master bath has many amenities, such as a lovely walk-in shower, whirlpool tub and large walk-in closet

The bonus room on the second floor had an additional 563 square feet of living area

5 bedrooms, 3 1/2 baths, 3-car side entry garage

Basement foundation, drawings also include crawl space and slab foundations

Price Code S1

Second Floor
1,941 sq. ft.

First Floor
3,062 sq. ft.

Dramatic gazebo!

DEVORA

PLANFEATURES

2,921 total square feet of living area

Width: 57'-0" Depth: 81'-10"

The impressive two-story gathering room has a fireplace and access to the rear covered terrace

A sizable island with eating bar in the kitchen is a definite gathering spot on the first floor

Two walk-in closets and a private bath are some of the features of the master suite

The bonus room on the second floor has an additional 393 square feet of living area

3 bedrooms, 3 1/2 baths, 2-car detached side entry garage

Crawl space foundation

Price Code G

Enchanting covered rear terrace

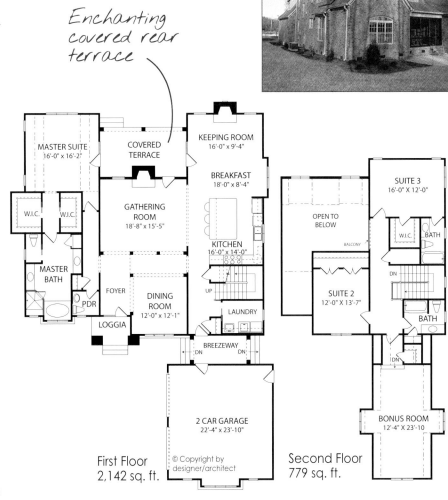

First Floor
2,142 sq. ft.

© Copyright by designer/architect

Second Floor
779 sq. ft.

Second Floor
1,002 sq. ft.

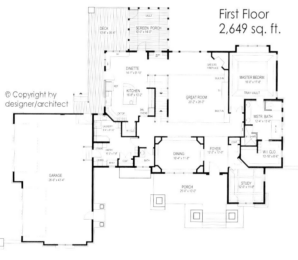

© Copyright by designer/architect

First Floor
2,649 sq. ft.

Lower Level
1,426 sq. ft.

Indoor sport court!!

PLANFEATURES

5,077 total square feet of living area

Width: 92'-0" Depth: 79'-6"

The spacious great room has built-in shelves and a corner gas fireplace to keep warm

Enjoying the outdoors is a breeze with the cozy screen porch and cheerful deck

Enter through double-doors to the master suite complete with a vaulted tray ceiling, a lavish bath and a large walk-in closet

5 bedrooms, 4 1/2 baths, 4-car side entry garage

Walk-out basement foundation

Price Code S3

houseplansandmore.com

Photo, above: A wall of windows with transoms above effortlessly ties the family room with the outdoors offering tranquil water views. And with the breakfast room just steps away, it's the ideal extension for all family activities.

Photo, right: This homeowner chose an extra-wide staircase that commands full attention in the beautiful foyer. With the addition of detailed carpentry such as crown molding and a chair rail, this entry has the feel of an older home but with a refreshing new home feel.

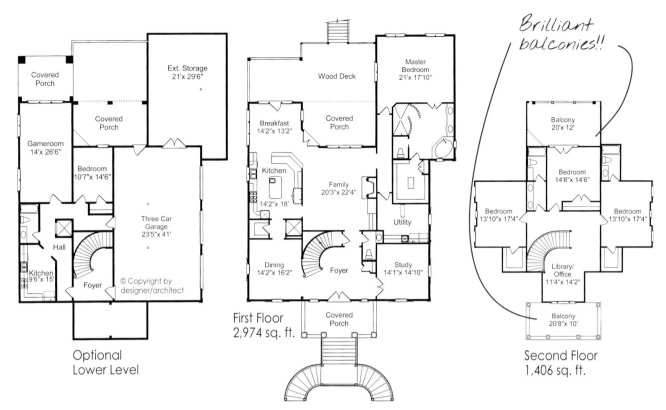

Optional Lower Level

Covered Porch

Ext. Storage 21'x 29'6"

Covered Porch

Gameroom 14'x 26'6"

Bedroom 10'7"x 14'6"

Three Car Garage 23'5"x 41'

Hall

Kitchen 9'6"x 15'

Foyer

© Copyright by designer/architect

First Floor 2,974 sq. ft.

Wood Deck

Master Bedroom 21'x 17'10"

Breakfast 14'2"x 13'2"

Covered Porch

Kitchen 14'2"x 18'

Family 20'3"x 22'4"

Utility

Dining 14'2"x 16'2"

Foyer

Study 14'1"x 14'10"

Covered Porch

Brilliant balconies!!

Second Floor 1,406 sq. ft.

Balcony 20'x 12'

Bedroom 14'6"x 14'6"

Bedroom 13'10"x 17'4"

Bedroom 13'10"x 17'4"

Library/ Office 11'4"x 14'2"

Balcony 20'8"x 10'

Photo, below: The owners of this home chose to make the library/office into a lovely parlor featuring a stunning grand piano. Located at the top of the stairs on the second floor, this room is a flexible and open space perfect for whatever amenities your family desires.

PLAN FEATURES

4,380 total square feet of living area

Width: 57'-0" Depth: 82'-0"

11' ceilings on the first floor and 9' ceilings on the second floor create a spacious interior

Intricate porch details display one-of-a-kind craftsmanship

The impressive foyer has a curved staircase creating a grand entry

One second floor bedroom accesses a private balcony

The optional lower level has an additional 1,275 square feet of living area

4 bedrooms, 3 1/2 baths, 3-car drive under side entry garage

Walk-out basement foundation

Price Code S1

houseplansandmore.com

229

PLAN FEATURES

2,277 total square feet of living area

Width: 54'-0" Depth: 49'-0"

Energy efficient home with 2" x 6" exterior walls

Lots of windows in the vaulted great room create an inviting feeling

The first floor den/bedroom #4 would make an ideal home office

The enormous dining area and kitchen combine to create a large gathering area overlooking the great room

4 bedrooms, 3 baths, 3-car garage

Crawl space foundation

Price Code E

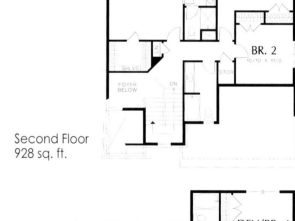

Second Floor
928 sq. ft.

Open & airy vaulted great room

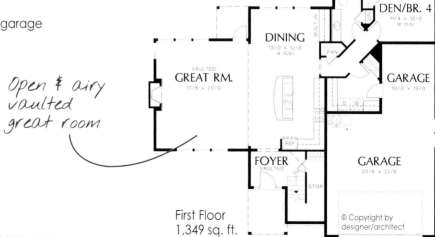

First Floor
1,349 sq. ft.

© Copyright by designer/architect

houseplansandmore.com

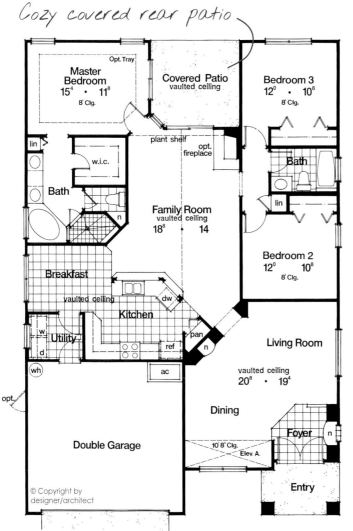

Cozy covered rear patio

PLANFEATURES

1,768 total square feet of living area

Width: 40'-0" Depth: 60'-0"

Uniquely designed vaulted living and dining rooms combine making great use of space

Informal family room has a vaulted ceiling, plant shelf accents and a kitchen overlook

The sunny breakfast area conveniently accesses the kitchen

3 bedrooms, 2 baths, 2-car garage

Slab foundation

Price Code B

© Copyright by designer/architect

PLANFEATURES

2,606 total square feet of living area

Width: 67'-6" Depth: 73'-10"

A corner fireplace in the great room warms the area and the adjoining dining room

French doors lead into the study/bedroom #4 that features a bay window and has access to a private patio

The garage includes a convenient storage space

The optional second floor has an additional 751 square feet of living space

4 bedrooms, 2 1/2 baths, 2-car side entry garage

Slab, basement, crawl space or walk-out basement foundation, please specify when ordering

Price Code F

Delightful master bath

Optional Second Floor

First Floor
2,606 sq. ft.

PLANFEATURES

1,468 total square feet of living area

Width: 35'-0" Depth: 30'-0"

Energy efficient home with 2" x 6" exterior walls

The family room has a beautiful cathedral ceiling adding spaciousness and a fireplace creating a cozy feel

The large kitchen has plenty of room for dining

3 bedrooms, 2 baths

Basement foundation

Price Code C

15'-0" X 11'-0"
4,50 X 3,30

10'-0" X 11'-0"
3,00 X 3,30

Second Floor
510 sq. ft.

13'-0" X 9'-0"
3,90 X 2,70

© Copyright by designer/architect

14'-0" X 13'-0"
4,20 X 3,90

19'-8" X 14'-0"
5,90 X 4,20

12'-0" X 12'-0"
3,60 X 3,60

Separated entryway for energy efficiency

First Floor
958 sq. ft.

houseplansandmore.com

KIMBERLY MANOR

PLAN#651-129S-0002

PLANFEATURES

5,277 total square feet of living area

Width: 63'-10" Depth: 85'-6"

A cheerful loft overlooks the two-story great room with fireplace and a wall of windows to brighten the area

The exceptional sunroom is the perfect space for entertaining guests

Two walk-in closets, a fireplace and an amazing private bath are some of the features of the master suite

The bonus room on the second floor has an additional 400 square feet of living area

4 bedrooms, 4 1/2 baths, 3-car side entry garage

Walk-out basement foundation

Price Code S2

© Copyright by designer/architect

First Floor
2,391 sq. ft.

Second Floor
922 sq. ft.

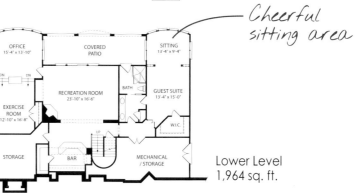

Cheerful sitting area

Lower Level
1,964 sq. ft.

houseplansandmore.com

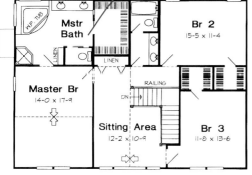

Vaulted master bedroom with private bath

Second Floor
1,269 sq. ft.

Mstr Bath

LINEN

Br 2
15-5 x 11-4

LINEN

Master Br
14-0 x 17-9

RAILING

DN

Sitting Area
12-2 x 10-9

Br 3
11-8 x 13-6

First Floor
1,378 sq. ft.

DN

BOOKS

Family Rm
21-4 x 15-1

Brkfst
10-6 x 15-1

Kit.
9-6 x 15-1

DW

Shop
14-5 x 15-5

DESK

PANTRY

Study/Guest
11-8 x 14-0

DN

Foyer

UP

Dining Rm
11-8 x 14-0

Garage
21-5 x 22-0

Porch

DN

© Copyright by designer/architect

PLANFEATURES

2,647 total square feet of living area

Width: 71'-0" Depth: 45'-0"

The master bath is luxurious with a corner whirlpool tub

The vaulted second floor sitting area is a great place to relax

The breakfast room has pocket doors that separate it from the family room

4 bedrooms, 3 baths, 2-car side entry garage

Basement or crawl space foundation, please specify when ordering

Price Code E

houseplansandmore.com

PLAN FEATURES

4,957 total square feet of living area

Width: 87'-0" Depth: 103'-0"

10' ceilings on the first floor and 9' ceilings on the second floor

A terrific screen porch can be accessed from the living room and master bedroom

A peninsula style spa whirlpool tub is the main focal point of the luxurious private master bath

The future second floor media room, game room and den have an additional 1,047 square feet of living area

5 bedrooms, 5 1/2 baths, 3-car side entry garage

Floating slab foundation

Price Code S2

Cozy study with fireplace!

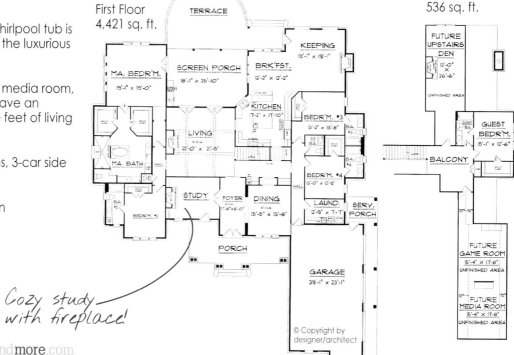

First Floor 4,421 sq. ft.

Second Floor 536 sq. ft.

© Copyright by designer/architect

Appealing two-sided fireplace!!

Second Floor
1,089 sq. ft.

First Floor
2,651 sq. ft.

© Copyright by designer/architect

PLANFEATURES

3,740 total square feet of living area

Width: 92'-5" Depth: 64'-0"

The grand entrance has a vaulted two-story foyer

A two-sided fireplace warms both the formal living room and master bedroom

The second floor bedrooms have their own window seats

The bonus room above the garage has an additional 497 square feet of living area

4 bedrooms, 3 1/2 baths, 3-car side entry garage

Basement, crawl space or slab foundation, please specify when ordering

Price Code S1

houseplansandmore.com

PLAN FEATURES
6,622 total square feet of living area

Width: 88'-9" Depth: 88'-5"

Double-doors open to the cozy study with fireplace and flanking shelves

The second floor balcony overlooks the spacious family room with warming fireplace

All the bedroom suites enjoy a private bath and spacious closets

5 bedrooms, 5 full baths, 3 half baths, 2-car side entry garage, 1-car garage

Walk-out basement foundation

Price Code S3

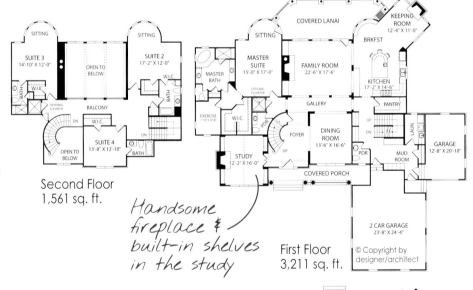

Second Floor
1,561 sq. ft.

Handsome fireplace & built-in shelves in the study

First Floor
3,211 sq. ft.

© Copyright by designer/architect

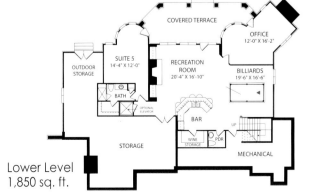

Lower Level
1,850 sq. ft.

houseplansandmore.com

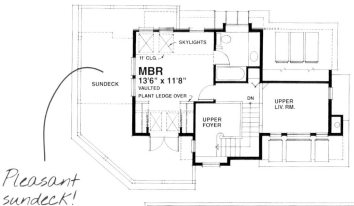

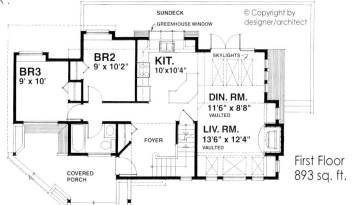

PLANFEATURES

1,235 total square feet of living area

Width: 46'-0" Depth: 28'-0"

Energy efficient home with 2" x 6" exterior walls

A greenhouse window adorns the kitchen and looks out over the sundeck

The entire second floor is dedicated to the master bedroom with amenities including a private bath and skylights

Abundant skylights and a window wall ensure maximum daylight for the vaulted living and dining rooms

3 bedrooms, 2 baths

Basement foundation

Price Code B

SKYLIGHTS

11' CLG.

MBR
13'6" x 11'8"
VAULTED

PLANT LEDGE OVER

SUNDECK

UPPER FOYER

DN

UPPER LIV. RM.

Second Floor
342 sq. ft.

Pleasant sundeck!

SUNDECK

GREENHOUSE WINDOW

© Copyright by designer/architect

BR2
9' x 10'2"

KIT.
10'x10'4"

BR3
9' x 10'

SKYLIGHTS

DIN. RM.
11'6" x 8'8"
VAULTED

FOYER

LIV. RM.
13'6" x 12'4"
VAULTED

COVERED PORCH

First Floor
893 sq. ft.

LEFFINGWELL

PLANFEATURES

1,900 total square feet of living area

Width: 69'-0" Depth: 59'-0"

The master bath enjoys two large walk-in closets, a jet tub and double vanities

The dining/office area is a versatile space that connects directly to the kitchen

Two secondary bedrooms skillfully share a full bath

The optional second floor has an additional 317 square feet of living area

3 bedrooms, 2 1/2 baths, 2-car side entry garage

Slab, crawl space or basement foundation, please specify when ordering

Price Code D

Optional Second Floor

Linen
Shwr
DN
Bonus Bath
Attic Access
Closet
Sloped Clg.
Sloped Clg.
Attic Access
Future Bonus Room
13-2 x 12-6
8' Clg. Ht.

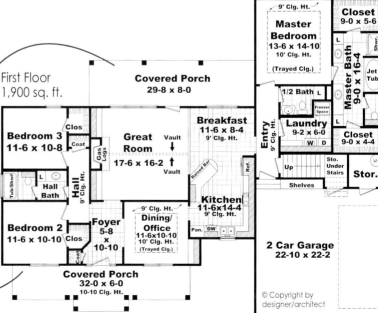

Wonderful covered porches!

First Floor
1,900 sq. ft.

Covered Porch 29-8 x 8-0

Bedroom 3 11-6 x 10-8

Clos
Coat
Gas Logs

Great Room 17-6 x 16-2
Vault
Vault

Breakfast 11-6 x 8-4
9' Clg. Ht.

9' Clg. Ht.

Master Bedroom 13-6 x 14-10
10' Clg. Ht.
(Trayed Clg.)

Closet 9-0 x 5-6
L

Master Bath 9-0 x 16-4
Shwr
Jet Tub

Tub/Shwr
L
Hall Bath
Hall
9' Clg. Ht.

Raised Bar
Ref.

Entry
9' Clg. Ht.

1/2 Bath
L
Freezer Space

Laundry 9-2 x 6-0
W
D

Closet 9-0 x 4-4

Up
Sto. Under Stairs
Stor.
WH

Shelves

Bedroom 2 11-6 x 10-10
Clos
Coat

Foyer 5-8 x 10-10

Dining/Office 11-6x10-10
10' Clg. Ht.
(Trayed Clg.)
9' Clg. Ht.
Pan.
DW

Kitchen 11-6x14-4
9' Clg. Ht.

2 Car Garage 22-10 x 22-2

Covered Porch 32-0 x 6-0
10-10 Clg. Ht.

© Copyright by designer/architect

PLAN FEATURES

3,905 total square feet of living area

Width: 53'-4" Depth: 63'-4"

The two-story grand room enjoys a warming fireplace, built-in shelves and double-door access to the rear deck/terrace

All bedrooms suites have ample closet space

The bonus room on the second floor has an additional 697 square feet of living area

3 bedrooms, 3 1/2 baths, 2-car side entry garage

Walk-out basement foundation

Price Code S1

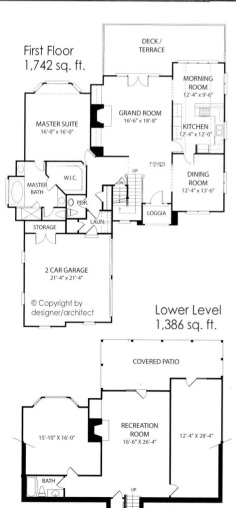

First Floor
1,742 sq. ft.

DECK / TERRACE

MORNING ROOM
12'-4" x 9'-6"

GRAND ROOM
16'-6" x 18'-8"

KITCHEN
12'-4" x 12'-0"

MASTER SUITE
16'-0" x 16'-0"

DINING ROOM
12'-4" x 13'-6"

FOYER

W.I.C.

MASTER BATH

PDR.

LOGGIA

STORAGE

LAUN.

UP

DN

2 CAR GARAGE
21'-4" x 21'-4"

© Copyright by designer/architect

Lower Level
1,386 sq. ft.

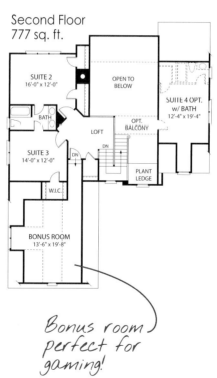

Second Floor
777 sq. ft.

SUITE 2
16'-0" x 12'-0"

OPEN TO BELOW

SUITE 4 OPT. w/ BATH
12'-4" x 19'-4"

BATH

LOFT

OPT. BALCONY

SUITE 3
14'-0" x 12'-0"

DN

DN

PLANT LEDGE

W.I.C.

BONUS ROOM
13'-6" x 19'-8"

Bonus room perfect for gaming!

COVERED PATIO

RECREATION ROOM
16'-6" X 26'-4"

15'-10" X 16'-0"

12'-4" X 28'-4"

BATH

UP

houseplansandmore.com

WOODTRAIL

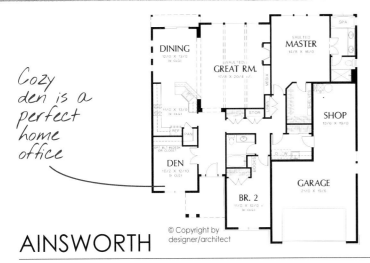

Cozy den is a perfect home office

© Copyright by designer/architect

1,902 total square feet of living area

Width: 52'-0" Depth: 56'-0"

Energy efficient home with 2" x 6" exterior walls

A vaulted great room maintains an open feeling

Sliding glass doors in the dining area lead to the outdoors

The garage includes a spacious workshop area perfect for hobbies and gardening

2 bedrooms, 2 baths, 2-car garage

Crawl space foundation

Price Code F

AINSWORTH

PLAN #651-028D-0040

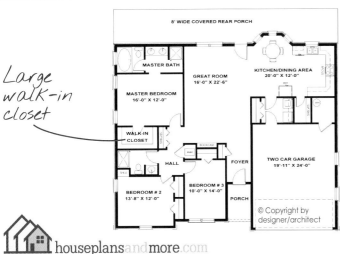

Large walk-in closet

© Copyright by designer/architect

1,609 total square feet of living area

Width: 52'-0" Depth: 50'-0"

Energy efficient home with 2" x 6" exterior walls

The foyer leads into the impressive great room that features access onto the rear porch ideal for relaxing

A bay window adds charm to the kitchen/dining area which also features a walk-in pantry and plenty of counterspace

The inviting master bedroom enjoys a walk-in closet and deluxe bath

The laundry area is conveniently located between the kitchen and the garage

3 bedrooms, 2 baths, 2-car garage

Slab foundation

Price Code B

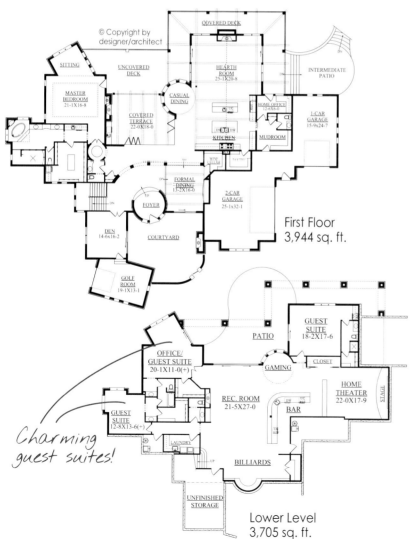

© Copyright by designer/architect

First Floor
3,944 sq. ft.

Charming guest suites!

Lower Level
3,705 sq. ft.

PLANFEATURES

7,649 total square feet of living area

Width: 118'-6" Depth: 104'-0"

Energy efficient home with 2" x 6" exterior walls

The first floor features patio doors that extend living spaces to the covered terrace

A luxurious master bedroom boasts a sitting area, a private bath with a corner tub, and a walk-in closet

The expansive lower level is no doubt an attention getter with an open recreation room, three guest suites, a home theater and a bar for convenient meals

4 bedrooms, 3 full baths, 3 half baths, 2-car side entry garage, 1-car garage

Walk-out basement or basement foundation, please specify when ordering

Price Code S4

PLAN FEATURES

3,171 total square feet of living area

Width: 86'-2" Depth: 63'-8"

An enormous walk-in closet is located in the master bath and dressing area

The great room, breakfast area and kitchen combine with 12' ceilings to create an open feel

The optional lower level has an additional 1,897 square feet of living area and is designed for entertaining featuring a wet bar with seating, a billiards room, large media room, two bedrooms and a full bath

3 bedrooms, 2 1/2 baths, 3-car side entry garage

Walk-out basement or basement foundation, please specify when ordering

Price Code E

First Floor
3,171 sq. ft.

Great area for entertaining!

Optional
Lower Level

Spectacular wrap-around deck!

SEAT

LIV./DIN.
23' x 9'4" & 14'6"

WOOD STOVE

8'10" x 8'

GUEST
10'8" x 9'

© Copyright by designer/architect

First Floor
672 sq. ft.

STUDIO
15'4" x 11'8"

OPEN

10' CLG.

BED RM.
15' x 9'

Second Floor
482 sq. ft.

PLANFEATURES

1,154 total square feet of living area

Width: 36'-0" Depth: 42'-6"

Energy efficient home with 2" x 6" exterior walls

The multi-purpose vaulted great room is up to the challenges of evolving cottage activities

Designed for relaxed living, this home enjoys access all around onto the large deck

A wrap-around window seat in the living/dining room is a cozy place to curl up with a book

The second floor studio would make a perfect artist's retreat, a home office or private escape perfect for taking in views on the balcony

2 bedrooms, 2 baths

Crawl space foundation

Price Code B

houseplansandmore.com

PLANFEATURES

3,421 total square feet of living area

Width: 84'-6" Depth: 69'-4"

The gourmet kitchen with island and snack bar combines with the spacious breakfast and hearth rooms to create a warm and friendly atmosphere

The luxurious master bedroom with sitting area and fireplace is complemented by a deluxe bath designed to pamper

The optional lower level has an additional 1,777 square feet of living area and offers fun and excitement

3 bedrooms, 3 1/2 baths, 4-car side entry garage

Walk-out basement foundation

Price Code F

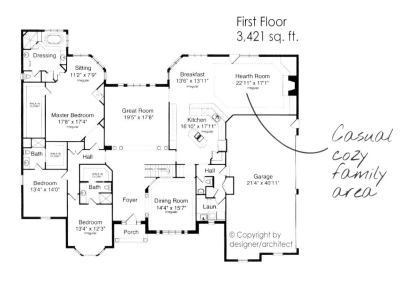

First Floor
3,421 sq. ft.

Casual cozy family area

© Copyright by designer/architect

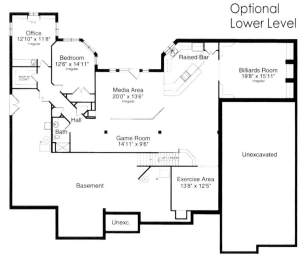

Optional Lower Level

PLANFEATURES

3,198 total square feet of living area

Width: 48'-0" Depth: 44'-0"

Energy efficient home with 2" x 6" exterior walls

The master bedroom has a large walk-in closet

The family and dining rooms are combined making the space feel more open

The front facade of the home is contemporary and unique, but not overdone

4 bedrooms, 2 1/2 baths, 1-car garage

Basement foundation

Price Code H

Convenient planning center

Second Floor
915 sq. ft.

Lower Level
763 sq. ft.

First Floor
1,520 sq. ft.

© Copyright by designer/architect

PLANFEATURES

3,101 total square feet of living area

Width: 68'-0" Depth: 44'-0"

Energy efficient home with 2" x 6" exterior walls

The spacious great room is open to the oversized dining area with nearby kitchen island

A fun-packed lower level is great for entertaining including a family and games room as well as plenty of bedrooms for guests

The lower level exercise room provides the perfect spot for staying in great shape right in your own home

3 bedrooms, 2 1/2 baths, 3-car garage

Walk-out basement foundation

Price Code D

Gorgeous owner's suite!

First Floor
1,680 sq. ft.

© Copyright by designer/architect

Lower Level
1,421 sq. ft.

houseplansandmore.com

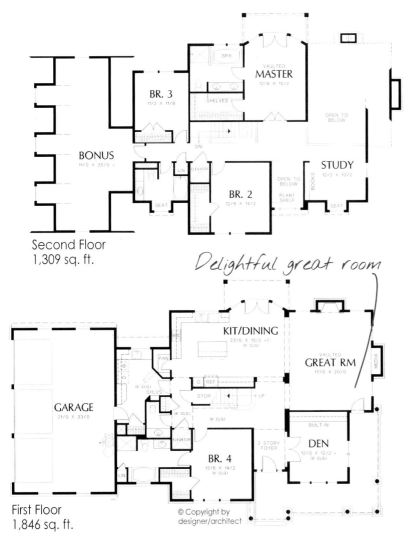

Second Floor
1,309 sq. ft.

Delightful great room

First Floor
1,846 sq. ft.

© Copyright by
designer/architect

PLANFEATURES

3,155 total square feet of living area

Width: 77'-6" Depth: 48'-8"

The large wrap-around front porch can be accessed by the vaulted great room

The kitchen/dining area offers a center island with enough casual dining space for three people

The second floor includes a quiet study with a built-in window seat

The bonus room on the second floor has an additional 563 square feet of living area

4 bedrooms, 3 1/2 baths, 3-car side entry garage

Crawl space foundation

Price Code F

PLANFEATURES

2,826 total square feet of living area

Width: 60'-6" Depth: 74'-0"

9' ceilings throughout

The fully appointed master bedroom has a luxurious bath

The second floor bedrooms include private dressing areas and walk-in closets

The large, well-planned kitchen features a center island

4 bedrooms, 3 1/2 baths, 2-car side entry garage

Slab foundation, drawings also include crawl space foundation

Price Code F

Decorative plant shelf in the foyer

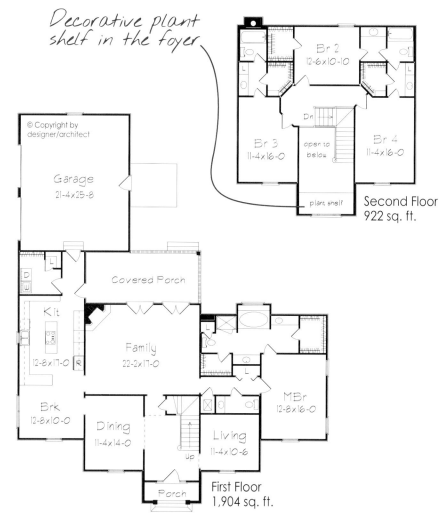

© Copyright by designer/architect

Garage
21-4x25-8

Second Floor
922 sq. ft.

Br 2
12-6x10-10

Br 3
11-4x16-0

open to below

Br 4
11-4x16-0

Dn

plant shelf

Covered Porch

Kit
12-8x17-0

Family
22-2x17-0

MBr
12-8x16-0

Brk
12-8x10-0

Dining
11-4x14-0

Living
11-4x10-6

up

Porch

First Floor
1,904 sq. ft.

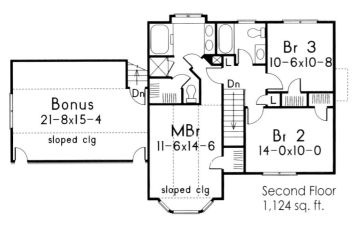

Bonus
21-8x15-4

sloped clg

MBr
11-6x14-6

sloped clg

Br 3
10-6x10-8

Br 2
14-0x10-0

Dn

Dn

L

L

Second Floor
1,124 sq. ft.

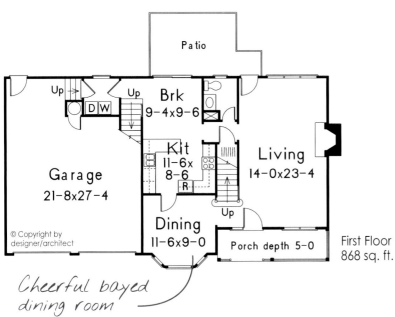

Patio

Up

Up

D W

Brk
9-4x9-6

Kit
11-6x
8-6

R

Up

Living
14-0x23-4

Garage
21-8x27-4

Dining
11-6x9-0

Porch depth 5-0

First Floor
868 sq. ft.

© Copyright by
designer/architect

*Cheerful bayed
dining room*

PLAN FEATURES

1,992 total square feet of living area

Width: 54'-0" Depth: 30'-0"

Distinct living, dining and breakfast
areas

The master bedroom boasts a full-
end bay window and a cathedral
ceiling

The storage and laundry areas are
located adjacent to the garage

The bonus room over the garage for
future office or playroom is included
in the square footage

3 bedrooms, 2 1/2 baths,
2-car garage

Crawl space foundation, drawings
also include basement foundation

Price Code A

houseplansandmore.com

ANTARES

PLAN #651-080D-0014

PLAN FEATURES

1,923 total square feet of living area

Width: 49'-6" Depth: 42'-0"

Energy efficient home with 2" x 6" exterior walls

This beautiful house has a unique second floor covered porch that wraps around for great outdoor living space

The combination living/dining room has handsome exposed beams above and a gas fireplace

An enjoyable screened porch is the perfect spot for alfresco dining throughout the year

2 bedrooms, 2 baths

Crawl space foundation

Price Code B

houseplansandmore.com

252

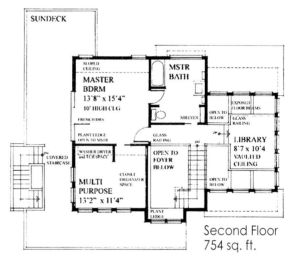

SUNDECK

SLOPED CEILING

MASTER BDRM
13'8" x 15'4"
10' HIGH CLG

FRENCH DRS

PLANT LEDGE OPEN TO MSTR

WASHER DRYER and TCB SPACE

MULTI PURPOSE
13'2" x 11'4"

CLOSET ORGANIZER SPACE

PLANT LEDGE

MSTR BATH

SHELVES

OPEN TO BELOW

OPEN TO FOYER BELOW

GLASS RAILING

EXPOSED FLOOR BEAMS

GLASS RAILING

LIBRARY
8'7 x 10'4
VAULTED CEILING

OPEN TO BELOW

Second Floor
754 sq. ft.

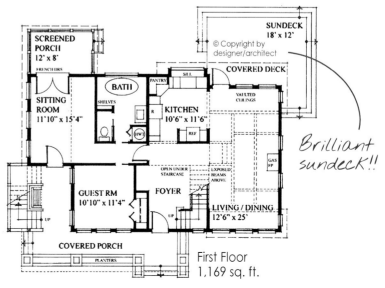

SUNDECK
18' x 12'

© Copyright by designer/architect

COVERED DECK

SCREENED PORCH
12' x 8'

FRENCH DRS

BATH

SHELVES

SITTING ROOM
11'10" x 15'4"

PANTRY

SILL

VAULTED CEILINGS

KITCHEN
10'6" x 11'6"

REF

OPEN UNDER STAIRCASE

EXPOSED BEAMS ABOVE

GAS FP

GUEST RM
10'10" x 11'4"

FOYER

LIVING / DINING
12'6" x 25'

UP

UP

COVERED PORCH

PLANTERS

Brilliant sundeck!!

First Floor
1,169 sq. ft.

Second Floor
1,561 sq. ft.

Sunny family
room with
fireplace

First Floor
1,930 sq. ft.

© Copyright by
designer/architect

PLANFEATURES

3,491 total square feet of living area

Width: 90'-3" Depth: 65'-8"

Energy efficient home with 2" x 6" exterior walls

The two-story entry leads into the grand living room that features a bowed window and a cozy fireplace

The bayed nook and family room create a relaxing area

All of the bedrooms are located on the second floor for additional privacy

The second floor bonus room has an additional 440 square feet of living area

4 bedrooms, 3 1/2 baths, 3-car side entry garage

Basement foundation

Price Code S1

houseplansandmore.com

PLANFEATURES

2,635 total square feet of living area

Width: 56'-6" Depth: 92'-6"

A private full bath bridges the guest room and study making the study an ideal third bedroom

On the opposite side of the home is the luxurious master bedroom equipped with a deluxe bath, his and hers closets and sliding glass doors to the covered deck

A grand fireplace warms the entire living area consisting of the great room, nook and kitchen

2 bedrooms, 2 1/2 baths, 3-car side entry garage

Basement foundation

Price Code E

French doors open to the lovely study

houseplansandmore.com

PLANFEATURES

2,613 total square feet of living area

Width: 47'-0" Depth: 56'-0"

Energy efficient home with 2" x 6" exterior walls

The cheerful breakfast nook features outdoor access

The sunny master suite is sure to be enjoyed with a deluxe bath

A quiet den/parlor in the front of the home is a great place to retreat

The bonus room above the garage is included in the total square footage

3 bedrooms, 2 1/2 baths, 2-car garage

Crawl space foundation

Price Code E

Second Floor
1,305 sq. ft.

Big bonus room!

First Floor
1,308 sq. ft.

© Copyright by designer/architect

houseplansandmore.com

LAUREN

PLANFEATURES

2,240 total square feet of living area

Width: 56'-8" Depth: 57'-4"

A lovely L-shaped staircase greets guests as soon as they enter the two-story foyer

The large and open vaulted great room boasts a cozy centered fireplace with planking windows for natural light

The kitchen enjoys an efficient layout with a wrap-around breakfast bar with seating for four people

A bayed master bedroom on the first floor has a large walk-in closet and fully appointed bath

3 bedrooms, 2 1/2 baths, 2-car side entry garage

Basement foundation

Price Code C

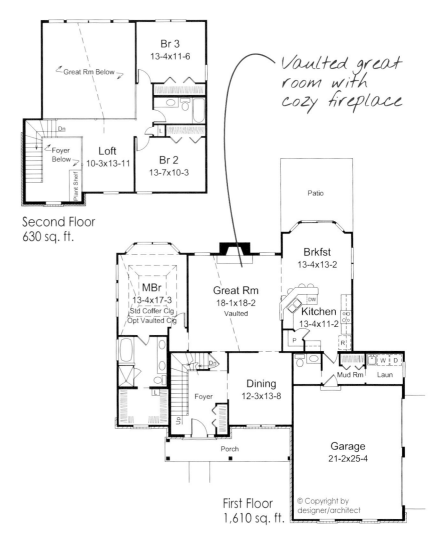

Vaulted great room with cozy fireplace

Second Floor
630 sq. ft.

Br 3
13-4x11-6

Great Rm Below

Dn

Foyer Below

Loft
10-3x13-11

Br 2
13-7x10-3

Plant Shelf

First Floor
1,610 sq. ft.

Patio

Brkfst
13-4x13-2

MBr
13-4x17-3
Std Coffer Clg
Opt Vaulted Clg

Great Rm
18-1x18-2
Vaulted

Kitchen
13-4x11-2

DW

Dn

Dining
12-3x13-8

Foyer

Mud Rm Laun W D

Garage
21-2x25-4

Porch

© Copyright by designer/architect

WOODFIELD MANOR

PLAN #651-007D-0212

1,568 total square feet of living area

Width: 72'-8" Depth: 37'-4"

A walk-in pantry is featured in the lovely kitchen and is adjacent to a convenient laundry room

3 bedrooms, 2 baths, 2-car garage

Crawl space foundation, drawings also include slab foundation

Price Code A

HAMILTON HILL

PLAN #651-053D-0031

1,908 total square feet of living area

Width: 74'-0" Depth: 50'-0"

The distinguished front entry includes a circle-top window and prominent center gable

The vaulted ceiling and floor-to-ceiling windows in the family and breakfast rooms create an open space

3 bedrooms, 2 baths, 2-car garage

Crawl space foundation, drawings also include slab foundation

Price Code A

POCKPOINT

PLAN #651-011D-0075

1,728 total square feet of living area

Width: 55'-0" Depth: 48'-0"

The vaulted great room boasts a wall of windows and a warming fireplace

2 bedrooms, 2 baths, 3-car garage

Crawl space foundation

Price Code C

REBECCA

PLAN #651-121D-0015

1,983 total square feet of living area

Width: 60'-0" Depth: 61'-0"

The optional attic space above the garage has an additional 273 square feet of living area

3 bedrooms, 2 1/2 baths, 2-car side entry garage

Basement foundation

Price Code B

houseplansandmore.com

PLANFEATURES

3,870 total square feet of living area

Width: 107'-7" Depth: 58'-7"

The large family room has a fireplace, two-story windows and a cantilevered balcony

French doors lead to a spacious porch with multiple skylights allowing generous amounts of light

A convenient second staircase to the second floor is located between the family room and the kitchen

The bonus room above the garage has an additional 809 square feet of living area

4 bedrooms, 4 1/2 baths, 3-car side entry garage

Walk-out basement foundation

Price Code S3

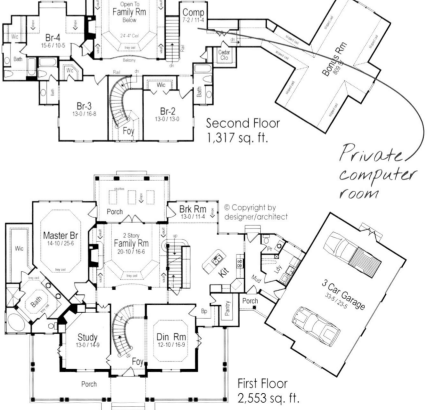

Second Floor
1,317 sq. ft.

Private computer room

© Copyright by designer/architect

First Floor
2,553 sq. ft.

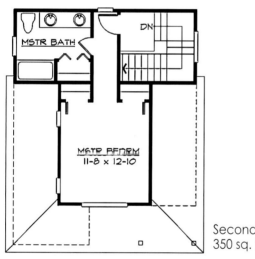

MSTR BATH

DN

MSTR BDRM
11-8 x 12-10

Second Floor
350 sq. ft.

PLANFEATURES

1,000 total square feet of living area

Width: 24'-0" Depth: 30'-0"

The lovely U-shaped kitchen is highly functional and cozy

The romantic master bedroom is privately located on the second floor and features a large window

Simple, yet beautiful window accents bring interest to the exterior of this home

2 bedrooms, 2 baths

Crawl space foundation

Price Code AA

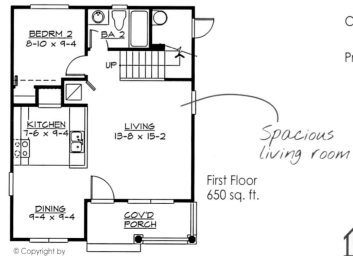

BEDRM 2
8-10 x 9-4

BA 2

UP

KITCHEN
7-6 x 9-4

LIVING
13-8 x 15-2

Spacious living room

First Floor
650 sq. ft.

DINING
9-4 x 9-4

COV'D PORCH

© Copyright by designer/architect

houseplansandmore.com

FRUITLAND

PLAN #651-013D-0025

2,097 total square feet of living area

Width: 70'-2" Depth: 59'-0"

The bonus room above garage has an additional 452 square feet of living space

3 bedrooms, 3 baths, 3-car side entry garage

Basement, crawl space or slab foundation, please specify when ordering

Price Code D

MELANIE

PLAN #651-121D-0017

1,379 total square feet of living area

Width: 40'-0" Depth: 52'-0"

The kitchen shares the center island and eating bar with the open great room for easy meals

2 bedrooms, 1 bath, 2-car garage

Basement foundation

Price Code AA

houseplansandmore.com

PRAIRIE GROVE

PLAN #651-028D-0021

2,775 total square feet of living area

Width: 81'-10" Depth: 77'-10"

The bonus room above garage has an additional 192 square feet of living area

3 bedrooms, 3 baths, 2-car side entry garage

Slab foundation

Price Code E

NATALIE

PLAN #651-121D-0024

1,994 total square feet of living area

Width: 62'-2" Depth: 56'-0"

The vaulted entry flows into the spacious great room with corner fireplace and a wall of windows

The kitchen has a walk-in pantry and eating bar that has lovely views of the sunny breakfast area

3 bedrooms, 2 baths, 2-car garage

Basement foundation

Price Code B

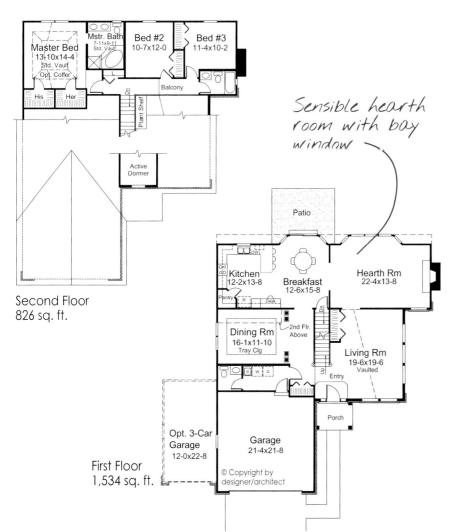

Second Floor
826 sq. ft.

Sensible hearth room with bay window

First Floor
1,534 sq. ft.

© Copyright by designer/architect

PLANFEATURES

2,360 total square feet of living area

Width: 50'-4" Depth: 56'-8"

The U-shaped kitchen enjoys the convenience of a large walk-in pantry, desk area and an extended counterspace with enough casual dining space for three people

An enormous hearth room extends off the bayed breakfast area and features a cozy fireplace and an oversized bay window

Luxury can be found in the second floor master bedroom including his and her walk-in closets and a private bath with a corner tub

The balcony overlooks the spacious living room with an arched window and has views out the active dormer

3 bedrooms, 2 1/2 baths, 2-car garage

Basement foundation

Price Code C

PLANFEATURES

4,241 total square feet of living area

Width: 70'-5" Depth: 82'-2"

The second floor loft is easily accessible from both of the bedrooms and overlooks the grand foyer below

The formal dining room attaches directly to the kitchen ideal when entertaining

A full bath on the first floor has direct access to the outdoors perfect when gardening or cleaning up from other outdoor activities

Framing - only concrete block available

4 bedrooms, 5 1/2 baths, 3-car garage

Slab foundation

Price Code S1

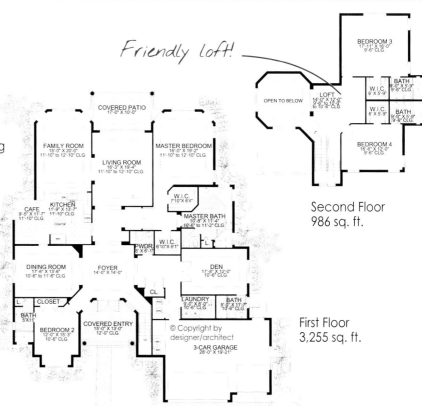

Friendly Loft!

Second Floor
986 sq. ft.

First Floor
3,255 sq. ft.

© Copyright by designer/architect

PLANFEATURES

1,470 total square feet of living area

Width: 35'-0" Depth: 42'-0"

The vaulted breakfast room is cheerful and sunny

The private second floor master bedroom has a bath and walk-in closet

The large utility room has access to the outdoors

3 bedrooms, 2 baths

Basement, crawl space or slab foundation, please specify when ordering

Price Code A

Enchanting rear deck great for sunny days

Deck

Brkfst
9-0 x 6-0

Kit.
11-6 x 9-8

flat clg.

Br #2
12-2 x 9-11

UP

DN

Foyer
flat clg.

Utility

Living Rm
18-11 x 12-11

Br #3
12-2 x 9-3

Porch

© Copyright by designer/architect

First Floor
1,035 sq. ft.

DN

Master Br
14-3 x 12-11

Second Floor
435 sq. ft.

houseplansandmore.com

PLANFEATURES

2,797 total square feet of living area

Width: 68'-0" Depth: 60'-0"

Energy efficient home with 2" x 6" exterior walls

The second floor game room has a wet bar perfect for entertaining

A private guest room with its own bath is situated near the garage

The formal dining room has decorative corner columns

3 bedrooms, 3 1/2 baths, 3-car garage

Crawl space foundation

Price Code F

Fun game room!

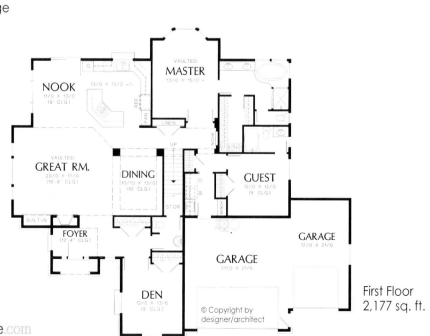

BR. 3
10/0 X 13/0 +/-
(9' CLG)

WET BAR

GAME RM.
16/0 X 15/0 +/-
(9' CLG)

Second Floor
620 sq. ft.

VAULTED
MASTER
13/0 X 15/0 +/-

NOOK
11/0 X 13/0
(9' CLG)

LINEN

UP

GREAT RM.
VAULTED
20/0 X 17/0
(15'-9" CLG)

DINING
10/0 X 13/0
(10' CLG)

GUEST
12/0 X 12/0
(9' CLG)

STOR

BUILT-IN

FOYER
(12'-4" CLG)

GARAGE
12/0 X 21/0

GARAGE
21/0 X 25/6

DEN
12/0 X 13/6
(9' CLG)

First Floor
2,177 sq. ft.

houseplansandmore.com

PLAN#651-051D-0189

PEBBLE RIDGE

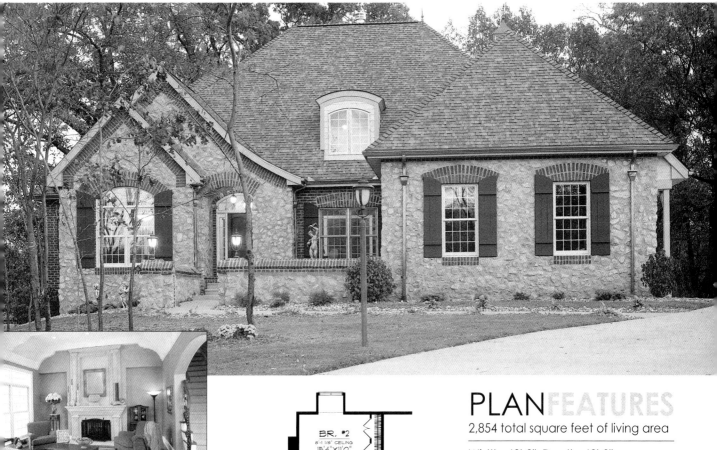

PLANFEATURES

2,854 total square feet of living area

Width: 63'-0" Depth: 68'-0"

Energy efficient home with 2" x 6" exterior walls

The elegant entry leads into the quiet great room that is perfect for relaxing with family or partying with friends

The stunning kitchen features a walk-in pantry, snack bar island and opens to the casual nook and formal dining room

A lovely three-season porch allows you to enjoy the great outdoors in any weather

4 bedrooms, 2 1/2 baths, 3-car side entry garage

Walk-out basement foundation

Price Code G

Second Floor Plan

BR. #2
8'-1 1/8" CEILING
15'4"X11'0"

BR. #3
8'-1 1/8" CEILING
13'6"X11'0"

BR. #4
8'-1 1/8" CEILING
13'0"X12'0"

Second Floor
792 sq. ft.

First Floor Plan

WOOD DECK

3 SEASON PORCH
14'8"X15'6"

GRT. RM.
12'-1 1/8" CEILING
21'4"X16'0"

MBR.
9'-1 1/8" CEILING
13'8"X18'4"

NOOK
9'-1 1/8" CEILING
13'8"X11'0"

KIT.
9'-1 1/8" CEILING
15'8"X13'0"

BENCH   LOCKERS

E.
12'-1 1/8" CEILING

STUDY
9'-1 1/8" CEILING
13'0"X12'8"

DIN.
10'-1 1/8" CEILING
12'0"X12'4"

3 CAR GARAGE
21'4"X31'6"

COURTYARD

Elegant 3 season porch with a wood deck!

First Floor
2,062 sq. ft.

© Copyright by designer/architect

PLANFEATURES

3,385 total square feet of living area

Width: 75'-2" Depth: 89'-6"

High ceilings throughout the house create a wonderful sense of space

Distinctive brick arched openings frame the great room

The second floor game room over the garage is sure to be popular with children

4 bedrooms, 4 baths, 3-car side entry garage

Slab or crawl space foundation, please specify when ordering

Price Code S1

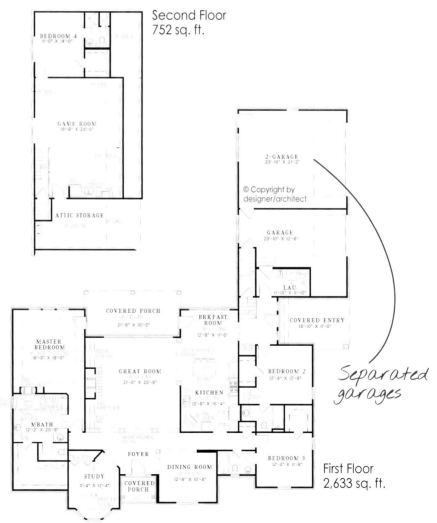

Second Floor
752 sq. ft.

First Floor
2,633 sq. ft.

Separated garages

© Copyright by designer/architect

houseplansandmore.com

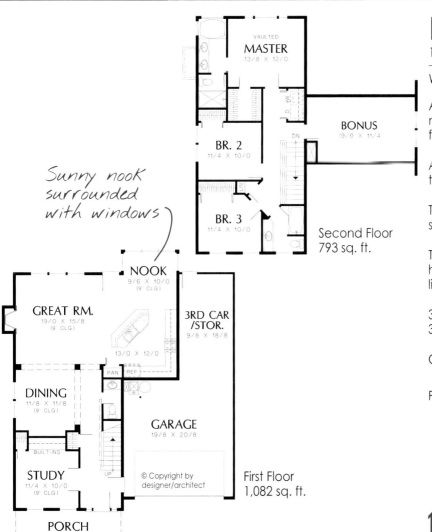

Sunny nook surrounded with windows

VAULTED MASTER
13/8 X 12/0

BONUS
19/0 X 11/4

BR. 2
11/4 X 10/0

BR. 3
11/4 X 10/0

DN

Second Floor
793 sq. ft.

NOOK
9/6 X 10/0
(9' CLG.)

GREAT RM.
19/0 X 15/8
(9' CLG.)

3RD CAR /STOR.
9/8 X 18/8

13/0 X 12/0

PAN   REF

DINING
11/8 X 11/8
(9' CLG.)

GARAGE
19/8 X 20/8

BUILT-INS

STUDY
11/4 X 10/0
(9' CLG.)

UP

© Copyright by
designer/architect

First Floor
1,082 sq. ft.

PORCH

PLAN**FEATURES**

1,875 total square feet of living area

Width: 40'-0" Depth: 52'-0"

All of the bedrooms are located near each other on the second floor for privacy and convenience

A sunny breakfast nook extends off the kitchen

The oversized garage has extra space for a third car or storage area

The bonus room on the second floor has an additional 250 square feet of living area

3 bedrooms, 2 1/2 baths, 3-car garage

Crawl space foundation

Price Code C

houseplansandmore.com

STARLA

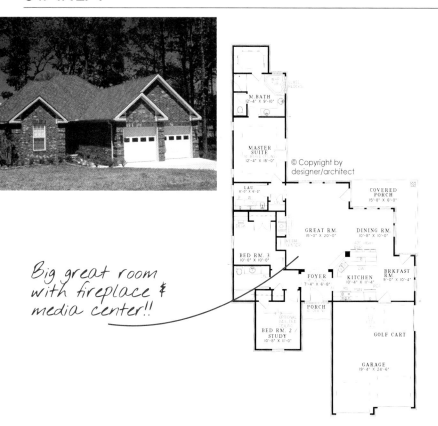

Big great room with fireplace & media center!!

PLAN #651-055D-0283

1,601 total square feet of living area

Width: 44'-0" Depth: 86'-2"

A feeling of spaciousness occurs upon entering the great room that is open to the dining room and flooded with light from the surrounding windows

Bedroom #3 enjoys a built-in desk

A centralized laundry room near the bedrooms will keep the laundry from being a chore

3 bedrooms, 2 baths, 2-car garage

Slab or crawl space foundation, please specify when ordering

Price Code C

GRAYBROOKE

Cute kid's nook with desk

PLAN #651-055D-0309

1,832 total square feet of living area

Width: 39'-0" Depth: 81'-0"

The large dining area is an extension of the kitchen

Ideal for school projects, the computer center is located near the secondary bedrooms

Built-ins surround the fireplace in the great room adding space for media equipment storage

3 bedrooms, 2 baths, 2-car rear entry garage

Slab or crawl space foundation, please specify when ordering

Price Code C

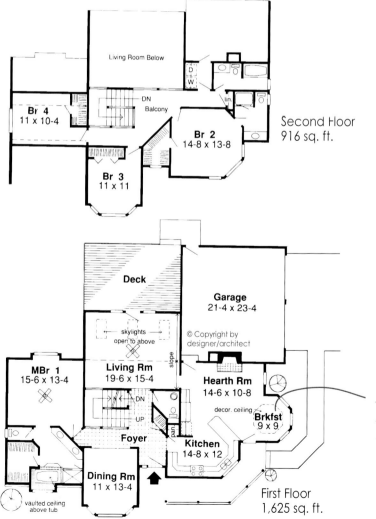

Living Room Below

Br 4
11 x 10-4

DN
Balcony

Br 2
14-8 x 13-8

Br 3
11 x 11

Second Floor
916 sq. ft.

Deck

Garage
21-4 x 23-4

© Copyright by
designer/architect

skylights
open to above

slope

MBr 1
15-6 x 13-4

Living Rm
19-6 x 15-4

Hearth Rm
14-6 x 10-8

DN

UP

decor. ceiling

Brkfst
9 x 9

Illuminated
breakfast
area

Foyer

pan.

Kitchen
14-8 x 12

Dining Rm
11 x 13-4

vaulted ceiling
above tub

First Floor
1,625 sq. ft.

PLAN FEATURES

2,541 total square feet of living area

Width: 59'-8" Depth: 55'-8"

Energy efficient home with 2" x 6" exterior walls

The living room is full of natural light shining down from the three skylights above

The front porch opens to the foyer and wraps around to the breakfast room

4 bedrooms, 3 1/2 baths, 2-car side entry garage

Basement foundation

Price Code F

houseplansandmore.com

Photo, right: Great efficiency can easily occur with this functional kitchen layout featuring a center island for added workspace.

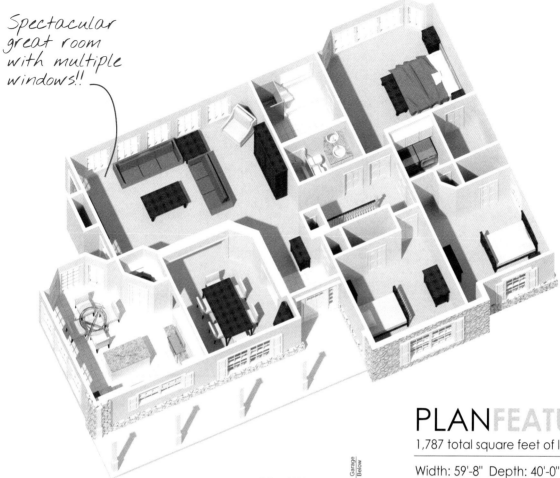

Spectacular great room with multiple windows!!

Photo, below:
A large double window fills the kitchen with plenty of sunlight and gives the dish washer of the family a way to enjoy the outdoor view during this task.

Deck

Great Rm
23-8x15-4
vaulted

skylights above

plant shelf above

© Copyright by designer/architect

Garage Below

MBr
15-8x14-6
vaulted

Brk'ft

P

Hall

W D

Laun.

Kitchen
14-7x15-8

Dining
11-1x13-8

Entry

Dn

Br 3
12-0x12-0

Br 2
12-0x12-0

Shelves

Porch

vaulted

PLANFEATURES

1,787 total square feet of living area

Width: 59'-8" Depth: 40'-0"

The large great room with fireplace and vaulted ceiling features three large skylights and windows galore

Cooking is sure to be a pleasure in this L-shaped well-appointed kitchen that includes a bayed breakfast area with access to the rear deck

Every bedroom offers a spacious walk-in closet with a convenient laundry room just steps away

415 square feet of optional living area available on the lower level

3 bedrooms, 2 baths, 2-car drive under rear entry garage

Walk-out basement foundation

Price Code B

houseplansandmore.com

DENBEIGH

PLAN FEATURES
3,108 total square feet of living area

Width: 66'-8" Depth: 60'-4"

The two-story great room features French doors to the rear deck

The kitchen and breakfast room combine and include a cooktop island, walk-in pantry and TV cabinet

Second floor bonus rooms provide an additional 485 square feet of living space

3 bedrooms, 2 1/2 baths, 3-car side entry garage

Slab or crawl space foundation, please specify when ordering

Price Code G

Master suite with all the amenities

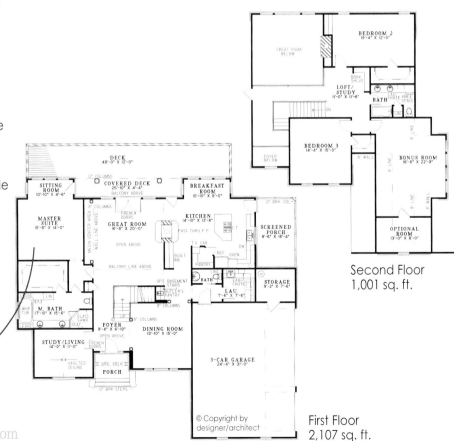

Second Floor
1,001 sq. ft.

First Floor
2,107 sq. ft.

© Copyright by designer/architect

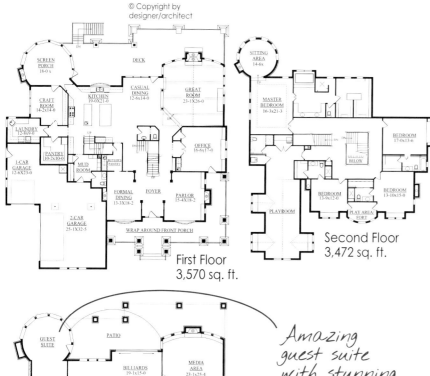

© Copyright by
designer/architect

First Floor
3,570 sq. ft.

Second Floor
3,472 sq. ft.

Amazing guest suite with stunning windows!!

Lower Level
3,184 sq. ft.

PLANFEATURES

10,226 total square feet of living area

Width: 85'-0" Depth: 92'-6"

Energy efficient home with 2" x 6" exterior walls

The open kitchen boasts two islands and flows seamlessly into the casual dining area

Entertaining is a breeze with the remarkable lower level featuring a media area, billiards and gaming areas, plus a bar for convenience

The master bedroom has a circular sitting area surrounded with windows that is perfect for relaxing

6 bedrooms, 7 full baths, 2 half baths, 2-car side entry garage, 1-car garage

Walk-out basement foundation

Price Code S4

PLAN FEATURES

3,457 total square feet of living area

Width: 70'-0" Depth: 100'-6"

A sunny nook off the kitchen accesses the rear vaulted porch

The spacious vaulted great room boasts two sets of double-doors to the outdoors, a fireplace, and a built-in media center

The impressive master bedroom features three walk-in closets, a bathtub, a separate shower, and French doors leading outdoors

4 bedrooms, 3 full baths, 2 half baths, 4-car side entry garage

Crawl space foundation

Price Code S1

Welcoming two-story foyer

© Copyright by designer/architect

First Floor
2,222 sq. ft.

Second Floor
1,235 sq. ft.

houseplansandmore.com

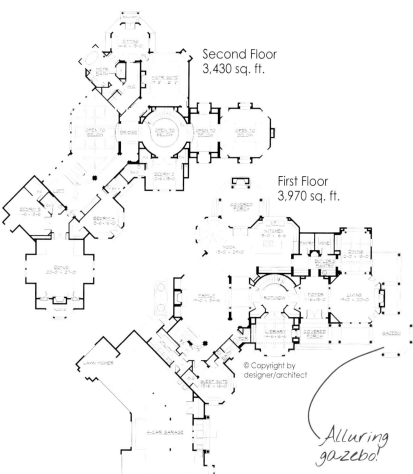

PLANFEATURES

7,400 total square feet of living area

Width: 136'-0" Depth: 126'-0"

This beautiful home offers numerous amenities including a library and a covered gazebo rear patio with a cozy outdoor fireplace

Upon entering, guests will be greeted by a grand curved staircase in the impressive rotunda

The master suite with fireplace is loaded with special features including a sitting area with private balcony and a lavish bath

5 bedrooms, 5 1/2 baths, 4-car side entry garage

Crawl space foundation

Price Code H

Second Floor
3,430 sq. ft.

First Floor
3,970 sq. ft.

© Copyright by designer/architect

Alluring gazebo!

BELLEFONTE

PLAN FEATURES

2,336 total square feet of living area

Width: 58'-0" Depth: 32'-0"

The two-story foyer with large second floor window creates a sunny, spacious entrance area

The second floor play room is conveniently located near the bedrooms as well as the laundry room

The master bath has a vaulted ceiling and luxurious appointments

A coffered ceiling enhances the master bedroom

4 bedrooms, 2 1/2 baths, 2-car garage

Walk-out basement foundation

Price Code B

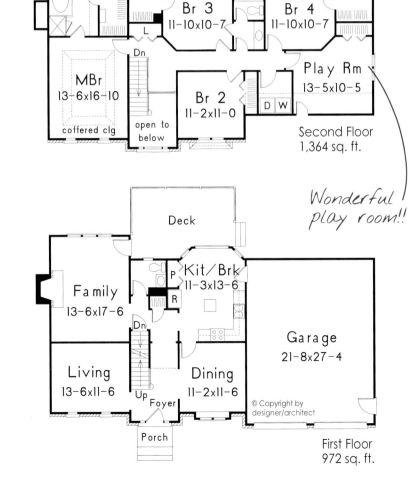

Br 3
11-10x10-7

Br 4
11-10x10-7

MBr
13-6x16-10
coffered clg

Dn

Br 2
11-2x11-0

open to below

Play Rm
13-5x10-5

D W

Second Floor
1,364 sq. ft.

Wonderful play room!!

Deck

Family
13-6x17-6

Kit/Brk
11-3x13-6

Dn

Living
13-6x11-6

Up Foyer

Dining
11-2x11-6

Garage
21-8x27-4

© Copyright by designer/architect

Porch

First Floor
972 sq. ft.

houseplansandmore.com

DECK
COVERED AREA
DINING
13-1x16-8
DECK
COVERED AREA

GUEST ROOM
12-0x12-0

GREAT ROOM
18-1X21-0

MASTER BEDROOM
17-8X18-5

KITCHEN

LAUNDRY

MUD ROOM

PANTRY

OPEN TO BELOW

FOYER

2-CAR GARAGE
37-6x23-1

© Copyright by designer/architect

OFFICE
14-1X14-1

FRONT PORCH

1-CAR GARAGE
37-6x13-1

First Floor
2,887 sq. ft.

lower level perfect for entertaining!

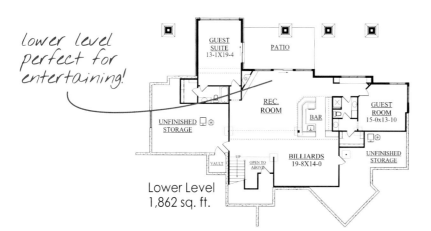

GUEST SUITE
13-1X19-4

PATIO

REC. ROOM

BAR

GUEST ROOM
15-0x13-10

UNFINISHED STORAGE

VAULT

UP

OPEN TO ABOVE

BILLIARDS
19-8X14-0

UNFINISHED STORAGE

Lower Level
1,862 sq. ft.

PLAN FEATURES

4,749 total square feet of living area

Width: 96'-0" Depth: 80'-0"

Energy efficient home with 2" x 6" exterior walls

The walk-out lower level includes an oversized recreation room with a corner fireplace, a large wet bar and an adjacent billiards space

Upon entering the home from the garage, there is a convenient mud room, laundry room, half bath, guest room with private bath and a kitchen with a center island

A roomy office is located off the entrance foyer and is highlighted with a fireplace and a storage closet

4 bedrooms, 5 1/2 baths, 1-car side entry garage, 2-car garage

Walk-out basement or basement foundation, please specify when ordering

Price Code S1

houseplansandmore.com

PLANFEATURES

3,655 total square feet of living area

Width: 87'-0" Depth: 76'-0"

A double-door entry opens to view the magnificent open living area of the kitchen, dining and hearth rooms

The adjoining great room enjoys a multitude of windows and a handsome fireplace

The owner's suite is secluded on the first floor with an office nearby, while two additional bedroom suites are located on the second floor

The bonus room above the garage has an additional 835 square feet of living area

3 bedrooms, 4 1/2 baths, 3-car side entry garage

Crawl space foundation

Price Code S1

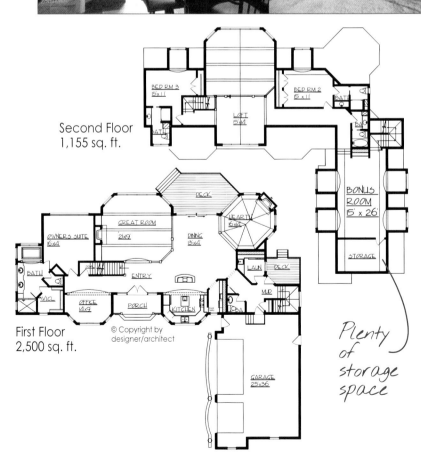

Second Floor
1,155 sq. ft.

BED RM 3
15 x 11

BED RM 2
15 x 11

LOFT
15 x 14

BONUS
ROOM
15' x 26'

STORAGE

First Floor
2,500 sq. ft.

© Copyright by designer/architect

OWNER'S SUITE
16 x 14

GREAT ROOM
21 x 9

DECK

HEARTH
16 x 16

DINING
13 x 14

BATH

W.I.C.

OFFICE
14 x 9

ENTRY

PORCH

KITCHEN

LAUN

MUD

GARAGE
25 x 36

Plenty of storage space

PLAN #651-011D-0079

SCARSDALE POINT

2,775 total square feet of living area

Width: 74'-0" Depth: 59'-0"

Energy efficient home with 2" x 6" exterior walls

The massive master bath provides the utmost luxury including a whirlpool spa tub, oversized closet and a double vanity

A charming see-through fireplace warms the cozy study as well as the casual family room equally

The quaint breakfast nook enjoys easy outdoor access onto a deck

3 bedrooms, 2 1/2 baths, 3-car garage

Crawl space foundation

Price Code F

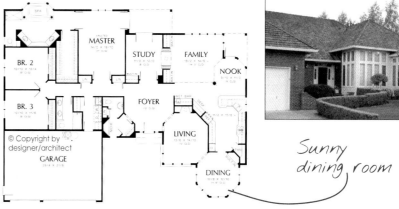

Sunny dining room

PLAN #651-011D-0082

ST. CLAIR

2,596 total square feet of living area

Width: 75'-0" Depth: 74' 0"

Energy efficient home with 2" x 6" exterior walls

An open entry foyer is flanked by a formal dining room and cozy den

The great room enjoys a warm fireplace as well as a built-in media center

An angled island in the kitchen contains a cooktop stove and extended dining space

3 bedrooms, 2 1/2 baths, 3-car garage

Crawl space foundation

Price Code F

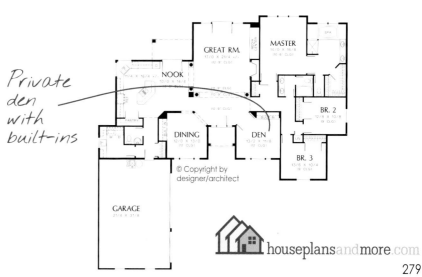

Private den with built-ins

houseplansandmore.com

Photo, above: Luxury abounds in this masterpiece home. As soon as you enter, the massive great room with atrium windows will catch your eye.

Photo, right: Sleek built-in shelving surrounds the fireplace in the great room offering the perfect spot for treasured family heirlooms, favorite novels or prized family photography.

Photo, left: Even in the kitchen, the homeowners will never be far from the action with this open floor plan.

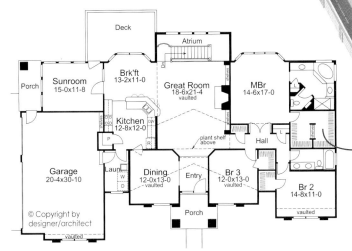

First Floor
2,398 sq. ft.

© Copyright by designer/architect

Optional Lower Level

Large master bedroom walk-in closet

Photo, below: The open kitchen floor plan is designed for easy cooking and casual dining all in one.

PLANFEATURES

2,398 total square feet of living area

Width: 78'-8" Depth: 51'-0"

The porch leads to a dramatic vaulted entry foyer with a plant shelf

The great room enjoys a 12' vaulted ceiling and atrium featuring 2 1/2 story windows and a fireplace with flanking bookshelves

A conveniently located sunroom and side porch adjoin the breakfast room and garage

There is 763 square feet of optional living area on the lower level with a family room, bedroom #4 and a bath

2" x 6" exterior walls available, please order plan #651-007E-0098

3 bedrooms, 2 baths, 3-car side entry garage

Walk-out basement foundation

Price Code D

houseplansandmore.com

POMEROY MANOR

PLAN FEATURES

3,800 total square feet of living area

Width: 103'-0" Depth: 75'-6"

The stunning double-door entry leads into the open foyer and adjacent dining room with bay window

Ample space in both garage areas is perfect for workshop space or storage of lawn equipment

The beautiful great room features a wall of windows with access to a covered porch and an inviting corner fireplace

The bonus room on the second floor has an additional 826 square feet of living area

3 bedrooms, 2 full baths, 2 half baths, 2-car and 1-car side entry garages

Basement, crawl space or slab foundation, please specify when ordering

Price Code S1

houseplansandmore.com

282

Spacious upstairs bonus room!

UPSTAIRS BONUS ROOM
28'-0"x35'-0"

Optional Second Floor

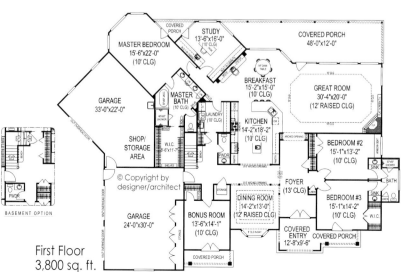

First Floor
3,800 sq. ft.

© Copyright by designer/architect

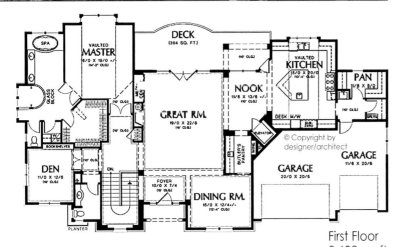

First Floor
2,602 sq. ft.

© Copyright by designer/architect

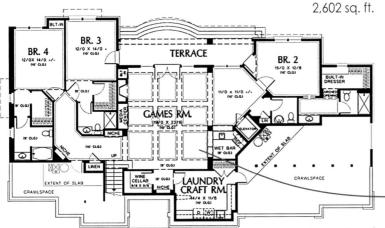

Lower Level
2,440 sq. ft.

PLANFEATURES

5,042 total square feet of living area

Width: 88'-0" Depth: 50'-0"

The kitchen enjoys an enormous walk-in pantry, a built-in desk and a nearby butler's pantry

The vaulted master suite promises pampering with a spacious bath including a whirlpool spa, glass block oversized shower and even its own laundry room

The lower level is filled with just as much luxury including an oversized games room, a laundry craft room, a wine cellar, and a stunning terrace

This home even includes a handy elevator

4 bedrooms, 4 full baths,
2 half baths, 3-car garage

Walk-out basement foundation

Price Code S1

Huge games room!!

houseplansandmore.com

HOLMES PLACE

PLANFEATURES

3,806 total square feet of living area

Width: 67'-10" Depth: 56'-4"

The morning room is brightened by a bay window and shares the eating bar area with the kitchen

The luxurious master bath boasts a large walk-in closet, two separate vanities and a corner tub

A spacious recreation room on the lower level enjoys a fireplace and access to the rear terrace

5 bedrooms, 4 1/2 baths, 2-car side entry garage

Walk-out basement foundation

Price Code S1

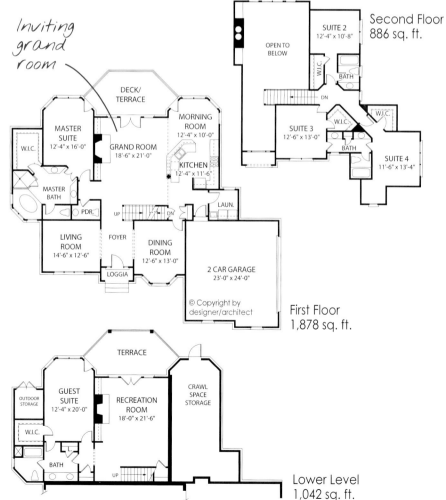

Inviting grand room

Second Floor
886 sq. ft.

First Floor
1,878 sq. ft.

Lower Level
1,042 sq. ft.

houseplansandmore.com

PLANFEATURES

3,109 total square feet of living area

Width: 91'-8" Depth: 66'-8"

Energy efficient home with 2" x 6" exterior walls

A double-door entry elegantly leads into this home

The homeowners will enjoy the openness of the combined kitchen, nook and great room

Relax in the master bedroom equipped with a pampering bath and walk-in closet

4 bedrooms, 2 1/2 baths, 2-car side entry garage, 1-car garage

Basement foundation

Price Code F

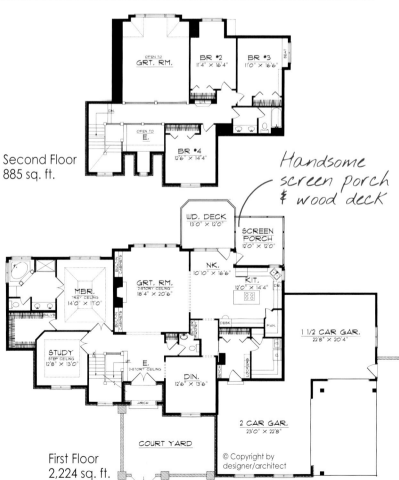

Second Floor
885 sq. ft.

Handsome screen porch & wood deck

First Floor
2,224 sq. ft.

© Copyright by designer/architect

houseplansandmore.com

NATCHEZ

PLANFEATURES

3,770 total square feet of living area

Width: 69'-6" Depth: 55'-6"

Energy efficient home with 2" x 6" exterior walls

The spacious kitchen has a center island with a double sink and a snack bar

The sitting room near the kitchen features a corner fireplace and has access to the rear deck and lovely vaulted screen porch

The luxurious, second floor master bedroom has abundant storage space and a plush bath

The bonus room above the garage has an additional 256 square feet of living space

4 bedrooms, 3 1/2 baths, 3-car garage

Basement foundation

Price Code G

houseplansandmore.com

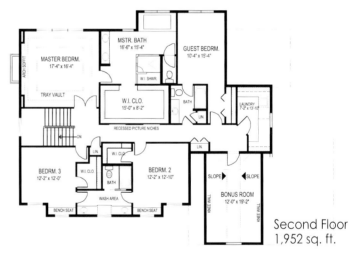

Second Floor
1,952 sq. ft.

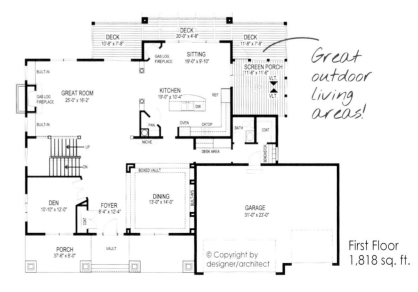

Great outdoor living areas!

© Copyright by designer/architect

First Floor
1,818 sq. ft.

PLANFEATURES

3,445 total square feet of living area

Width: 71'-8" Depth: 39'-10"

The flow of the first floor enhances the enjoyment of entertaining guests in the formal living and dining rooms, while the kitchen, hearth room and breakfast area combine for a comfortable casual atmosphere

The second floor bayed master bedroom enjoys the warmth of a fireplace, a walk-in closet and a spacious dressing area

The screened-in porch connects to the bayed breakfast area and an outdoor deck with the eye-catching gazebo

4 bedrooms, 3 1/2 baths, 3-car side entry garage

Walk-out basement or crawl space foundation, please specify when ordering

Price Code F

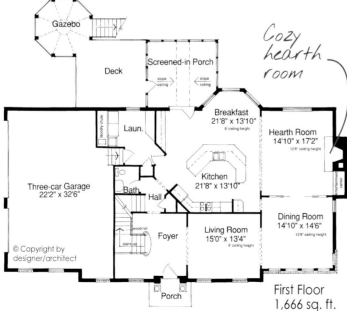

Second Floor
1,779 sq. ft.

Bedroom
13"7" x 17'1"
8' ceiling height

Master Bedroom
16'11" x 20'8"
9' ceiling height

Dressing

walk-in closet

laundry chute

Dressing

Hall

Bedroom
16'10" x 12'9"
8' ceiling height

walk-in closet

stairs dn
4 risers

Bath

walk in closet

Bedroom
15'10" x 12'0"
9' ceiling height

Balcony

Gazebo

Deck

Screened-in Porch

slope ceiling

slope ceiling

Cozy hearth room

Breakfast
21'8" x 13'10"
9' ceiling height

Hearth Room
14'10" x 17'2"
12'8" ceiling height

Laun.

laundry chute

Kitchen
21'8" x 13'10"

Three-car Garage
22'2" x 32'6"

Bath

Hall

Dining Room
14'10" x 14'6"
12'8" ceiling height

wood rail

Foyer

stairs up

Living Room
15'0" x 13'4"
9' ceiling height

© Copyright by designer/architect

First Floor
1,666 sq. ft.

Porch

SHADYVIEW

PLAN #651-007D-0124

1,944 total square feet of living area

Width: 65'-0" Depth: 51'-0"

A luxury bath, walk-in closet and doors to the porch are a few of the amenities of the master bedroom

3 bedrooms, 2 baths, 3-car detached garage

Basement foundation

Price Code C

ROSE WAY

PLAN #651-048D-0008

2,089 total square feet of living area

Width: 61'-8" Depth: 50'-4"

The kitchen overlooks the family room and features a pantry and desk

4 bedrooms, 3 baths, 2-car garage

Slab foundation

Price Code C

MILLIGAN

PLAN #651-028D-0029

2,605 total square feet of living area

Width: 78'-0" Depth: 61'-0"

Arched openings grace the entrances to the formal dining room and the great room

4 bedrooms, 3 1/2 baths, 2-car side entry garage

Basement, slab or crawl space foundation, please specify when ordering

Price Code E

RILEY

PLAN #651-121D-0021

1,562 total square feet of living area

Width: 65'-0" Depth: 46'-4"

A convenient eating bar in the kitchen is perfect for casual meals

The spacious great room boasts a vaulted ceiling and warming corner fireplace

3 bedrooms, 2 baths, 2-car garage

Basement foundation

Price Code A

PLAN #651-077D-0156

WELLSHIRE

2,200 total square feet of living area

Width: 65'-6" Depth: 79'-6"

Step inside this inviting home to find an exquisite great room topped with a tray ceiling and featuring a gas fireplace flanked by built-in shelves

The nearby kitchen is centrally located, offering a walk-in pantry and raised snack bar, and easily serves both the formal dining room and the casual breakfast area

The optional second floor has an additional 371 square feet of living area

4 bedrooms, 2 1/2 baths, 2-car side entry garage

Crawl space or slab foundation, please specify when ordering

Price Code E

Comfortable rear covered porch

© Copyright by designer/architect

Optional Second Floor

First Floor
2,200 sq. ft.

PLAN #651-121D-0014

AUTUMN

2,360 total square feet of living area

Width: 50'-4" Depth: 56'-8"

A gracious hearth room is brightened by windows and is perfect for relaxing with family next to the cozy fireplace

The kitchen features a walk-in pantry and eating bar for convenience

The vaulted master bedroom has a private bath with a whirlpool tub, a separate shower and a double-bowl vanity

3 bedrooms, 2 1/2 baths, 2-car garage

Basement foundation

Price Code C

Kitchen enjoys a walk-in pantry

© Copyright by designer/architect

Second Floor
826 sq. ft.

First Floor
1,534 sq. ft.

houseplansandmore.com

SOMERFIELD

PLANFEATURES

2,695 total square feet of living area

Width: 50'-0" Depth: 44'-0"

The view from the front door to the family room's two-story fireplace wall is amazing

The expansive kitchen and breakfast area feature a perfect place for the family computer

The master bedroom features a window seat dramatized by a stepped ceiling and large windows overlooking the backyard

The second floor laundry area and computer desk complete this well-appointed design

5 bedrooms, 3 baths, 2-car side entry garage

Walk-out basement foundation

Price Code G

Second Floor
1,380 sq. ft.

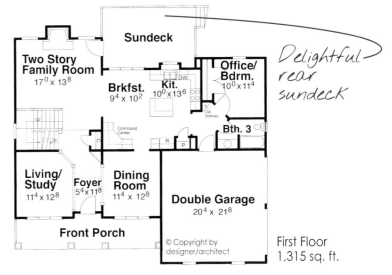

Delightful rear sundeck

First Floor
1,315 sq. ft.

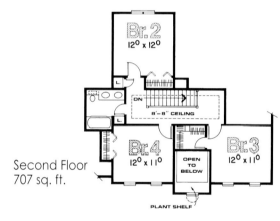

Second Floor
707 sq. ft.

Inviting master bedroom with a private bath

First Floor
1,570 sq. ft.

© Copyright by designer/architect

PLAN FEATURES

2,277 total square feet of living area

Width: 54'-0" Depth: 52'-0"

The two-story entry is impressive with a view to the formal dining room defined by decorative columns

An efficient kitchen includes a pantry and work island with a nearby bayed breakfast area for easy meals

Transom windows, a grand fireplace and cathedral ceiling create a stunning atmosphere in the great room

4 bedrooms, 2 1/2 baths, 2-car garage

Basement foundation

Price Code H

houseplansandmore.com

PLANFEATURES

3,438 total square feet of living area

Width: 64'-0" Depth: 61'-6"

Double doors off the front entry lead to a private den with a unique corner window style and built-in bookcases

The two-story living room flows into the formal dining room making a perfect combination when entertaining

All of the bedrooms are located on the second floor for plenty of peace and quiet

4 bedrooms, 2 1/2 baths, 3-car garage

Crawl space foundation

Price Code S1

Two-story living room with a curved window wall

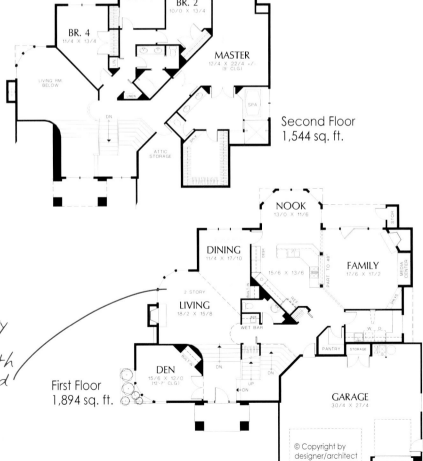

Second Floor
1,544 sq. ft.

First Floor
1,894 sq. ft.

houseplansandmore.com

PLANFEATURES

1,758 total square feet of living area

Width: 48'-0" Depth: 63'-0"

A terrific deck can be found off the screened porch, perfect for a barbecue grill

A cozy corner fireplace warms all the surroundings in the combination great room/dining area

The kitchen is compact in design and features a spacious center island full of workspace and dining space for three people

The optional lower level has an additional 997 square feet of living area and includes two bedrooms, a full bath and recreation room

2 bedrooms, 2 baths, 2-car side entry garage

Basement foundation

Price Code B

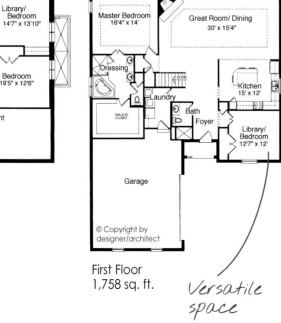

Optional Lower Level

- Unexcavated
- Rec Room 22'6" x 20'1"
- Bath
- Library/Bedroom 14'7" x 13'10"
- Bedroom 19'5" x 12'6"
- Basement
- Unexcavated
- Unex.

First Floor
1,758 sq. ft.

- Screened Porch 14' x 11'8"
- Deck
- Master Bedroom 16'4" x 14'
- Great Room/Dining 30' x 15'4"
- Dressing
- Laundry
- WALK-IN CLOSET
- Bath
- Foyer
- Kitchen 15' x 12'
- Library/Bedroom 12'7" x 12'
- Garage

© Copyright by designer/architect

Versatile space

houseplansandmore.com

MONTERRA MANOR

PLAN#651-051S-0021

PLAN FEATURES

3,259 total square feet of living area

Width: 69'-8" Depth: 74'-8"

Energy efficient home with 2" x 6" exterior walls

The cheerful sun room is surrounded with windows for added openness

The double-door entry into the den keeps this space private

A sink and extra counterspace extends to the dining room entrance for entertaining ease

4 bedrooms, 3 1/2 baths, 3-car side entry garage

Basement foundation

Price Code S1

Exquisite master bedroom

First Floor
2,402 sq. ft.

Second Floor
857 sq. ft.

© Copyright by designer/architect

houseplansandmore.com

294

PLANFEATURES

6,366 total square feet of living area

Width: 110'-6" Depth: 79'-5"

A unique office is tucked away behind the kitchen and is brightened by multiple windows

A morning kitchen, private luxurious bath and huge walk-in closet are some of the amenities of the master suite

The recreation room on the second floor steps down into the media room with bar and seating space

4 bedrooms, 4 full baths, 2 half baths, 3-car side entry garage

Crawl space foundation

Price Code S3

Second Floor
2,603 sq. ft.

Distinctive fireplace warms the family room

First Floor
3,763 sq. ft.

© Copyright by designer/architect

CANYONCOVE

PLANFEATURES

4,351 total square feet of living area

Width: 59'-0" Depth: 81'-0"

The U-shaped kitchen enjoys a center island, a walk-in pantry and a peninsula with a convenient eating bar

A vaulted ceiling, shelves and a window seat are some of the amenities of the sunny den

Entertaining is a breeze on the lower level, complete with a large games room, wine cellar, wet bar and access to the patio

4 bedrooms, 3 1/2 baths, 3-car garage

Partial crawl space/walk-out basement foundation

Price Code S1

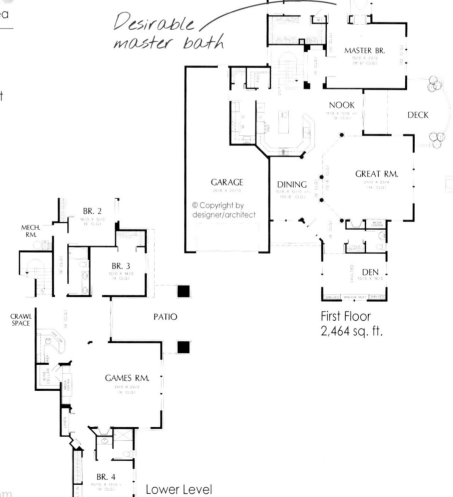

Desirable master bath

© Copyright by designer/architect

First Floor
2,464 sq. ft.

Lower Level
1,887 sq. ft.

PATTON

PLAN #651-011D-0007

1,580 total square feet of living area

Width: 50'-0" Depth: 48'-0"

Energy efficient home with 2" x 6" exterior walls

A covered porch extends the great room into the outdoors

3 bedrooms, 2 1/2 baths, 2-car garage

Crawl space foundation

Price Code C

HUGES HILL

PLAN #651-065D-0170

1,537 total square feet of living area

Width: 59'-8" Depth: 42'-2"

A corner fireplace in the great room is visible from the foyer offering a dramatic first impression

The private master bedroom enjoys its own bath, walk-in closet and access to the rear porch

3 bedrooms, 2 baths, 2-car garage

Basement foundation

Price Code B

CARRABELLE

PLAN #651-047D-0135

2,503 total square feet of living area

Width: 60'-0" Depth: 78'-4"

A stunning whirlpool tub is the highlight of the master bath and enjoys sunlight from a curved window wall above

3 bedrooms, 3 baths, 2-car side entry garage

Slab foundation

Price Code F

PARC CREST

PLAN #651-111D-0009

2,112 total square feet of living area

Width: 68'-1" Depth: 74'-0"

The bonus room above the garage has an additional 304 square feet of living area

3 bedrooms, 2 1/2 baths, 2-car side entry garage

Basement, crawl space or slab foundation, please specify when ordering

Price Code C

houseplansandmore.com

ROSECROFT

2,529 total square feet of living area

Width: 63'-0" Depth: 34'-2"

A distinguished exterior appearance enhances this home's classic interior arrangement

A private bath with garden tub, a walk-in closet and a coffered ceiling enhance the master bedroom suite

The bonus room over the garage, that is included in the square footage, has direct access from the attic and the second floor hall

4 bedrooms, 2 1/2 baths, 2-car garage

Basement foundation

Price Code B

Cheerful breakfast area

Second Floor
1,410 sq. ft.

First Floor
1,119 sq. ft.

OAKCREST MANOR

1,811 total square feet of living area

Width: 34'-10" Depth: 83'-0"

Designed for a narrow lot, this exciting home features an open living space with the great room, dining area and kitchen flowing together and defined by decorative columns and a snack bar counter

The rear master suite offers a pampering bath with two vanities, a whirlpool tub and a walk-in closet

Two secondary bedrooms also enjoy walk-in closets for easy organization

3 bedrooms, 2 baths, 2-car rear entry garage

Crawl space or slab foundation, please specify when ordering

Price Code C

Amazing open living area with decorative columns

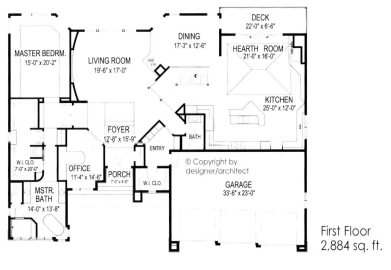

First Floor
2,884 sq. ft.

MASTER BEDRM.
15'-0" x 20'-2"

LIVING ROOM
19'-6" x 17'-0"

DINING
17'-3" x 12'-6"

DECK
22'-0" x 6'-6"

HEARTH ROOM
21'-0" x 16'-0"

KITCHEN
25'-0" x 12'-0"

GAS F.P.

W.I. CLO.
7'-0" x 20'-0"

FOYER
12'-8" x 15'-9"

ENTRY

BATH

OFFICE
11'-4" x 14'-6"

PORCH
7'-0" x 4'-6"

W.I. CLO.

GARAGE
33'-6" x 23'-0"

MSTR. BATH
14'-0" x 13'-8"

© Copyright by
designer/architect

Lower Level
2,681 sq. ft.

BEDROOM 3
14'-6" x 15'-0"

REC. ROOM
19'-8" x 18'-8"

GAME AREA
10'-8" x 12'-4"

EXERCISE
12'-6" x 16'-10"

BEDROOM 2
14'-6" x 16'-2"

W.I. CLO.

BATH

BILLIARDS
16'-0" x 17'-6"

WET BAR

BATH

MECHANICAL

LAUNDRY
7'-0" x 11'-0"

BATH

W.I. CLO.

BEDROOM 4
14'-6" x 14'-0"

UNEXCAVATED

WINE

UNEXCAVATED

STORAGE

Gorgeous billiards & recreation room!

PLANFEATURES

5,565 total square feet of living area

Width: 75'-0" Depth: 60'-0"

The living and dining rooms share a warming see-through fireplace

A built-in bench wraps around the kitchen creating additional seating and cozy spaces for entertaining

The lower level is spacious with a recreational room, an exercise space and three additional large bedrooms

4 bedrooms, 3 full baths, 2 half baths, 3-car garage

Walk-out basement foundation

Price Code S1

BRISTOL FERRY

PLAN #651-032D-0613

1,217 total square feet of living area

Width: 36'-0" Depth: 38'-0"

Energy efficient home with 2" x 6" exterior walls

A cozy corner fireplace warms the living room and makes an inviting atmosphere

Triple sliding glass doors in the kitchen offer plenty of sunlight and direct access outdoors

A large spa-style tub creates a relaxing retreat in the full bath

2 bedrooms, 1 bath

Basement foundation

Price Code D

Lovely corner fireplace

© Copyright by designer/architect

PALM BEACH

PLAN #651-047D-0103

1,433 total square feet of living area

Width: 40'-0" Depth: 55'-0"

Bedroom #3 offers a spacious feel with a vaulted ceiling

A step-up whirlpool tub and a double-bowl vanity provide a feeling of luxury in the master bath

The combined vaulted living and dining areas make the main living areas of this home feel open and larger than their true size

3 bedrooms, 2 baths, 2-car garage

Slab foundation

Price Code C

Charming breakfast area

© Copyright by designer/architect

houseplansandmore.com

Perfect 3 seasons room!!

First Floor
3,487 sq. ft.

© Copyright by designer/architect

Second Floor
1,659 sq. ft.

Optional
Lower Level

PLANFEATURES

5,146 total square feet of living area

Width: 89'-8" Depth: 76'-0"

Energy efficient home with 2" x 6" exterior walls

The expansive kitchen is a chef's dream with an abundance of counterspace, a large pantry and a cooktop island

The second floor bonus room has an additional 546 square feet of living space

The optional lower level has an additional 2,534 square feet of living area and includes two bedrooms, two baths, a media room and game room

4 bedrooms, 5 1/2 baths, 3-car side entry garage

Basement foundation

Price Code S1

PLAN FEATURES

2,240 total square feet of living area

Width: 56'-8" Depth: 57'-4"

The master bedroom enjoys a private first floor location along with an amenity-filled bath and walk-in closet

A flexible loft space can be found on the second floor perfect for a home office or children's play area

The functional kitchen offers an eating bar and a corner walk-in pantry for added storage space

3 bedrooms, 2 1/2 baths, 2-car side entry garage

Basement foundation

Price Code C

Two-story great room with a vaulted ceiling

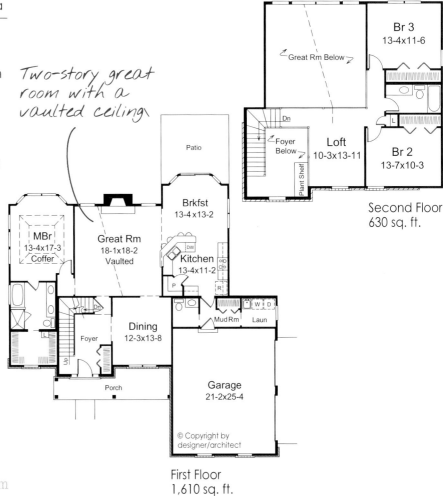

Second Floor
630 sq. ft.

Br 3
13-4x11-6

Great Rm Below

Dn

Foyer Below

Loft
10-3x13-11

Br 2
13-7x10-3

Plant Shelf

Patio

Brkfst
13-4 x13-2

MBr
13-4x17-3
Coffer

Great Rm
18-1x18-2
Vaulted

Kitchen
13-4x11-2

P

DW

R

Foyer

Dn

Up

Dining
12-3x13-8

Mud Rm

W D

Laun

Porch

Garage
21-2x25-4

© Copyright by designer/architect

First Floor
1,610 sq. ft.

COUNTRY MANOR

PLAN #651-007D-0048

2,758 total square feet of living area

Width: 72'-8" Depth: 68'-4"

Energy efficient home with 2" x 6" exterior walls

The trendsetting kitchen and breakfast area adjoin the spacious screened porch

4 bedrooms, 2 1/2 baths, 3-car side entry garage

Walk-out basement foundation

Price Code E

BAY RANCH

PLAN #651-053D-0002

1,668 total square feet of living area

Width: 56'-0" Depth: 40'-0"

A handy covered porch graces the front entry

The large living room has a fireplace, built-in bookshelves and a sloped ceiling

3 bedrooms, 2 baths, 2-car side entry drive under garage

Walk-out basement foundation

Price Code A

BUSHNELL HILL

PLAN #651-028D-0044

2,052 total square feet of living area

Width: 50'-0" Depth: 68'-0"

The grand arched entryway is accented with elegant columns

3 bedrooms, 2 baths, 2-car detached garage

Slab or crawl space foundation, please specify when ordering

Price Code D

BRIANNA

PLAN #651-121D-0031

1,308 total square feet of living area

Width: 46'-0" Depth: 36'-0"

The great room and kitchen/dining combine

3 bedrooms, 2 baths, 2-car side entry detached garage

Basement foundation

Price Code AA

houseplansandmore.com

PLAN FEATURES

6,664 total square feet of living area

Width: 65'-0" Depth: 75'-0"

The master bedroom has his and her baths and closets, with a shared dressing area and private morning kitchen

All of the bedrooms have private balcony access, increasing the open air feel of the floor plan

In addition to the V.I.P. suite, this home has a maid's room located on the first floor

Framing - only concrete block available

6 bedrooms, 6 1/2 baths, 3-car garage

Slab foundation

Price Code S1

Impressive staircase

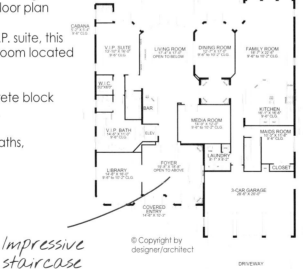

© Copyright by designer/architect

First Floor
3,515 sq. ft.

Second Floor
3,149 sq. ft.

houseplansandmore.com

Master Suite
15-8 x 18-6
pan vault

whirlpool

chimney

Lin

Br 2
12-0 x 11-4

niche

Br 4
12-0 x 13-0

LIN

DN

open to foyer

railing

Br 3
11-0 x 13-0

Second Floor
1,472 sq. ft.

Friendly deck great for entertaining!

Deck

Brkfst
15-8 x 10-0

Kitchen

snack bar

Family Rm
17-0 x 22-0

built-ins

15-8 x 14-10

pantry

deck

Study
12-8 x 13-1

D

W

Ldry

DN

Dining Rm
11-0 x 17-0

Foyer

UP

Living Rm
13-0 x 19-7

Garage
31-8 x 23-8

© Copyright by
designer/architect

First Floor
2,054 sq. ft.

PLANFEATURES

3,526 total square feet of living area

Width: 78'-0" Depth: 60'-0"

Energy efficient home with 2" x 6" exterior walls

The breakfast and family rooms have enormous windows overlooking the backyard

The living room has an elegant sloped ceiling and broad hearth fireplace

The study is a secluded room providing peace and quiet

4 bedrooms, 3 1/2 baths, 3-car garage

Walk-out basement foundation

Price Code H

Photo, right: Standing at the sink in the kitchen right behind the wrap-around counter offers pleasant views through the dining bay window, the French door leading to the patio and the cozy roaring fireplace.

houseplansandmore.com

Relaxed dining area with a vaulted ceiling & bay window

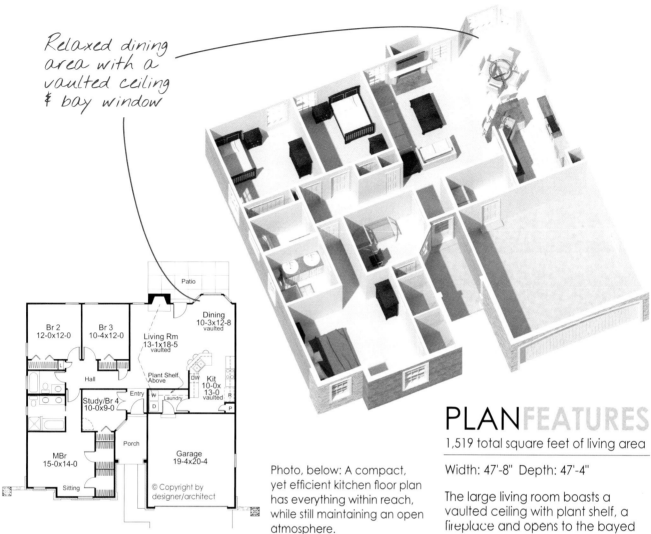

Patio

Br 2
12-0x12-0

Br 3
10-4x12-0

Dining
10-3x12-8
vaulted

Living Rm
13-1x18-5
vaulted

Hall

Plant Shelf
Above

Kit
10-0x
13-0
vaulted

DW

L

Entry

W

D

Laundry

R

Study/Br 4
10-0x9-0

P

MBr
15-0x14-0

Porch

Garage
19-4x20-4

Sitting

© Copyright by
designer/architect

Photo, below: A compact, yet efficient kitchen floor plan has everything within reach, while still maintaining an open atmosphere.

PLANFEATURES

1,519 total square feet of living area

Width: 47'-8" Depth: 47'-4"

The large living room boasts a vaulted ceiling with plant shelf, a fireplace and opens to the bayed dining area

Two walk-in closets, a stylish bath and a small sitting area accompany the master bedroom

The kitchen has an adjoining laundry room and features a vaulted ceiling, a snack counter open to the living and dining areas, and a built-in pantry

4 bedrooms, 2 baths, 2-car garage

Crawl space foundation, drawings also include slab and basement foundations

Price Code B

houseplansandmore.com

307

PLANFEATURES

3,055 total square feet of living area

Width: 72'-8" Depth: 69'-1"

The great room features a fireplace with flanking shelves and sliding glass doors to the rear terrace/deck

A gorgeous sunroom with a vaulted ceiling is perfect for relaxing

The bonus room on the second floor has an additional 374 square feet of living area

4 bedrooms, 3 1/2 baths, 2-car side entry garage

Crawl space foundation

Price Code G

Spectacular master suite!!

Second Floor
657 sq. ft.

SUITE 4
12'-6" x 12'-6"

BATH

W.I.C.

OPEN TO BELOW

BALCONY

DN

SUITE 3
15'-0" x 11'-0"

UP

W.I.C.

BONUS ROOM
14'-0" x 20'-0"

First Floor
2,398 sq. ft.

© Copyright by designer/architect

MASTER SUITE
15'-6" x 17'-6"

TERRACE / DECK

SUNROOM
14'-6" x 11'-6"

MASTER BATH

W.I.C.

GREAT ROOM
19'-6" x 16'-6"

DINING ROOM
12'-0" x 14'-6"

BAR

PDR.

BREAKFAST
14'-6" x 12'-6"

BATH

FOYER

UP

W.I.C.

STUDY/ GUEST/ LIBRARY
12'-6" x 13'-6"

LOGGIA

LAUNDRY

KITCHEN
14'-6" x 15'-6"

P.

2 CAR GARAGE
23'-6" x 23'-6"

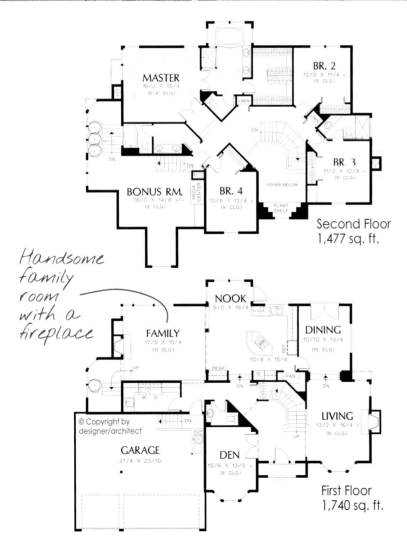

Second Floor
1,477 sq. ft.

Handsome family room with a fireplace

First Floor
1,740 sq. ft.

© Copyright by designer/architect

PLANFEATURES

3,217 total square feet of living area

Width: 63'-0" Depth: 52'-0"

A spacious den features a cheerful bay window

A secondary staircase can be found by the casual family room and leads to the spacious second floor bonus room

The formal dining room enjoys double French doors leading outdoors

The bonus room on the second floor has an additional 382 square feet of living area

4 bedrooms, 3 1/2 baths, 3-car garage

Crawl space foundation

Price Code F

houseplansandmore.com

VALLEY CREST HILL

PLAN FEATURES

2,525 total square feet of living area

Width: 62'-0" Depth: 47'-0"

Energy efficient home with 2" x 6" exterior walls

The cheerful kitchen has a double-bowl sink in the island, a large corner pantry and opens up nicely to the dining area and sunroom

Double doors off the entry hall lead to a sophisticated study with plenty of peace and quiet

The owner's suite is topped with a coffered ceiling and offers a generous closet and a private bath with a double-bowl vanity, amazing walk-in shower and a whirlpool tub

4 bedrooms, 2 1/2 baths, 3-car garage

Walk-out basement foundation

Price Code C

Second Floor
1,280 sq. ft.

Beautiful windows!!

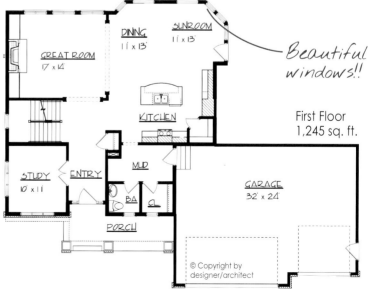

First Floor
1,245 sq. ft.

houseplansandmore.com

PLAN FEATURES

3,581 total square feet of living area

Width: 92'-0" Depth: 66'-0"

Two stairwells provide easy access to the second floor bedrooms and the exciting gameroom

French doors in the dining room open to the covered front porch, inviting guests to enjoy some fresh air

The first floor full bath is accessible from the rear porch containing messy transitions from outdoors to inside

4 bedrooms, 4 baths, 3-car side entry garage

Slab foundation

Price Code J

Second Floor
912 sq. ft.

Gameroom
15'1"x 26'1"

Attic Storage

Bedroom
13'1"x 13'1"

Bath

Hall

Bath

Open to Below

Bedroom
12'x 13'3"

Huge walk-in closet!!

Master Bedroom
14'1"x 18'1"

Porch

Three-Car Garage
23'7"x 35'7"

Pantry

Master Bath

Bath

Living
22'1"x 18'1"

Kitchen
14'7"x 18'1"

© Copyright by designer/architect

Walk-In Closet

Hall

Storage

Utility

Bedroom
11'7"x 11'3"

Study
11'10"x 10'9"

Dining
11'7"x 14'9"

Breakfast
11'9"x 13'1"

Porch

First Floor
2,669 sq. ft.

Foyer

Porch

houseplansandmore.com

AQUAMARINE

PLAN FEATURES

2,551 total square feet of living area

Width: 68'-0" Depth: 36'-6"

Energy efficient home with 2" x 6" exterior walls

A see-through fireplace provides a warm glow in the living and dining rooms

A secluded home office provides peace and quiet

A gorgeous sun room off the living room offers a beautiful extension that makes you feel surrounded by the outdoors

3 bedrooms, 2 1/2 baths, 2-car garage

Basement foundation

Price Code G

Pleasant see-through fireplace

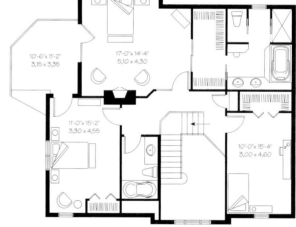

10'-6"x 11'-2"
3,15 x 3,35

17'-0"x 14'-4"
5,10 x 4,30

11'-0"x 15'-2"
3,30 x 4,55

10'-0"x 15'-4"
3,00 x 4,60

Second Floor
1,153 sq. ft.

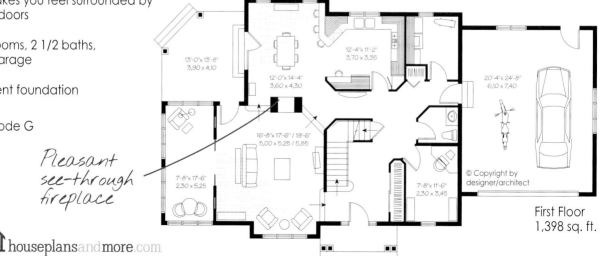

13'-0"x 13'-8"
3,90 x 4,10

12'-0"x 14'-4"
3,60 x 4,30

12'-4"x 11'-2"
3,70 x 3,35

20'-4"x 24'-8"
6,10 x 7,40

16'-8"x 17'-6" / 19'-6"
5,00 x 5,25 / 5,85

7'-8"x 17'-6"
2,30 x 5,25

7'-8"x 11'-6"
2,30 x 3,45

© Copyright by
designer/architect

First Floor
1,398 sq. ft.

houseplansandmore.com

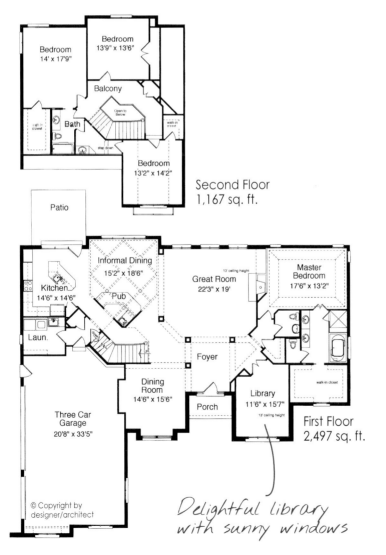

Bedroom
14' x 17'9"

Bedroom
13'9" x 13'6"

Balcony

Bath

Open to Below

walk in closet

step down

Bedroom
13'2" x 14'2"

Second Floor
1,167 sq. ft.

Patio

Informal Dining
15'2" x 18'6"

Kitchen
14'6" x 14'6"

Pub

13' ceiling height

Great Room
22'3" x 19'

Master Bedroom
17'6" x 13'2"

Laun.

Foyer

Three Car Garage
20'8" x 33'5"

Dining Room
14'6" x 15'6"

Porch

Library
11'6" x 15'7"

walk-in closet

13' ceiling height

First Floor
2,497 sq. ft.

© Copyright by designer/architect

Delightful library with sunny windows

PLANFEATURES

3,664 total square feet of living area

Width: 72'-4" Depth: 65'-0"

A delightful pub and informal dining area invites family members and guests to relax and enjoy the good times

Decorative columns define the foyer, the formal dining room and the great room

Boasting a tray ceiling treatment, the master bedroom showcases a bath with a whirlpool tub, a double-bowl vanity and a large walk-in closet

4 bedrooms, 2 1/2 baths, 3-car side entry garage

Basement foundation

Price Code F

houseplansandmore.com

PLATTSBURGH

PLAN FEATURES

4,579 total square feet of living area

Width: 89'-4" Depth: 67'-0"

Energy efficient home with 2" x 6" exterior walls

The wood beam ceiling adds spectacular dimension to the great room and dining room

The open kitchen is a chef's dream with a nearby walk-in pantry and utility room with a built-in locker system

A cathedral ceiling adds spaciousness and elegance to the master bedroom that also enjoys a private covered porch

Retreat to the lower level and find an amazing recreation room with a wet bar and nearby media room

4 bedrooms, 3 baths, 3-car side entry garage

Walk-out basement foundation

Price Code S1

houseplansandmore.com

314

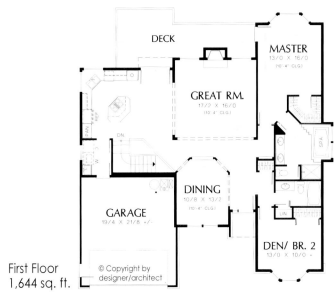

DECK

MASTER
13/0 X 16/0
(10' 4" CLG)

GREAT RM.
17/2 X 16/0
(10' 4" CLG)

DINING
10/8 X 13/2
(10' 4" CLG)

GARAGE
19/4 X 21/8 +/-

DEN/ BR. 2
13/0 X 10/0

First Floor
1,644 sq. ft.

© Copyright by
designer/architect

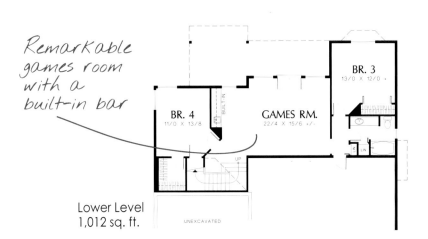

Remarkable
games room
with a
built-in bar

BR. 4
11/0 X 13/8

GAMES RM.
22/4 X 15/6

BR. 3
13/0 X 12/0

BUILT-IN

UP

Lower Level
1,012 sq. ft.

UNEXCAVATED

PLANFEATURES

2,656 total square feet of living area

Width: 52'-0" Depth: 55'-0"

Energy efficient home with 2" x 6" exterior walls

The den/bedroom #2 is a flexible space that can adapt to your family's needs

The lower level features a popular games room with outdoor access and a wet bar

An unbelievably open kitchen offers great function for the chef of the family while enjoying plenty of space for entertaining

4 bedrooms, 3 baths, 2-car garage

Crawl space foundation

Price Code F

houseplansandmore.com

PLANFEATURES

3,057 total square feet of living area

Width: 71'-0" Depth: 57'-0"

Covered front porches and amazing bay windows grace the front of this Plantation style home

The enticing family room features a warming fireplace and access to the rear deck area

The kitchen/breakfast area boasts a two-story ceiling

A whirlpool tub, a walk-in closet and a double-bowl vanity are some of the amenities of the master bath

The future recreation room on the second floor has an additional 459 square feet of living area

4 bedrooms, 3 1/2 baths, 2-car side entry garage

Partial crawl space/walk-out basement foundation

Price Code E

Second Floor
1,062 sq. ft.

Luxurious master bath with a whirlpool tub

First Floor
1,995 sq. ft.

houseplansandmore.com

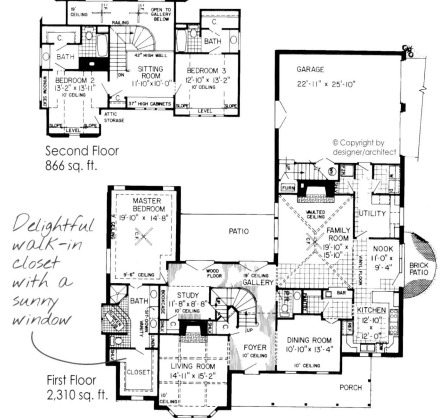

PLAN FEATURES

3,176 total square feet of living area

Width: 78'-0" Depth: 64'-0"

Energy efficient home with 2" x 6" exterior walls

Varied ceiling heights throughout

The beautifully designed foyer has a prominent center staircase and a lovely adjacent gallery space

A casual sitting room connects the secondary bedrooms

3 bedrooms, 3 1/2 baths, 2-car side entry garage

Basement, crawl space or slab foundation, please specify when ordering

Price Code E

Second Floor
866 sq. ft.

Delightful walk-in closet with a sunny window

First Floor
2,310 sq. ft.

© Copyright by designer/architect

houseplansandmore.com

PLANFEATURES

2,795 total square feet of living area

Width: 72'-0" Depth: 42'-0"

The cozy parlor with fireplace and formal dining room combine for a pleasant dining experience

All of the bedrooms are located on the second floor for peace and quiet from the main living areas

The bayed den makes the perfect home office

The bonus room on the second floor has an additional 538 square feet of living area

4 bedrooms, 2 1/2 baths, 3-car garage

Crawl space foundation

Price Code E

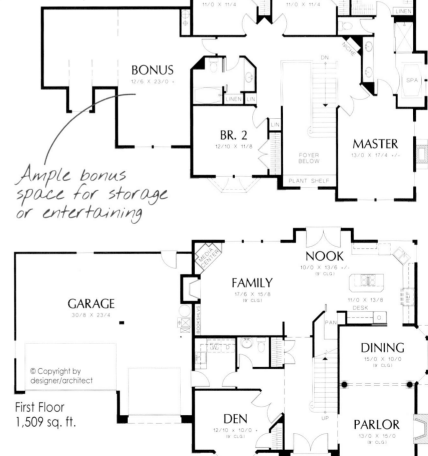

Second Floor
1,286 sq. ft.

BR. 3
11/0 X 11/4

BR. 4
11/0 X 11/4

BONUS
12/6 X 23/0 +/-

BR. 2
12/10 X 11/8

MASTER
13/0 X 17/4 +/-

Ample bonus space for storage or entertaining

First Floor
1,509 sq. ft.

GARAGE
30/8 X 23/4

FAMILY
17/6 X 15/8
(9' CLG)

NOOK
10/0 X 13/6 +/-
(9' CLG)

11/0 X 13/8

DINING
15/0 X 10/0
(9' CLG)

DEN
12/10 X 10/0 +/-
(9' CLG)

PARLOR
13/0 X 15/0
(9' CLG)

© Copyright by designer/architect

WOODSTONE

PLAN #651-011D-0076

1,975 total square feet of living area

Width: 52'-0" Depth: 58'-0"

The spacious great room boasts a fireplace, a media area and a vaulted ceiling

2 bedrooms, 2 baths, 3-car garage

Crawl space foundation

Price Code C

STEINHAUER

PLAN #651-028D-0030

1,856 total square feet of living area

Width: 58'-0" Depth: 68'-0"

The centrally located kitchen easily serves the formal dining room and informal breakfast area

4 bedrooms, 3 baths, 2-car side entry garage

Slab or crawl space foundation, please specify when ordering

Price Code C

EVERGLADE POINT

PLAN #651-047D-0210

2,041 total square feet of living area

Width: 60'-4" Depth: 56'-0"

The corner fireplace adds a cozy feel to the casual family room

Large round columns adorn the entries of the formal living and dining rooms

4 bedrooms, 2 baths, 2-car garage

Slab foundation

Price Code D

HARRAHILL

PLAN #651-055D-0031

2,133 total square feet of living area

Width: 58'-6" Depth: 64'-6"

The kitchen is designed for efficiency

3 bedrooms, 2 baths, 2-car side entry garage

Slab or crawl space foundation, please specify when ordering; basement and walk-out basement foundations available for an additional fee

Price Code C

houseplansandmore.com

PLAN FEATURES

4,299 total square feet of living area

Width: 105'-0" Depth: 69'-0"

A charming covered front porch greets guests as they enter the home

The enchanting foyer connects the dining room through arched openings and the living room/library with pocket transomed doors

Beautiful wood beams and trusses grace the open family room, breakfast area and the kitchen

The second floor bedrooms each have access to its own private bath

The future rooms above the garage have an additional 1,171 square feet of living area

4 bedrooms, 4 full baths, 2 half baths, 3-car side entry garage

Crawl space foundation

Price Code F

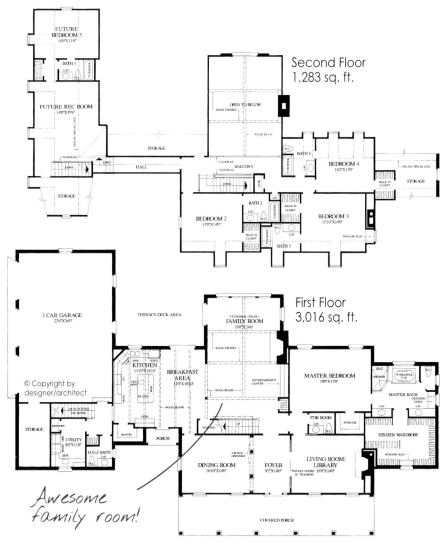

Second Floor
1,283 sq. ft.

First Floor
3,016 sq. ft.

© Copyright by designer/architect

Awesome family room!

houseplansandmore.com

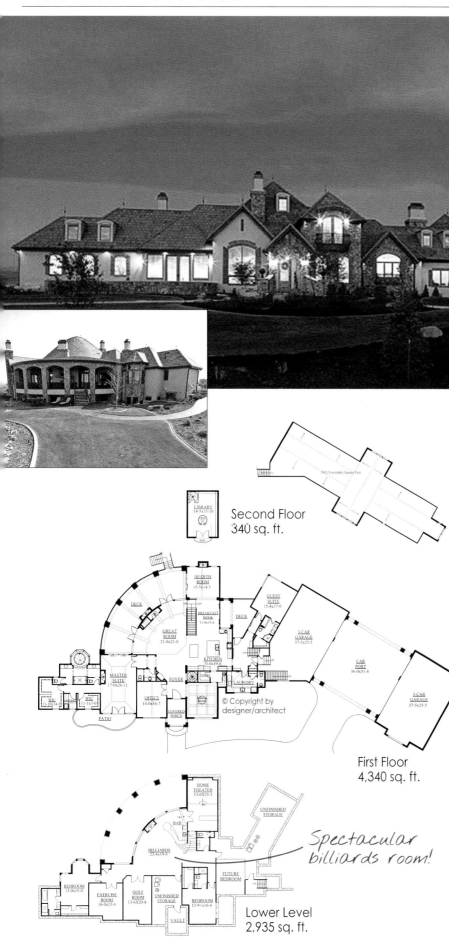

Second Floor
340 sq. ft.

First Floor
4,340 sq. ft.

Spectacular billiards room!

Lower Level
2,935 sq. ft.

PLANFEATURES

7,615 total square feet of living area

Width: 201'-6" Depth: 87'-0"

The amazing great room enjoys a fireplace and spans outward onto the spacious covered deck

An immense lower level boasts a billiards area with a bar, home theater and several extra rooms to fit the homeowner's needs

There is ample parking space with two separate 3-car garages and a carport

The large bonus room above the garage has an additional 1,921 square feet of living area

4 bedrooms, 4 full baths, 2 half baths, 6-car side entry garage and carport

Walk-out basement or basement foundation, please specify when ordering

Price Code S4

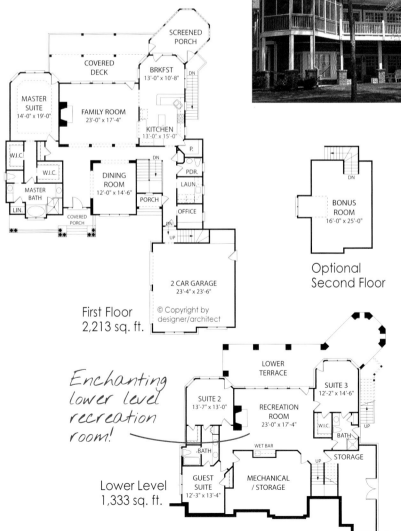

PLANFEATURES

3,546 total square feet of living area

Width: 67'-2" Depth: 93'-2"

The sunny breakfast room shares the eating bar with the kitchen and has access to the lovely screened porch

A warming fireplace and a wall of windows are featured in the family room

The recreation room on the lower level enjoys a fireplace and a wet bar

The bonus room on the second floor has an additional 430 square feet of living area

4 bedrooms, 3 1/2 baths, 2-car side entry garage

Walk-out basement foundation

Price Code S1

First Floor 2,213 sq. ft.

© Copyright by designer/architect

Optional Second Floor

Enchanting lower level recreation room!

Lower Level 1,333 sq. ft.

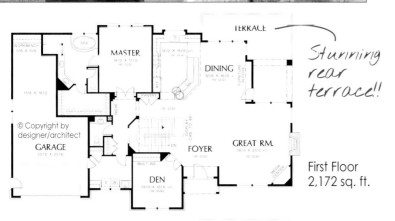

Stunning rear terrace!!

© Copyright by designer/architect

First Floor
2,172 sq. ft.

Lower Level
1,813 sq. ft.

PLANFEATURES

3,985 total square feet of living area

Width: 75'-0" Depth: 51'-0"

The impressive great room features a fireplace, a corner media center and flows into the open foyer and dining areas

A spa tub, double-bowl vanity and spacious walk-in closet are some of the amenities of the private master bath

The lower level is perfect for entertaining with the immense games room, wet bar and wine cellar

4 bedrooms, 3 1/2 baths, 3-car garage

Slab/walk-out basement foundation

Price Code S1

houseplansandmore.com

VALLEJO

PLAN #651-011D-0085

2,562 total square feet of living area

Width: 40'-0" Depth: 60'-0"

Energy efficient home with 2" x 6" exterior walls

The lower level enjoys a large games room with two additional bedrooms and a full bath

4 bedrooms, 3 baths, 2-car garage

Partial slab/walk-out basement foundation

Price Code E

CATALINA PLACE

PLAN #651-065D-0250

2,959 total square feet of living area

Width: 76'-0" Depth: 68'-1"

A beamed ceiling tops the great room and a fireplace with built-ins decorate one wall

3 bedrooms, 2 1/2 baths, 3-car side entry garage

Walk-out basement foundation

Price Code E

houseplansandmore.com

HILGARD

PLAN #651-055D-0532

1,933 total square feet of living area

Width: 37'-0" Depth: 74'-4"

Bedroom #2/study is a versatile space that can adapt to your family's needs

3 bedrooms, 2 baths, 2-car rear entry garage

Crawl space or slab foundation, please specify when ordering

Price Code C

CALVERT CREEK

PLAN #651-111D-0002

1,738 total square feet of living area

Width: 68'-0" Depth: 58'-4"

The fireplace becomes a natural barrier between the kitchen and living room

The second floor bonus room has an additional 337 square feet of living area

3 bedrooms, 2 baths, 2-car side entry garage

Basement, crawl space or slab foundation, please specify when ordering

Price Code B

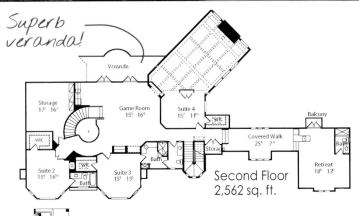

PLANFEATURES

6,457 total square feet of living area

Width: 143'-0" Depth: 86'-11"

Energy efficient home with 2" x 6" exterior walls

The gently sweeping staircase is the center jewel of this home, creating a beautiful view upon every entrance

The covered walk on both floors reveals private guest spaces, with the second floor including a charming balcony

In addition to the walk-in closets and spacious tub, the master bath includes a personal exercise area

6 bedrooms, 5 full baths, 2 half baths, 3-car side entry detached garage

Slab foundation

Price Code J

Superb veranda!

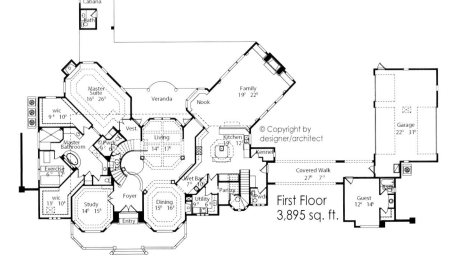

Second Floor
2,562 sq. ft.

First Floor
3,895 sq. ft.

© Copyright by designer/architect

PLAN FEATURES

1,710 total square feet of living area

Width: 28'-0" Depth: 32'-0"

Energy efficient home with 2" x 6" exterior walls

Clerestory windows brighten the second floor and living room below

The lower level recreation room includes a luxurious whirlpool tub and wet bar

A unique centered fireplace separates the dining and living rooms

3 bedrooms, 2 baths, 1-car drive under garage

Basement foundation

Price Code B

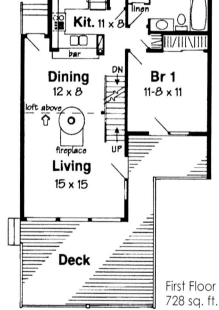

First Floor
728 sq. ft.

Kit. 11 x 8

linen

Dining
12 x 8

Br 1
11-8 x 11

loft above

fireplace

Living
15 x 15

DN

UP

Deck

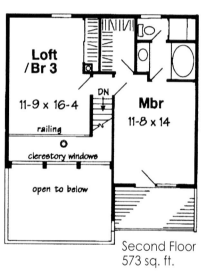

Second Floor
573 sq. ft.

Loft /Br 3
11-9 x 16-4

railing

clerestory windows

open to below

Mbr
11-8 x 14

DN

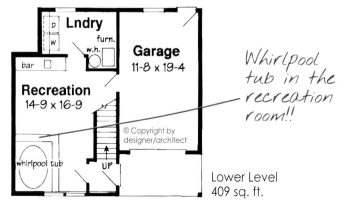

Lower Level
409 sq. ft.

Lndry

D
W

furn.

w.h.

bar

Recreation
14-9 x 16-9

Garage
11-8 x 19-4

whirlpool tub

UP

Whirlpool tub in the recreation room!!

© Copyright by designer/architect

PLAN #651-011D-0088

LINWORTH

2,837 total square feet of living area

Width: 96'-0" Depth: 51'-0"

Energy efficient home with 2" x 6" exterior walls

Dramatic decorative columns maintain an open and airy feel in the formal living and dining rooms

Both the casual family room and the formal living room enjoy the warmth of their own fireplaces

The cheerful breakfast nook leads to the open and sunny terrace

4 bedrooms, 2 1/2 baths, 3-car garage

Crawl space foundation

Price Code E

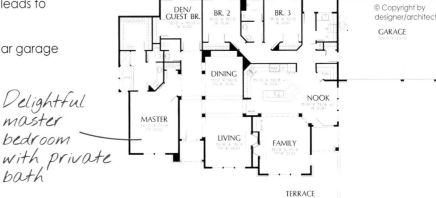

Delightful master bedroom with private bath

PLAN #651-011D-0094

LA SERENA

3,242 total square feet of living area

Width: 118'-0" Depth: 73'-9"

Energy efficient home with 2" x 6" exterior walls

The kitchen is lined with plenty of cabinets and counterspace plus there's a large center island with space for dining

A beautiful bow window adds elegance and sunlight to the great room

The den has a double-door entry, a closet for storage and a built-in counter

3 bedrooms, 2 1/2 baths, 3-car garage

Crawl space foundation

Price Code F

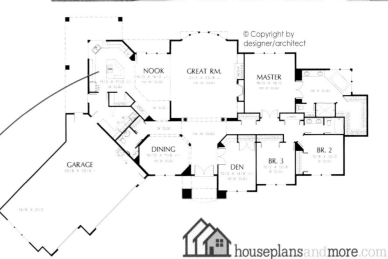

Extraordinary Kitchen!

PLANFEATURES

4,258 total square feet of living area

Width: 84'-8" Depth: 82'-4"

French doors lead into the private study that includes a separate computer area with a built-in desk

Soffits top the entryways to the formal dining room, the casual kitchen and the dinette

The lower level enjoys a massive recreation room with wet bar perfect for entertaining

4 bedrooms, 3 1/2 baths, 3-car side entry garage

Walk-out basement foundation

Price Code H

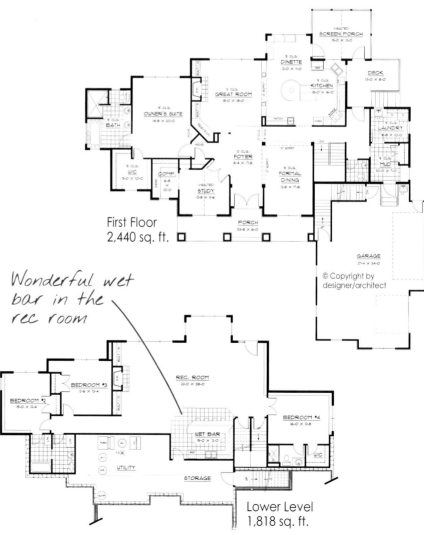

Wonderful wet bar in the rec room

Beautiful screen porch & rear deck

Second Floor
1,629 sq. ft.

First Floor
1,530 sq. ft.

© Copyright by designer/architect

PLANFEATURES

3,159 total square feet of living area

Width: 82'-0" Depth: 55'-0"

Energy efficient home with 2" x 6" exterior walls

An impressive master bath includes a spacious walk-in closet and built-in tub perfect for relaxing

The kitchen is open and efficient with a large, curved island for easy dining

The double-door entry to the study reveals a beautiful built-in work area and lovely windows for added light

4 bedrooms, 3 1/2 baths,
3-car garage

Basement foundation

Price Code F

houseplansandmore.com

PLANFEATURES

1,845 total square feet of living area

Width: 41'-4" Depth: 83'-8"

The master suite has privacy from the other bedrooms

The dining room is convenient to the kitchen and the great room

The breakfast room accesses an outdoor grilling porch

The optional bonus room has an additional 1,191 square feet of living area

3 bedrooms, 2 baths, 2-car rear entry garage

Crawl space or slab foundation, please specify when ordering; basement and walk-out basement foundations are available for an additional fee

Price Code C

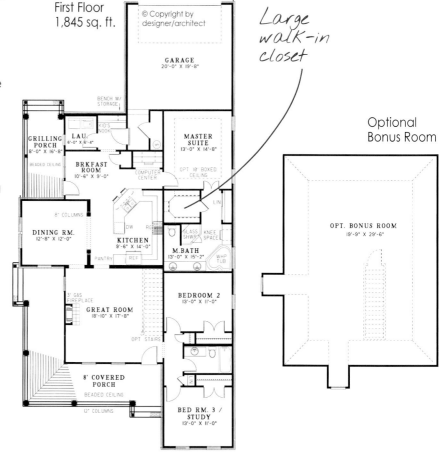

First Floor
1,845 sq. ft.

© Copyright by designer/architect

Large walk-in closet

Optional Bonus Room

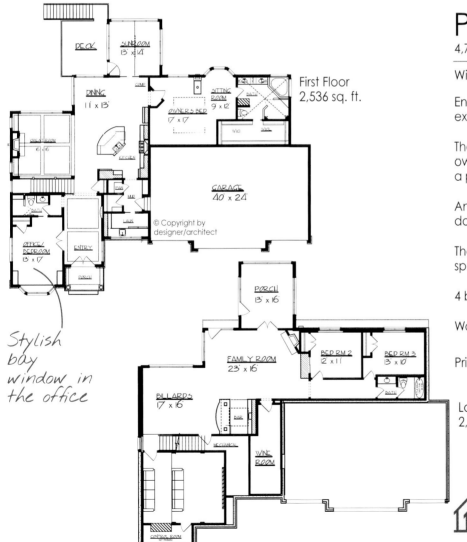

First Floor
2,536 sq. ft.

© Copyright by
designer/architect

Stylish bay window in the office

Lower Level
2,190 sq. ft.

PLANFEATURES

4,726 total square feet of living area

Width: 77'-0" Depth: 67'-0"

Energy efficient home with 2" x 6" exterior walls

The owner's bedroom features its own bath, a bayed sitting area and a peninsula style fireplace

An angled kitchen island contains a double sink and casual dining space

The lower level enjoys a billiards space ideal for entertaining

4 bedrooms, 3 baths, 4-car garage

Walk-out basement foundation

Price Code S1

houseplansandmore.com

PLANFEATURES

4,304 total square feet of living area

Width: 67'-2" Depth: 104'-2"

The kitchen boasts a large center island with an eating bar and flows into the breakfast area and sunroom

Two walk-in closets and a whirlpool tub sitting in a box-bay window are some of the amenities of the master bath

The lower level is perfect for entertaining guests with a large recreation room and spacious wet bar

The bonus room above the garage has an additional 686 square feet of living area

4 bedrooms, 3 1/2 baths,
3-car side entry garage

Walk-out basement foundation

Price Code S2

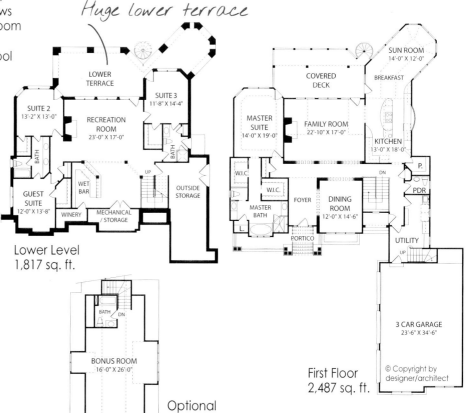

Huge lower terrace

Lower Level
1,817 sq. ft.

Optional Second Floor

First Floor
2,487 sq. ft.

© Copyright by designer/architect

PLANFEATURES

2,287 total square feet of living area

Width: 43'-0" Depth: 69'-0"

Energy efficient home with 2" x 6" exterior walls

The wrap-around porch creates an inviting feeling

The first floor windows have transom windows above

The den has a see-through fireplace into the family area

3 bedrooms, 2 1/2 baths, 2-car side entry garage

Crawl space foundation

Price Code E

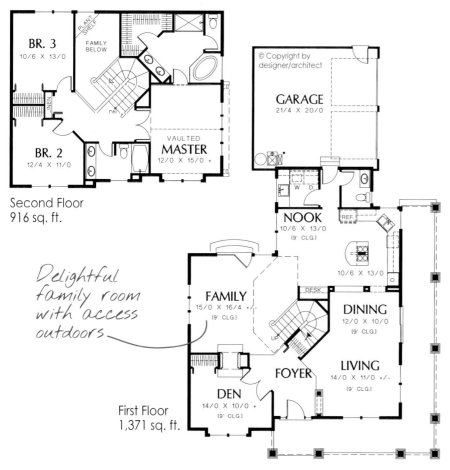

Second Floor
916 sq. ft.

Delightful family room with access outdoors

First Floor
1,371 sq. ft.

WESTOVER PARK

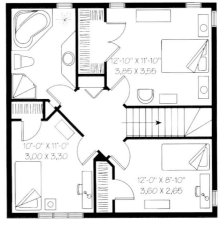

PLANFEATURES

1,432 total square feet of living area

Width: 38'-8" Depth: 32'-0"

Energy efficient home with 2" x 6" exterior walls

The comfortable family room is an easy place to relax with family or entertain friends

A snack bar in the kitchen makes quick meals a breeze and provides space for buffet-style dinners

The garage has separate access to the basement

3 bedrooms, 2 baths, 1-car garage

Basement foundation

Price Code D

Welcoming front porch

Second Floor
676 sq. ft.

12'-10" X 11'-10"
3,85 X 3,55

10'-0" X 11'-0"
3,00 X 3,30

12'-0" X 8'-10"
3,60 X 2,65

14'-4" X 10'-10"
4,30 X 3,25

10'-4" X 11'-10"
3,10 X 3,55

12'-0" X 24'-8"
3,60 X 7,40

12'-0" X 15'-2"
3,60 X 4,55

© Copyright by designer/architect

First Floor
756 sq. ft.

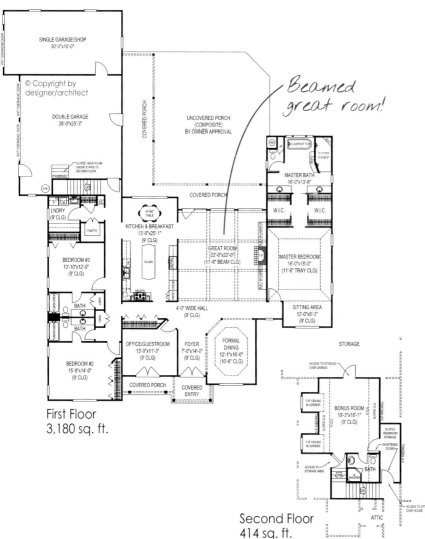

Beamed great room!

First Floor
3,180 sq. ft.

Second Floor
414 sq. ft.

PLANFEATURES

3,594 total square feet of living area

Width: 83'-6" Depth: 96'-6"

The master bedroom, secluded from the other bedrooms, has a tray ceiling, cozy sitting area and two walk-in closets

A workshop area in the garage is perfect for hobbies or storage of equipment

There is ample porch space at the rear of the home as well as a covered porch entry

4 bedrooms, 4 baths, 2-car and 1-car side entry garages

Slab foundation

Price Code S1

houseplansandmore.com

FOXRIDGE

PLAN #651-007D-0136

1,532 total square feet of living area

Width: 71'-8" Depth: 38'-0"

The optional lower level has an additional 740 square feet of living area

3 bedrooms, 2 baths, 2-car garage

Walk-out basement foundation

Price Code B

JILLIAN

PLAN #651-121D-0005

1,562 total square feet of living area

Width: 65'-0" Depth: 46'-4"

All of the bedrooms are located near each other for convenient family living

3 bedrooms, 2 baths, 2-car garage

Basement foundation

Price Code A

houseplansandmore.com

KAITLYN

PLAN #651-121D-0003

2,215 total square feet of living area

Width: 91'-10" Depth: 52'-6"

The open and spacious kitchen is outfitted with a large wrap-around counter with enough casual dining space for five people

3 bedrooms, 2 1/2 baths, 2-car garage

Basement foundation

Price Code C

ANGELINA

PLAN #651-121D-0012

1,281 total square feet of living area

Width: 37'-6" Depth: 52'-0"

The well-appointed kitchen enjoys an angled raised counter perfect for casual dining

The vaulted master bedroom enjoys a sizable walk-in closet and its own private bath

3 bedrooms, 2 baths, 2-car garage

Basement foundation

Price Code AA

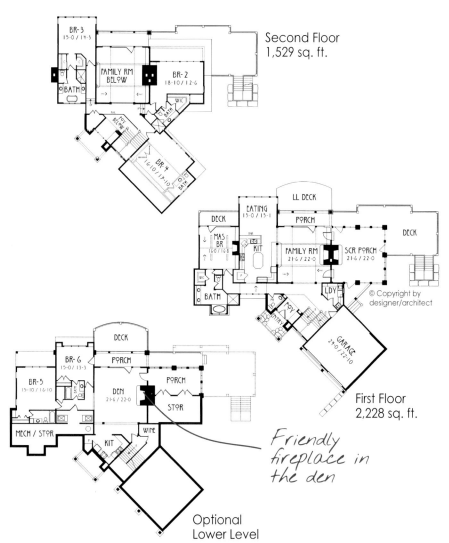

Second Floor
1,529 sq. ft.

First Floor
2,228 sq. ft.

Friendly fireplace in the den

Optional
Lower Level

© Copyright by designer/architect

PLANFEATURES

3,757 total square feet of living area

Width: 79'-5" Depth: 63'-7"

Step inside this magnificent home to find multiple windows, a see-through fireplace that connects the family room and screened porch, and a luxurious master bedroom

The second floor houses three additional bedroom suites

A den, second kitchen and two more bedrooms are offered on the optional lower level with 1,475 additional square feet

4 bedrooms, 4 1/2 baths, 2-car garage

Basement or walk-out basement foundation, please specify when ordering

Price Code S6

houseplansandmore.com

PLANFEATURES

2,800 total square feet of living area

Width: 84'-0" Depth: 63'-2"

Energy efficient home with 2" x 6" exterior walls

The open and airy great room boasts a vaulted ceiling, a gas fireplace and double-door access to the rear covered porch

The breakfast room is brightened by multiple windows and opens to the kitchen and great room

Located in the rear of the home is the master bedroom with a private master bath and spacious walk-in closet

4 bedrooms, 3 1/2 baths, 3-car side entry garage

Slab or crawl space foundation, please specify when ordering

Price Code F

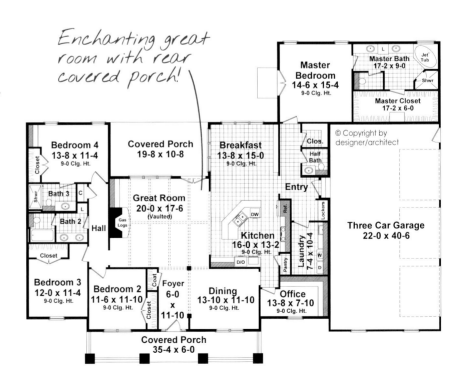

Enchanting great room with rear covered porch!

© Copyright by designer/architect

PLANFEATURES

3,682 total square feet of living area

Width: 65'-0" Depth: 58'-0"

The kitchen boasts a large center island with eating bar that is perfect for casual gatherings

Double-doors open to the den with built-ins on one wall that would be excellent for a home office

The games room on the lower level enjoys a corner fireplace, wet bar and access to the patio

4 bedrooms, 4 baths, 3-car garage

Partial crawl space/walk-out basement foundation

Price Code S1

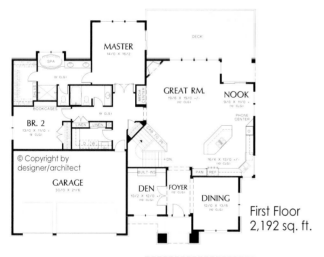

First Floor
2,192 sq. ft.

Lower Level
1,490 sq. ft.

Stunning games room with a fireplace!

houseplansandmore.com

PLANFEATURES

2,241 total square feet of living area

Width: 68'-4" Depth: 56'-0"

11' ceilings in the entry, great room, kitchen and dining room for added spaciousness

Joining the kitchen and great room is a unique see-through fireplace with convenient built-in shelving units on both sides

The kitchen features an amazing amount of dining space including a large island with breakfast table extension that has enough space for seven people

4 bedrooms, 2 1/2 baths, 2-car side entry garage

Basement foundation

Price Code C

Charming master bedroom with bay window

Floor plan labels:
- Patio
- Kitchen 15-4x18-4, 11' Clg
- Dining 12-2x16-4, 11' Clg
- Brkfst Area
- MBr 15-1x17-4, Coffer Clg
- Br 3 13-8x11-0
- Br 4/ Study 12-0x10-0
- Laun/ Mud Rm
- Dn
- Great Rm 20-1x16-11, 11' Clg
- Entry
- Br 2 13-8x11-6
- Garage 23-4x25-4
- Porch

SUMMERSET

PLAN #651-007D-0055

2,029 total square feet of living area

Width: 67'-0" Depth: 51'-4"

2" x 6" exterior walls available, please order plan #651-007E-0055

3 bedrooms, 2 baths, 2-car side entry garage

Basement foundation, drawings also include crawl space and slab foundations

Price Code D

ZOEY

PLAN #651-121D-0023

1,762 total square feet of living area

Width: 41'-0" Depth: 60'-4"

The vaulted great room boasts a warming corner fireplace and flows into the vaulted dining area

An island with eating bar in the kitchen is a perfect gathering spot for casual meals

3 bedrooms, 2 baths, 2-car garage

Basement foundation

Price Code A

SPRINGFALL

PLAN #651-011D-0013

2,001 total square feet of living area

Width: 60'-0" Depth: 50'-0"

Energy efficient home with 2" x 6" exterior walls

The large wrap-around counter in the kitchen is accessible from the dining area

3 bedrooms, 2 baths, 3-car garage

Crawl space foundation

Price Code D

HANNAH

PLAN #651-121D-0029

1,366 total square feet of living area

Width: 40'-0" Depth: 55'-4"

The efficiently designed kitchen enjoys a sunny box-bay window and a convenient eating bar

2 bedrooms, 2 baths, 2-car garage

Basement foundation

Price Code AA

houseplansandmore.com

WRIGLEY

PLANFEATURES

2,157 total square feet of living area

Width: 54'-0" Depth: 46'-0"

Energy efficient home with 2" x 6" exterior walls

The dining room opens into a formal living room perfect for entertaining

The family/hearth room connects to the breakfast area with a beautiful see-through fireplace

The laundry facilities are conveniently located but tucked out of the way

3 bedrooms, 2 1/2 baths, 2-car garage

Basement, crawl space or slab foundation, please specify when ordering

Price Code D

First Floor
1,590 sq. ft.

Deck

Kit
10 x 13-10

Brkfst
9 x 11-8

MBr 1
13 x 15-4
decor. ceiling

Dining Rm
12 x 12-10

11'-0" ceil. height

Living Rm
12 x 19-4

Family/
Hearth Rm
12-10 x 15-4

Ldry
W D

Foyer

Garage
20-4 x 21-8

© Copyright by designer/architect

Second Floor
567 sq. ft.

Br 3
10-4 x 11

Br 2
12-8 x 10

Loft/
Media Rm
10 x 12-8

open to below

Practical loft/media room

PLANFEATURES

5,322 total square feet of living area

Width: 86'-0" Depth: 74'-10"

A large vaulted great room flows into an open kitchen where one can enjoy treats at the center eating island

Walk through the double-doors into the beautiful vaulted sunroom perfect for enjoying the nice weather

The lower level features a large recreation room and attached screen porch that is perfect for those gatherings that include indoor and outdoor activities

5 bedrooms, 5 1/2 baths, 3-car side entry garage

Walk-out basement foundation

Price Code S1

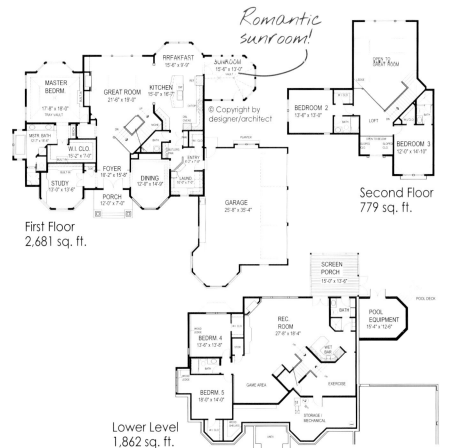

Romantic sunroom!

First Floor
2,681 sq. ft.

Second Floor
779 sq. ft.

Lower Level
1,862 sq. ft.

© Copyright by designer/architect

houseplansandmore.com

PLANFEATURES

3,701 total square feet of living area

Width: 112'-10" Depth: 69'-3"

Energy efficient home with 2" x 6" exterior walls

The magnificent box-bay windows along with the covered porch give this home exceptional detail

French doors throughout the home create a delightful atmosphere

A unique kitchen provides a large cooktop island with snack bar for entertaining

3 bedrooms, 2 1/2 baths, 3-car rear entry garage

Crawl space foundation

Price Code F

Spectacular living room with fireplace!

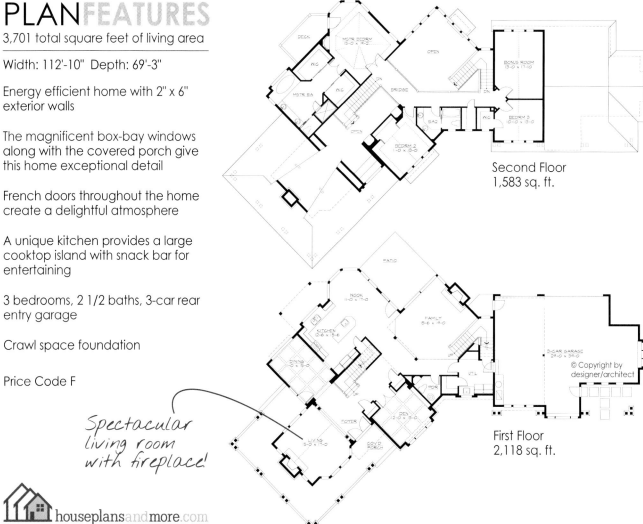

Second Floor
1,583 sq. ft.

First Floor
2,118 sq. ft.

© Copyright by designer/architect

PLANFEATURES

2,780 total square feet of living area

Width: 48'-0" Depth: 111'-0"

The covered rear porch is a delight in every season with a corner fireplace for added warmth

The living and dining rooms combine offering one large gathering space that is both beautiful and functional

In addition to the utility room is a handy mud room with plenty of storage space

The optional second floor has an additional 897 square feet of living area

3 bedrooms, 3 baths, 2-car rear entry garage

Floating slab foundation

Price Code K

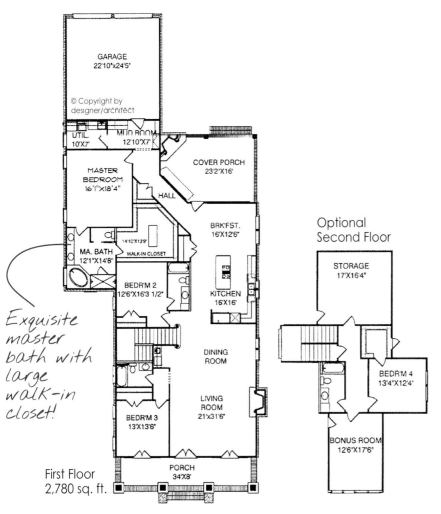

GARAGE 22'10"x24'5"

© Copyright by designer/architect

UTIL. 10'X7'

MUD ROOM 12'10"X7'

MASTER BEDROOM 16'1"X18'4"

HALL

COVER PORCH 23'2'X16'

BRK'FST. 16'X12'6'

14'10"X13'9"
WALK-IN CLOSET

MA. BATH 12'1"X14'8'

KITCHEN 16'X16'

BEDR'M 2 12'6"X16'3 1/2"

Exquisite master bath with large walk-in closet!

DINING ROOM

LIVING ROOM 21'X31'6'

BEDR'M 3 13'X13'6'

First Floor 2,780 sq. ft.

PORCH 34'X8'

Optional Second Floor

STORAGE 17'X16'4'

BEDR'M 4 13'4"X12'4'

BONUS ROOM 12'6"X17'6'

houseplansandmore.com

PLANFEATURES

2,367 total square feet of living area

Width: 45'-0" Depth: 48'-0"

The loft/bedroom 4 is a great versatile space ideal for additional bedroom space or a home office

An open floor plan reigns on the first floor with the vaulted family room and nook open to the kitchen

A private first floor master bedroom has its own bath and walk-in closet

4 bedrooms, 2 1/2 baths, 2-car garage

Crawl space foundation

Price Code D

Combined dining & living room with decorative column

BR. 2
12/2 X 12/6

OPEN TO BELOW

DN

LOFT/BR. 4
13/10 X 17/0

ATTIC STORAGE

LIN

BR. 3
12/8 X 10/8

ATTIC STORAGE

Second Floor
788 sq. ft.

VAULTED
NOOK
9/6 X 10/0

VAULTED
FAMILY
19/0 X 16/2

MASTER
15/2 X 12/2
(9' CLG)

NICHE

REF PAN

D W

DINING
12/0 X 10/0
(9' CLG)

GARAGE
20/8 X 20/8

LIVING
12/0 X 14/0
(11' CLG)

© Copyright by designer/architect

First Floor
1,579 sq. ft.

PLAN #651-007D-0001

OSBORNE

2,597 total square feet of living area

Width: 61'-8" Depth: 54'-4"

The large U-shaped kitchen features an island cooktop and breakfast bar

The entry and great room are enhanced by a sweeping balcony

Bedrooms #2 and #3 share a bath, while bedroom #4 has a private bath

The vaulted great room includes transomed arch windows

2" x 6" exterior walls available, please order plan #651-007E-0001

4 bedrooms, 3 1/2 baths, 2-car side entry garage

Walk-out basement foundation, drawings also include crawl space and slab foundations

Price Code E

Lovely screened porch

First Floor
1,742 sq. ft.

Second Floor
855 sq. ft.

PLAN #651-011D-0020

HAYDEN

2,304 total square feet of living area

Width: 40'-0" Depth: 52'-0"

Energy efficient home with 2" x 6" exterior walls

The private study is furnished with built-in storage

Impressive columns define the dining room

The master suite has a vaulted ceiling, and a private bath with a corner tub

The bonus room on the second floor is included in the square footage

3 bedrooms, 2 1/2 baths, 3-car garage

Crawl space foundation

Price Code D

Inviting study

First Floor
1,082 sq. ft.

Second Floor
1,222 sq. ft.

houseplansandmore.com

ELMBROOK

PLAN#651-053D-0014

PLANFEATURES

2,195 total square feet of living area

Width: 40'-0" Depth: 32'-0"

The striking facade is created by a gracious two-story window treatment

Bay windows add light and space throughout this home

The open family and kitchen/breakfast area exits onto the spacious rear deck

4 bedrooms, 2 1/2 baths, 2-car drive under side entry garage

Basement foundation, drawings also include walk-out basement foundation

Price Code A

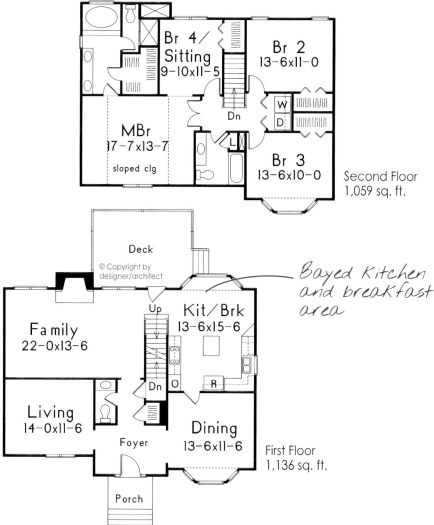

Br 4/ Sitting
9-10x11-5

Br 2
13-6x11-0

MBr
17-7x13-7

sloped clg

Dn

W
D

L

Br 3
13-6x10-0

Second Floor
1,059 sq. ft.

Deck

© Copyright by designer/architect

Bayed Kitchen and breakfast area

Up

Kit/Brk
13-6x15-6

Family
22-0x13-6

Dn

O

R

Living
14-0x11-6

Dn

Dining
13-6x11-6

Foyer

Porch

First Floor
1,136 sq. ft.

ELMBROOK
houseplansandmore.com

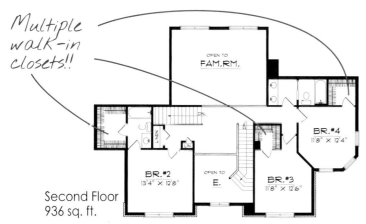

Multiple walk-in closets!!

Second Floor 936 sq. ft.

OPEN TO FAM.RM.

BR. #4
11'8" × 12'4"

BR. #2
13'4" × 12'8"

OPEN TO E.

BR. #3
11'8" × 12'6"

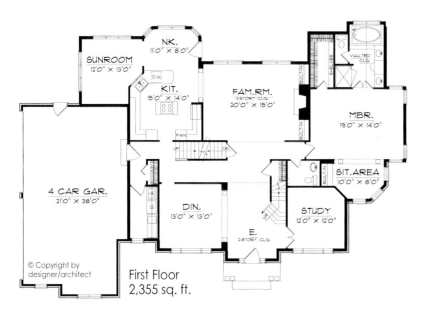

First Floor 2,355 sq. ft.

NK.
11'0" × 8'0"

SUNROOM
12'0" × 13'0"

KIT.
15'0" × 14'0"

FAM.RM.
2-STORY CLG.
20'0" × 15'0"

VAULTED CLG.

MBR.
19'0" × 14'0"

4 CAR GAR.
21'0" × 38'0"

DIN.
13'0" × 13'0"

SIT. AREA
10'0" × 8'0"

STUDY
12'0" × 12'0"

E.
2-STORY CLG.

© Copyright by designer/architect

PLANFEATURES

3,291 total square feet of living area

Width: 79'-0" Depth: 55'-0"

Energy efficient home with 2" x 6" exterior walls

The two-story family room boasts a grand fireplace flanked by built-in shelves

The sunroom creates a warm and cheerful atmosphere and connects with the bayed nook and kitchen

The elegant master bedroom features a bayed sitting area and double-door entry to the deluxe bath with vaulted ceiling

All of the secondary bedrooms enjoy walk-in closets

4 bedrooms, 3 1/2 baths, 4-car side entry garage

Basement foundation

Price Code S1

houseplansandmore.com

PLANFEATURES

1,873 total square feet of living area

Width: 44'-0" Depth: 44'-0"

Energy efficient home with 2" x 6" exterior walls

This stylish home fits perfectly on a narrow lot

The vaulted, two-story living room greets guests and offers a dramatic first impression

The kitchen, bayed dining room and family room combine for an easy flow of household activities

3 bedrooms, 2 1/2 baths, 2-car garage

Basement foundation

Price Code D

Second Floor
819 sq. ft.

MBR.
12'8" x 16'0"

BR.#2
12'4" x 11'0"

OPEN TO LIV.

BR.#3
11'4" x 12'0"

PLANT LEDGE

First Floor
1,054 sq. ft.

FAM.RM.
16'8" x 14'0"

DIN.
11'0" x 13'4"

KIT.
11'0" x 11'0"

SHELVES

LIV.
VAULTED CEILING
16'8" x 15'8"

2 CAR GAR.
21'8" x 23'4"

E.

Lovely laundry room with closet

© Copyright by designer/architect

houseplansandmore.com

PLANFEATURES

5,474 total square feet of living area

Width: 94'-0" Depth: 71'-0"

Upon entry guests are greeted by the stunning curved staircase

Two stories of verandas offer an abundance of outdoor living area as well as adding grand curb appeal

Three fireplaces warm this home and decorate the family room, den and sprawling master suite

4 bedrooms, 4 full baths, 2 half baths, 3-car side entry garage

Slab foundation

Price Code S2

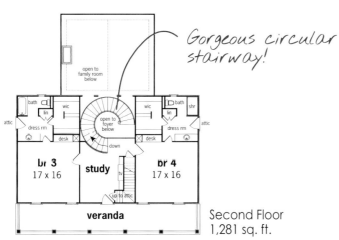

Gorgeous circular stairway!

Second Floor
1,281 sq. ft.

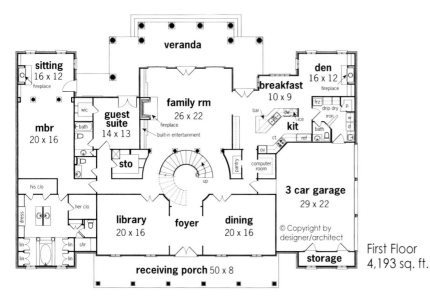

First Floor
4,193 sq. ft.

© Copyright by designer/architect

SHERIDAN MILL

PLAN #651-011D-0070

1,852 total square feet of living area

Width: 70'-0" Depth: 45'-0"

A very spacious great room is warmed by a fireplace and has a built-in shelf for a television

3 bedrooms, 2 baths, 3-car garage

Crawl space foundation

Price Code C

DELMAR

PLAN #651-053D-0037

1,388 total square feet of living area

Width: 48'-0" Depth: 48'-0"

The kitchen, breakfast and family rooms have vaulted ceilings, adding spaciousness to this central living area

3 bedrooms, 2 baths, 2-car garage

Crawl space foundation, drawings also include slab foundation

Price Code A

CHLEMSFORD TRAIL

PLAN #651-055D-0030

2,107 total square feet of living area

Width: 64'-8" Depth: 62'-1"

4 bedrooms, 2 1/2 baths, 2-car garage

Slab or crawl space foundation, please specify when ordering; basement and walk-out basement foundations available for an additional fee

Price Code D

VALENTINA MANOR

PLAN #651-129S-0015

7,017 total square feet of living area

Width: 75'-5" Depth: 76'-4"

The amazing two-story grand room boasts a fireplace and multiple windows to provide plenty of light

A convenient elevator can be used to access every floor easily

5 bedrooms, 5 1/2 baths, 3-car side entry garage

Walk-out basement foundation

Price Code S3

houseplansandmore.com

Bonus room above the garage perfect for entertaining!

BEDROOM 4
14'9" x 13'0"

OPEN BELOW

MECHANICAL/
STORAGE
7'5" x 8'8"

BEDROOM 3
14'9" x 13'0"

OPEN BELOW

BEDROOM 2
14'9" x 15'5"

LINEN

BONUS ROOM
11'9" x 32'1"

Second Floor
986 sq. ft.

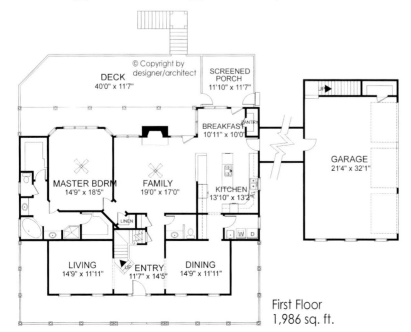

DECK
40'0" x 11'7"

© Copyright by
designer/architect

SCREENED PORCH
11'10" x 11'7"

BREAKFAST
10'11" x 10'0"

PANTRY

GARAGE
21'4" x 32'1"

MASTER BDRM
14'9" x 18'5"

FAMILY
19'0" x 17'0"

KITCHEN
13'10" x 13'2"

LINEN

W D

LIVING
14'9" x 11'11"

ENTRY
11'7" x 14'5"

DINING
14'9" x 11'11"

First Floor
1,986 sq. ft.

PLANFEATURES

2,972 total square feet of living area

Width: 93'-10" Depth: 61'-2"

Extra storage is available beyond bedroom #2 on the second floor

An angled staircase in the entry adds interest

A charming screened porch is accessible from the breakfast area

The bonus room above the garage has an additional 396 square feet of living area

4 bedrooms, 3 1/2 baths, 3-car side entry garage

Walk-out basement, crawl space or slab foundation, please specify when ordering

Price Code E

houseplansandmore.com

MERCEDES

PLANFEATURES

3,276 total square feet of living area

Width: 69'-0" Depth: 55'-6"

Skylights in the hip-vault ceiling let in extra light in the dining and living rooms

The octagon-shaped screened porch provides a panoramic view of the backyard

The kitchen has a bar with seating facing the dinette

The master bath has a corner whirlpool tub with windows overlooking the backyard

4 bedrooms, 2 1/2 baths, 2-car garage

Walk-out basement foundation

Price Code G

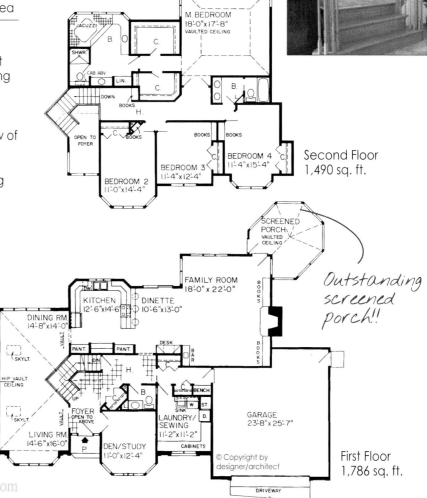

Second Floor
1,490 sq. ft.

Outstanding screened porch!!

First Floor
1,786 sq. ft.

houseplansandmore.com

PLAN #651-072D-1108

GREEN ORCHARD

2,445 total square feet of living area

Width: 64'-0" Depth: 60'-0"

Enjoy the spacious great room featuring a beautiful fireplace that creates a dramatic ambiance adding character and flair to this home

The efficient kitchen is quite charming and contains a breakfast island

The attractive sunroom provides a lovely space for relaxing

The theater on the lower level is 336 square feet and is included in the total square footage

The future finished space on the lower level features an additional 1,381 square feet of living area

2 bedrooms, 2 baths, 3-car garage

Walk-out basement foundation

Price Code B

Attractive lower level

Lower Level
336 sq. ft.

© Copyright by designer/architect

First Floor
2,109 sq. ft.

PLAN #651-080D-0008

PYRENEES

1,644 total square feet of living area

Width: 36'-0" Depth: 50'-6"

Energy efficient home with 2" x 6" exterior walls

A highly versatile great room with a wrap-around covered porch encourages relaxed entertaining and is perfectly suited for evolving family activities

The large U-shaped kitchen with raised breakfast bar is open to the great room ensuring that everyone is included in the fun

The second floor vaulted studio has a private covered balcony and easily transforms this space into a home office

2 bedrooms, 2 baths

Crawl space foundation

Price Code B

Stunning deck space!!

First Floor
955 sq. ft.

© Copyright by designer/architect

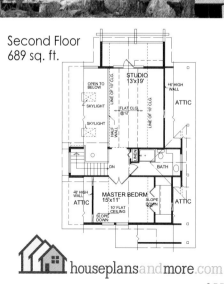

Second Floor
689 sq. ft.

houseplansandmore.com

PLAN FEATURES

2,738 total square feet of living area

Width: 63'-4" Depth: 48'-0"

An open entrance offers a spectacular view of the windowed rear wall and fireplace in the great room

The kitchen, breakfast and hearth rooms combine to offer an open and comfortable gathering place

The master bedroom is topped with an 11' ceiling and features a sitting alcove and deluxe bath

4 bedrooms, 3 1/2 baths, 2-car side entry garage

Basement foundation

Price Code E

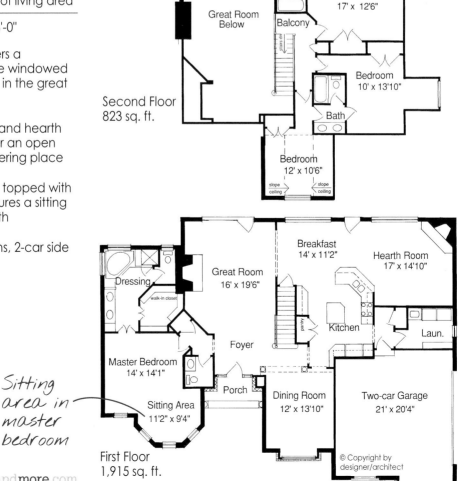

Second Floor
823 sq. ft.

Great Room Below

Balcony

Bedroom
17' x 12'6"

Bedroom
10' x 13'10"

Bath

Bedroom
12' x 10'6"

slope ceiling   slope ceiling

Breakfast
14' x 11'2"

Hearth Room
17' x 14'10"

Great Room
16' x 19'6"

Dressing

walk-in closet

Kitchen

pantry

Laun.

Foyer

Master Bedroom
14' x 14'1"

Sitting area in master bedroom

Sitting Area
11'2" x 9'4"

Porch

Dining Room
12' x 13'10"

Two-car Garage
21' x 20'4"

First Floor
1,915 sq. ft.

© Copyright by designer/architect

houseplansandmore.com

PLANFEATURES

3,339 total square feet of living area

Width: 74'-0" Depth: 64'-6"

An amazing two-story great room enjoys multiple windows and a warming fireplace

The efficient kitchen has an island with eating bar and is open to the casual dining area

The master bedroom is located on the first floor with a private bath that includes a double vanity, whirlpool tub and a large walk-in closet

4 bedrooms, 3 1/2 baths, 2-car side entry garage, 1-car garage

Basement foundation

Price Code G

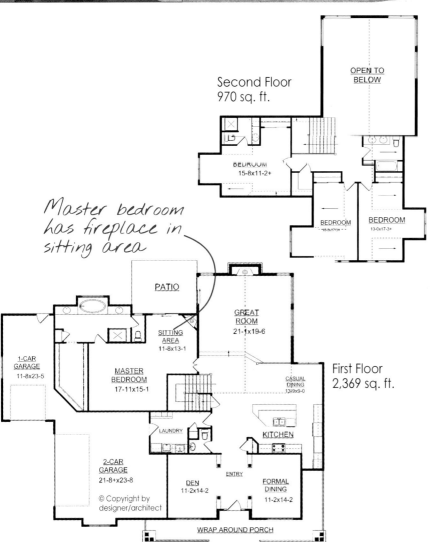

Second Floor
970 sq. ft.

Master bedroom has fireplace in sitting area

First Floor
2,369 sq. ft.

© Copyright by designer/architect

houseplansandmore.com

SAGAMORE

2,421 total square feet of living area

Width: 65'-2" Depth: 54'-0"

The charming courtyard on the side of the home easily accesses the porch leading into the breakfast area

French doors throughout the home create a sunny atmosphere

The master bedroom accesses a covered porch

4 bedrooms, 2 baths, optional 2-car detached garage

Crawl space or slab foundation, please specify when ordering

Price Code D

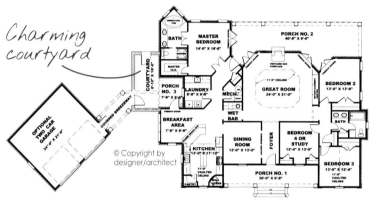

Charming courtyard

© Copyright by designer/architect

HARBINE

2,172 total square feet of living area

Width: 62'-0" Depth: 76'-0"

The fully-equipped kitchen contains a cooktop island, a walk-in pantry, a snack bar and a view out the breakfast area windows

The great room creates a cozy atmosphere with a tray ceiling, a fireplace and French door leading onto the rear covered porch

The secondary bedrooms all have walk-in closets and share a full bath

A luxury bath featuring a corner whirlpool tub, walk-in closet and double-bowl vanity graces the master bedroom

4 bedrooms, 2 baths, 2-car side entry garage

Slab or crawl space foundation, please specify when ordering

Price Code D

Spacious walk-in closet in the master bath

© Copyright by designer/architect

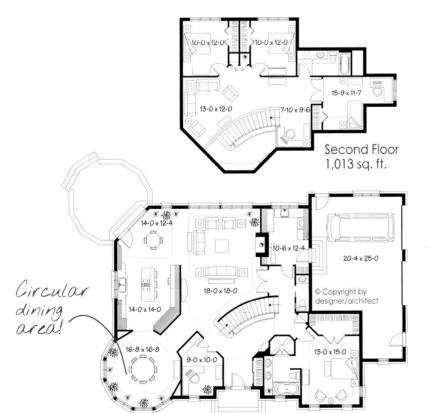

Second Floor
1,013 sq. ft.

Circular dining area!

© Copyright by designer/architect

First Floor
2,165 sq. ft.

PLANFEATURES

3,178 total square feet of living area

Width: 68'-4" Depth: 48'-0"

Energy efficient home with 2" x 6" exterior walls

The second floor has a spacious casual room that is great for entertaining guests or relaxing as a family

The master bedroom is located on the first floor and includes a private bath with double-bowl vanity and a walk-in closet

The giant kitchen has an oversized island/breakfast bar that is both great for preparing food and eating on the go

4 bedrooms, 2 1/2 baths, 2-car side entry garage

Basement foundation

Price Code H

houseplansandmore.com

CHARLESTON PLACE

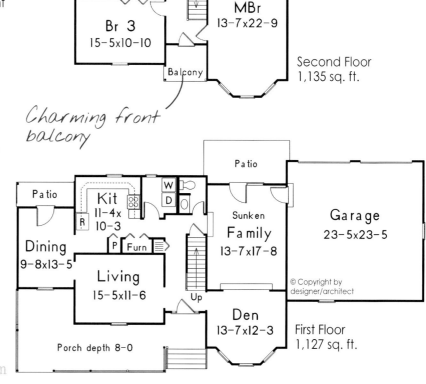

PLAN FEATURES

2,262 total square feet of living area

Width: 70'-10" Depth: 36'-0"

Energy efficient home with 2" x 6" exterior walls

Charming exterior features include a large front porch, two patios, a front balcony and double bay windows

The den provides an impressive entry to the sunken family room

The large master bedroom has a walk-in closet, dressing area and bath

3 bedrooms, 2 1/2 baths, 2-car rear entry garage

Crawl space foundation, drawings also include basement and slab foundations

Price Code D

Br 2
15-2x11-3

Br 3
15-5x10-10

MBr
13-7x22-9

Dn

Balcony

Second Floor
1,135 sq. ft.

Charming front balcony

Patio

Kit
11-4x
10-3

W
D

Dining
9-8x13-5

P Furn

Living
15-5x11-6

Sunken
Family
13-7x17-8

Garage
23-5x23-5

Up

Den
13-7x12-3

Porch depth 8-0

© Copyright by designer/architect

First Floor
1,127 sq. ft.

houseplansandmore.com

PLANFEATURES

5,250 total square feet of living area

Width: 71'-0" Depth: 91'-6"

Energy efficient home with 2" x 6" exterior walls

The spacious wrap-around covered porch features an outdoor fireplace and built-in barbecue grill perfect for entertaining

Each bedroom has its own bath and walk-in closet

The dramatic circular staircase is highlighted in the rotunda with a 27' ceiling

The master bath showcases an octagon-shaped space featuring a whirlpool tub

4 bedrooms, 4 1/2 baths, 4-car side entry garage

Crawl space foundation

Price Code H

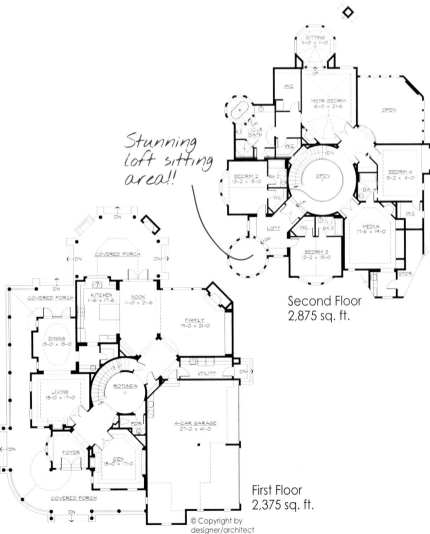

Stunning loft sitting area!!

Second Floor
2,875 sq. ft.

First Floor
2,375 sq. ft.

© Copyright by designer/architect

houseplansandmore.com

ALANA

PLANFEATURES

2,443 total square feet of living area

Width: 55'-10" Depth: 63'-6"

An impressive two-story family room has a fireplace with flanking shelves and double-door access to the rear patio

The sunny breakfast area sits in a bay window just steps away from the convenient eating bar

A large walk-in closet, private bath and access to the rear patio are some of the amenities of the master suite

The bonus room on the second floor has an additional 260 square feet of living area

3 bedrooms, 3 1/2 baths, 2-car side entry garage

Crawl space foundation

Price Code G

Generous rear patio perfect for entertaining!!

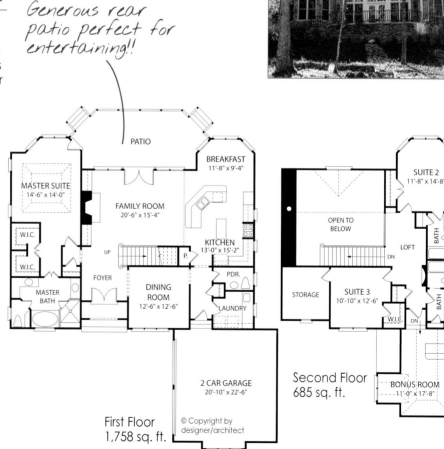

First Floor
1,758 sq. ft.

Second Floor
685 sq. ft.

© Copyright by designer/architect

PLANFEATURES

3,487 total square feet of living area

Width: 62'-7" Depth: 81'-3"

The great room continues the circular pattern and shares a see-through gas fireplace with the neighboring den

The open kitchen and dining room make entertaining a breeze

The barbecue deck and screen porch off the back give this home even more intriguing appeal

The second floor bonus room has an additional 425 square feet of living area

The optional finished lower level has an additional 1,202 square feet of living area

4 bedrooms, 3 1/2 baths, 3-car side entry garage

Walk-out basement foundation

Price Code S1

Second Floor
1,924 sq. ft.

- MSTR. BATH 11'-0" x 10'-0"
- BEDROOM 3 11'-1" x 11'-1"
- W.I. CLO. 9'-0" x 8'-0"
- W.I. CLO. 11'-5" x 5'-0"
- BATH
- BEDROOM 4 12'-0" x 14'-4"
- W.I. CLO.
- MASTER BEDROOM 18'-11" x 10'-0"
- LAUNDRY 11'-1" x 7'-0"
- BONUS ROOM 22'-11" x 20'-4"
- W.I. CLO.
- BEDROOM 2 12'-2" x 11'-8"
- BATH

Lovely screen porch

Optional Lower Level

- SCREEN PORCH ABOVE
- DECK ABOVE
- GAME ROOM 18'-5" x 15'-1"
- MECHANICAL
- MEDIA / REC. ROOM 24'-9" x 17'-4"
- WET BAR
- UNEXCAVATED
- WINE
- BEDROOM 5 11'-9" x 11'-6"
- BATH
- UNEXCAVATED

First Floor
1,563 sq. ft.

© Copyright by designer/architect

- SCREEN PORCH 12'-0" x 15'-5"
- BBQ. DECK 12'-8" x 7'-6"
- DECK 12'-9" x 16'-6"
- DINING ROOM 12'-2" x 15'-5"
- KITCHEN 14'-0" x 19'-6"
- MUDROOM
- W.I. CLO.
- GARAGE 23'-0" x 44'-2"
- BATH
- W.I. CLO.
- GREAT ROOM 18'-10" x 17'-4"
- SEE-THRU GAS FIREPLACE
- FOYER 8'-5" x 10'-1"
- DEN 12'-2" x 14'-7"
- W.I. PLANTER
- DECK
- PORCH 14'-0" x 16'-9"

houseplansandmore.com

ANDRIA

PLAN FEATURES

3,650 total square feet of living area

Width: 85'-0" Depth: 53'-4"

Energy efficient home with 2" x 6" exterior walls

The expansive kitchen and nook feature a cooktop island with seating, walk-in pantry and access to the outdoors

A two-story vaulted ceiling enhances the spacious great room that features a grand fireplace flanked by built-ins

Entertain with ease in the formal dining room with a step ceiling

Bedroom #4 is a wonderful suite with a study area, walk-in closet and private bath

4 bedrooms, 3 1/2 baths, 4-car side entry garage

Basement foundation

Price Code S1

houseplansandmore.com

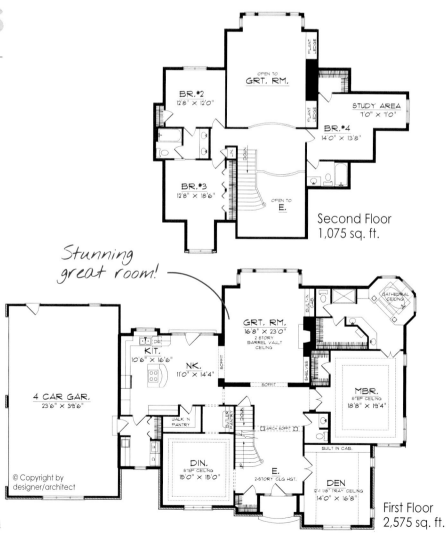

Stunning great room!

Second Floor
1,075 sq. ft.

First Floor
2,575 sq. ft.

© Copyright by designer/architect

KNIGHTS MANOR

PLAN #651-020D-0266

1,792 total square feet of living area

Width: 68'-0" Depth: 62'-0"

Energy efficient home with 2" x 6" exterior walls

A full wall of windows with access to the rear porch brightens the entire living space

3 bedrooms, 2 baths, 2-car side entry garage

Crawl space foundation

Price Code C

ICE CAP

PLAN #651-055D-0525

1,474 total square feet of living area

Width: 43'-0" Depth: 66'-6"

The stunning great room with tray ceiling includes a fireplace and access to the outdoor grilling porch

The private master bath includes both a whirlpool tub and a separate shower

2 bedrooms, 2 baths, 2-car side entry garage

Crawl space or slab foundation, please specify when ordering

Price Code B

AUGUSTA HILL

PLAN #651-055D-0034

1,787 total square feet of living area

Width: 54'-2" Depth: 56'-2"

The covered grilling porch is perfect for barbecues

3 bedrooms, 2 baths, 2-car garage

Slab or crawl space foundation, please specify when ordering; walk-out basement and basement foundations available for an additional fee

Price Code B

SKYMEADOW

PLAN #651-111D-0031

3,236 total square feet of living area

Width: 89'-4" Depth: 74'-2"

The entry rotunda will immediately intrigue guests as they enter this beautiful home

4 bedrooms, 3 baths, 3-car side entry garage

Slab, crawl space and basement foundation, please specify when ordering

Price Code E

PLANFEATURES

4,768 total square feet of living area

Width: 76'-6" Depth: 68'-6"

The private second floor master bedroom enjoys a private deck and massive bath with a spa tub, an oversized shower and plenty of closet space

The private study includes a charming window seat, built-in bookcases and a covered porch

All of the bedrooms are located on the second floor for peace and quiet

4 bedrooms, 4 1/2 baths, 3-car side entry garage

Crawl space foundation

Price Code S1

Enchanting study with a cozy fireplace!

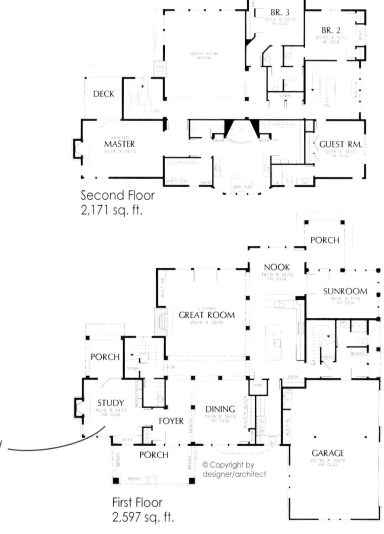

Second Floor
2,171 sq. ft.

First Floor
2,597 sq. ft.

© Copyright by designer/architect

houseplansandmore.com

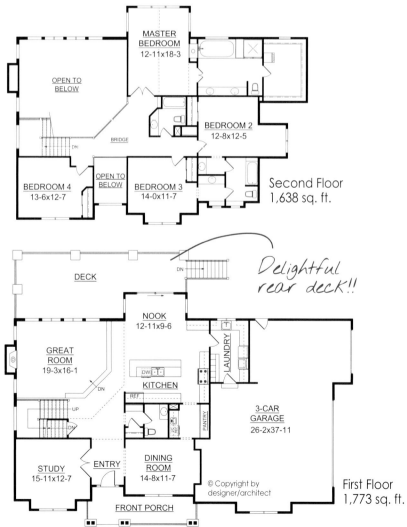

MASTER BEDROOM 12-11x18-3

OPEN TO BELOW

BRIDGE

BEDROOM 2 12-8x12-5

BEDROOM 4 13-6x12-7

OPEN TO BELOW

BEDROOM 3 14-0x11-7

Second Floor 1,638 sq. ft.

DECK

DN

Delightful rear deck!!

NOOK 12-11x9-6

GREAT ROOM 19-3x16-1

KITCHEN

LAUNDRY

DW

REF.

PANTRY

3-CAR GARAGE 26-2x37-11

STUDY 15-11x12-7

ENTRY

DINING ROOM 14-8x11-7

© Copyright by designer/architect

FRONT PORCH

First Floor 1,773 sq. ft.

PLAN FEATURES

3,411 total square feet of living area

Width: 74'-6" Depth: 57'-9"

Step down into the great room with a dramatic wall of windows for views to the deck, a balcony overlook above and fireplace

Dinner guests are easily served through the butler's pantry conveniently located between the kitchen and dining room

A centrally located bridge on the second floor overlooks the entry and great room

4 bedrooms, 3 1/2 baths, 3-car side entry garage

Basement or walk-out basement foundation, please specify when ordering

Price Code S1

houseplansandmore.com

Photo, above: The stunning ultra chic great room uses modern furnishings to accent the unique and glamorous fireplace centered between two transom style windows.

Photo, right: A quarter-circle shaped kitchen island creates a clean, sleek look with a glass-topped eating area and stainless steel appliances in the background.

Charming sitting area in the master bedroom

Photo, above: Whether it's a night of poker or pool, everyone will love the lower level game room.

Second Floor
1,814 sq. ft.

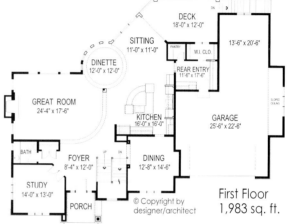

Lower Level
1,708 sq. ft.

© Copyright by designer/architect

First Floor
1,983 sq. ft.

Photo, below: The curved windowed wall of the dinette is anything but boring. This elegant dining space will make any meal seem more impressive.

PLAN FEATURES

5,505 total square feet of living area

Width: 77'-0" Depth: 58'-0"

The charming exterior of this home is graced with a covered porch and multiple focal windows

The kitchen is a chef's delight with an abundance of counter space for food prep and entertaining

The expansive great room boasts multiple windows and a fireplace

The master bedroom features an enormous bathroom with a walk-in shower and garden tub

5 bedrooms, 4 1/2 baths, 3-car garage

Walk-out basement foundation

Price Code S1

houseplansandmore.com

WILLINDA

Sunny breakfast area!!

1,379 total square feet of living area

Width: 38'-4" Depth: 68'-6"

The pass-through laundry area connects the garage and the kitchen and includes a pantry

A gas fireplace in the great room warms the entire room

3 bedrooms, 2 baths, 2-car garage

Slab or crawl space foundation, please specify when ordering

Price Code B

DEBALIVIERE

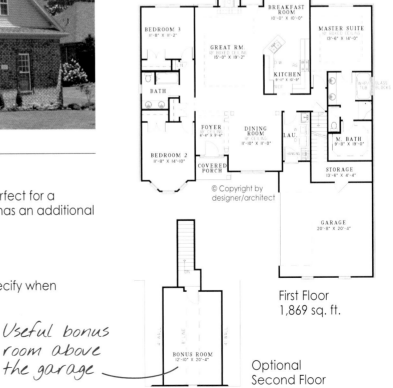

First Floor
1,869 sq. ft.

Useful bonus room above the garage

Optional
Second Floor

1,869 total square feet of living area

Width: 52'-0" Depth: 69'-6"

The second floor features a bonus room perfect for a children's play area or a home office and has an additional 288 square feet of living area

3 bedrooms, 2 baths, 2-car garage

Crawl space or slab foundation, please specify when ordering

Price Code C

houseplansandmore.com

CUNNINHAM COVE

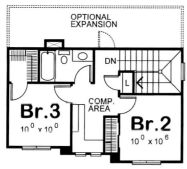

OPTIONAL EXPANSION

DN

Br.3
10⁰ x 10⁰

COMP. AREA

Br.2
10⁰ x 10⁶

Second Floor
431 sq. ft.

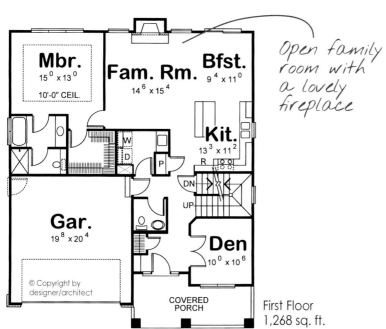

Mbr.
15⁰ x 13⁰
10'-0" CEIL.

Fam. Rm.
14⁶ x 15⁴

Bfst.
9⁴ x 11⁰

Open family room with a lovely fireplace

Kit.
13³ x 11²

DN
UP

Gar.
19⁸ x 20⁴

Den
10⁰ x 10⁶

© Copyright by designer/architect

COVERED PORCH

First Floor
1,268 sq. ft.

PLANFEATURES

1,699 total square feet of living area

Width: 40'-0" Depth: 47'-8"

A double-door entry off the foyer leads to a cozy den that would be ideal as a home office

At the rear, the kitchen, breakfast and family rooms combine for an easy flow of family activities

The second floor includes two secondary bedrooms, a handy computer area and an optional expansion area that can be finished as needed

3 bedrooms, 2 1/2 baths, 2-car garage

Basement foundation

Price Code H

houseplansandmore.com

WINSTON

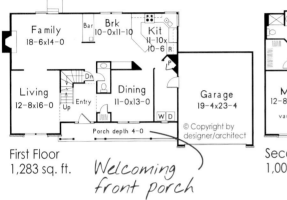

2,286 total square feet of living area

Width: 66'-0" Depth: 34'-0"

Fine architectural details make this home a showplace with its large windows, intricate brickwork and fine woodwork and trim

The stunning two-story entry has an attractive wood railing and balustrades in the foyer

The convenient wrap-around kitchen enjoys a window view, planning center and pantry

An oversized master bedroom includes a walk-in closet and master bath

4 bedrooms, 2 1/2 baths, 2-car garage

Basement foundation, drawings also include crawl space and slab foundations

Price Code E

First Floor
1,283 sq. ft.

Welcoming front porch

© Copyright by designer/architect

Second Floor
1,003 sq. ft.

LOWERY MANOR

5,191 total square feet of living area

Width: 111'-6" Depth: 71'-0"

The future areas on the second floor have an additional 929 square feet of living area

5 bedrooms, 4 full baths, 2 half baths, 3-car side entry garage

Crawl space foundation

Price Code S2

Second Floor
1,881 sq. ft.

© Copyright by designer/architect

Delightful study with fireplace

First Floor
3,310 sq. ft.

houseplansandmore.com

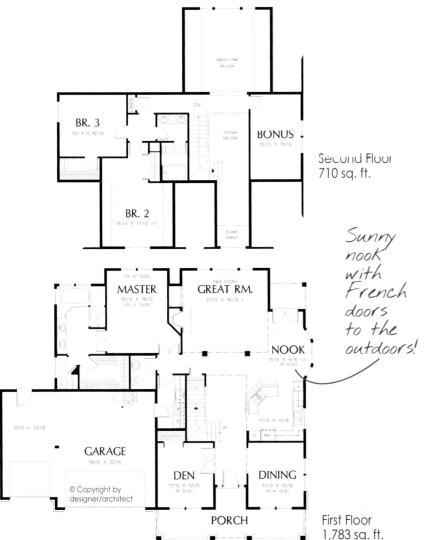

Second Floor
710 sq. ft.

BR. 3
13/1 X 10/0

BONUS
10/0 X 16/6

BR. 2
14/0 X 17/0 +/-

Sunny nook with French doors to the outdoors!

MASTER
12/0 X 16/2

GREAT RM.
17/0 X 16/0 +

NOOK
11/0 X 9/6 +/-

GARAGE
19/6 X 22/6

11/0 x 20/6

DEN
11/0 X 12/6

DINING
11/0 X 12/6

PORCH

First Floor
1,783 sq. ft.

© Copyright by designer/architect

PLANFEATURES

2,493 total square feet of living area

Width: 62'-6" Depth: 53'-0"

The first floor master bedroom enjoys a prime location, a private bath and walk-in closet

The bayed breakfast nook is a cheerful spot for a casual meal

The two-story great room enjoys a cozy fireplace and massive windows for taking in outdoor views

The bonus room on the second floor has an additional 184 square feet of living area

3 bedrooms, 2 1/2 baths, 3-car garage

Crawl space foundation

Price Code D

houseplansandmore.com

CHARLOTTE HOLLOW

PLANFEATURES
3,723 total square feet of living area

Width: 82'-4" Depth: 89'-0"

Formal and informal living spaces allow for ease of entertaining with friends and comfortable relaxation with family

This split-bedroom design ensures privacy for the master suite and house guests

Take parties to the outdoors with the expansive covered patio equipped with a summer kitchen

The optional second floor has an additional 490 square feet of living area

5 bedrooms, 4 baths, 3-car side entry garage

Slab foundation

Price Code G

Glorious Kitchen!!

Optional Second Floor

First Floor
3,723 sq. ft.

© Copyright by designer/architect

houseplansandmore.com

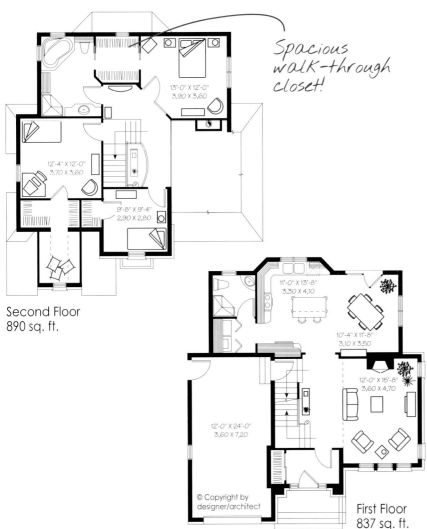

Spacious walk-through closet!

13'-0" X 12'-0"
3,90 X 3,60

12'-4" X 12'-0"
3,70 X 3,60

9'-8" X 9'-4"
2,90 X 2,80

Second Floor
890 sq. ft.

11'-0" X 13'-8"
3,30 X 4,10

10'-4" X 11'-8"
3,10 X 3,50

12'-0" X 15'-8"
3,60 X 4,70

12'-0" X 24'-0"
3,60 X 7,20

© Copyright by
designer/architect

First Floor
837 sq. ft.

PLAN FEATURES

1,727 total square feet of living area

Width: 36'-0"   Depth: 39'-8"

Energy efficient home with 2" x 6" exterior walls

Centered around a grand fireplace, the living room is a great place to visit with family and friends

A center work island in the kitchen offers organization, extra workspace and a preparation area

One of the second floor bedrooms has a unique layout with an enormous walk-in closet and a space beyond that is completely secluded

3 bedrooms, 2 baths, 1-car garage

Basement foundation

Price Code E

PINE RUN

PLAN #651-111D-0030

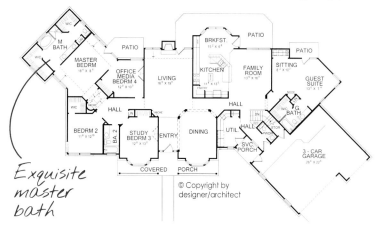

3,164 total square feet of living area

Width: 115'-0" Depth: 66'-8"

This sprawling ranch home has a terrific guest suite with a kitchenette, sitting area, private bath and patio

The handy service porch is a casual way to enter the home from the garage

The office/media/bedroom #4 is a versatile room that connects to the master bedroom

5 bedrooms, 3 1/2 baths, 3-car side entry garage

Basement, crawl space or slab foundation, please specify when ordering

Price Code E

Exquisite master bath

© Copyright by designer/architect

LEVITTOWN CREEK

PLAN #651-119D-0002

5,419 total square feet of living area

Width: 74'-9" Depth: 90'-4"

This stylish ranch home has a finished lower level with plenty of space for entertaining

The double doors off the foyer lead to a secluded den with built-ins under the front facing window

The lower level is designed for terrific entertaining including a bayed sitting area, a living/theater space, a billiards area, a game area, and a wrap-around wet bar

4 bedrooms, 3 1/2 baths, 3-car side entry garage

Walk-out basement foundation

Price Code F

Lower Level
2,324 sq. ft.

Awesome lower level bar!

© Copyright by designer/architect

First Floor
3,095 sq. ft.

houseplansandmore.com

PLANFEATURES

2,083 total square feet of living area

Width: 74'-0" Depth: 41'-6"

Energy efficient home with 2" x 6" exterior walls

The lovely breakfast nook accompanies the eating bar and bay window

A half wall with columns creates a lovely entry into the living room

The second floor landing has a cozy window seat surrounded by built-in bookshelves

3 bedrooms, 2 1/2 baths, 2-car side entry garage

Basement, slab or crawl space foundation, please specify when ordering

Price Code C

Second Floor
970 sq. ft.

Bdr 2 11'8" X 12'

Vaulted Ceiling

Dn

Linen

Lin

Desk

Mbr 11'7" X 14'6"

Open to Below

Bdr 3 11'8" X 11'6"

Balcony

Bookcase

Window Seat

Tranquil rear deck or patio

First Floor
1,113 sq. ft.

Deck or Patio (Optional)

Dn

Dn

2 Car Garage 21'3" X 21'3"

D W

Util

Kitchen 12'4" X 12'

Nook 9'6" X 9'

Family Rm 12'6" X 12'3"

© Copyright by designer/architect

Pantry Arch Desk Dn

Dn

Living Rm 12'8" X 14'

Fireplace

Arch

Raised Hearth

Dining Rm 11'8" X 14'

Up **Foyer**

Dn

Opt. Floor Plan Slab & Crawlspace

Covered Porch

Dn

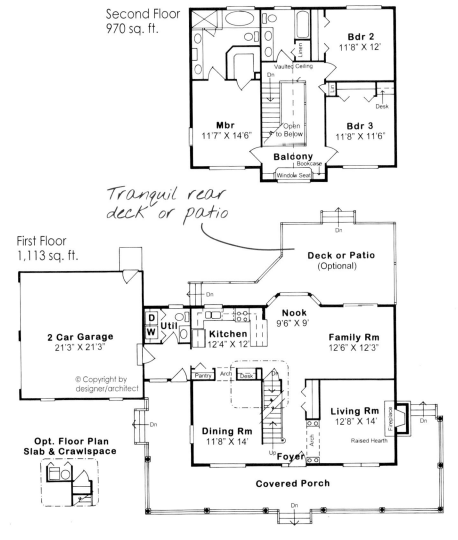

houseplansandmore.com

PLAN FEATURES

3,359 total square feet of living area

Width: 55'-0" Depth: 71'-5"

Entertaining outdoors is a breeze with the rear covered lanai including a stylish corner fireplace

The kitchen has a large center island with eating bar

The spacious master bath features a whirlpool tub, two separate vanities and a walk-in closet

The bonus room on the second floor has an additional 322 square feet of living area

3 bedrooms, 4 1/2 baths, 2-car garage

Crawl space foundation

Price Code S1

Exquisite covered lanai!!

First Floor
2,297 sq. ft.

Second Floor
1,062 sq. ft.

houseplansandmore.com

PLAN#651-047D-0187 GROVE CITY

PLANFEATURES

6,462 total square feet of living area

Width: 137'-8" Depth: 91'-7"

Enjoy being pampered with this elegant home including spaces such as a reception hall, a family gathering hall, dining hall, library and the grand suite

The outdoor living areas are equally impressive with a luxurious verandah, a pool area and an outdoor grill

A grand curved staircase continues the plush amenities on the second floor with two child's suites, a media presentation room, billiards/game area, and a student's retreat with a unique brain space

Framing - only concrete block available

4 bedrooms, 5 full baths, 3 half baths, 4-car side entry detached garage

Slab foundation

Price Code I

houseplansandmore.com

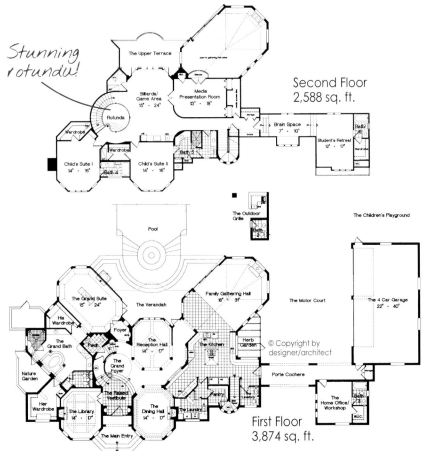

Stunning rotunda!

Second Floor 2,588 sq. ft.

First Floor 3,874 sq. ft.

© Copyright by designer/architect

PLAN FEATURES

1,365 total square feet of living area

Width: 26'-0" Depth: 26'-0"

Energy efficient home with 2" x 6" exterior walls

A European flair helps create a one-of-a-kind exterior sure to be eye-catching to passersby

Decorative columns at the entry from the living room into the dining room add a touch of elegance to this design

A large garden tub makes the perfect escape in the second floor bath

3 bedrooms, 1 1/2 baths

Basement foundation

Price Code C

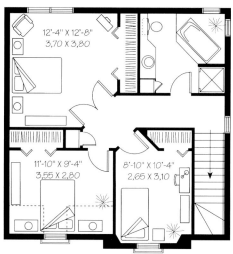

12'-4" X 12'-8"
3,70 X 3,80

11'-10" X 9'-4"
3,55 X 2,80

8'-10" X 10'-4"
2,65 X 3,10

Second Floor
686 sq. ft.

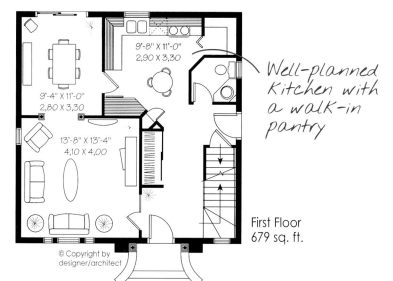

9'-8" X 11'-0"
2,90 X 3,30

9'-4" X 11'-0"
2,80 X 3,30

13'-8" X 13'-4"
4,10 X 4,00

Well-planned kitchen with a walk-in pantry

First Floor
679 sq. ft.

houseplansandmore.com

WASHINGTON

PLAN #651-011D-0091

2,650 total square feet of living area

Width: 94'-0" Depth: 53'-0"

Energy efficient home with 2" x 6" exterior walls

Bedrooms #2 and #3 share a functional Jack and Jill bath

3 bedrooms, 2 1/2 baths, 3-car side entry garage

Crawl space foundation

Price Code E

MANNINGTON

PLAN #651-013D-0022

1,992 total square feet of living area

Width: 66'-2" Depth: 62'-0"

The bonus room above the garage has an additional 299 square feet of living area

4 bedrooms, 3 baths, 2-car side entry garage

Basement, crawl space or slab foundation, please specify when ordering

Price Code C

LEWISTON

PLAN #651-053D-0051

2,731 total square feet of living area

Width: 74'-0" Depth: 70'-0"

The breakfast room includes a dramatic vaulted ceiling and plenty of windows

The family room has a fireplace flanked by shelves, a vaulted ceiling and access to ra ear deck

4 bedrooms, 3 1/2 baths, 2-car side entry garage

Basement foundation, drawings also include walk-out basement foundation

Price Code C

SABOURIN

PLAN #651-055D-0172

1,940 total square feet of living area

Width: 58'-0" Depth: 54'-10"

The kitchen features a bar with seating

4 bedrooms, 2 baths, 2-car garage

Slab, crawl space, basement or walk-out basement foundation, please specify when ordering

Price Code C

houseplansandmore.com

ULYSSES

First Floor
1,705 sq. ft.

© Copyright by
designer/architect

3,126 total square feet of living area

Width: 68'-0" Depth: 44'-0"

Energy efficient home with 2" x 6" exterior walls

A large and open entry greets guests upon arrival

3 bedrooms, 2 1/2 baths, 3-car garage

Walk-out basement foundation

Price Code D

Amazing family room!!

Lower Level
1,421 sq. ft.

CHILDERS HILL

Warming hearth room!

© Copyright by
designer/architect

First Floor
2,290 sq. ft.

3,980 total square feet of living area

Width: 86'-8" Depth: 53'-0"

Energy efficient home with 2" x 6" exterior walls

An expansive lower level has an immense bar area for entertaining with style and ease

3 bedrooms, 2 1/2 baths, 3-car garage

Walk-out basement foundation

Price Code F

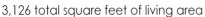
houseplansandmore.com

Lower Level
1,690 sq. ft.

PLANFEATURES

3,148 total square feet of living area

Width: 53'-6" Depth: 73'-0"

This home enjoys both front and rear covered porches creating two great points of entry

The lower level includes amenities such as a recreation room and a wine cellar

A large kitchen with plenty of counterspace overlooks the dining area

4 bedrooms, 3 1/2 baths, 3-car side entry garage

Partial crawl space/walk-out basement foundation

Price Code F

Second Floor
931 sq. ft.

Charming office

Lower Level
949 sq. ft.

First Floor
1,268 sq. ft.

© Copyright by designer/architect

houseplansandmore.com

383

PLANFEATURES

3,746 total square feet of living area

Width: 93'-0" Depth: 54'-0"

Energy efficient home with 2" x 6" exterior walls

The stovetop island in the kitchen overlooks the charming hearth next to the breakfast room

The two-story great room has a vaulted ceiling and a large, handsome hearth framed by bookshelves

The three-season porch provides a place to enjoy the fresh air, even when the weather is rough

4 bedrooms, 3 1/2 baths, 3-car garage

Basement foundation

Price Code H

Second Floor
1,768 sq. ft.

Delightful study

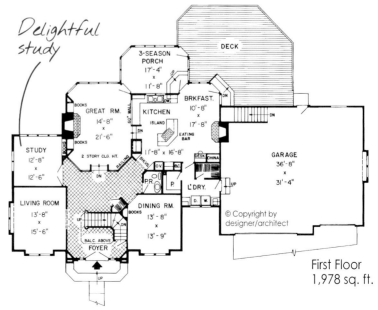

First Floor
1,978 sq. ft.

© Copyright by designer/architect

PLANFEATURES

5,555 total square feet of living area

Width: 72'-6" Depth: 107'-0"

An amazing walk-in wet bar provides an entertaining solution for the family and living rooms, while overlooking the covered patio

A large outdoor barbecue area allows the chef of the family to remain outdoors for all preparation and cooking efforts

Other amenities throughout this home include a courtyard off the formal dining room, a hobby room, an exercise room and an office

Framing - only concrete block available

4 bedrooms, 4 1/2 baths, 3-car side entry garage

Slab foundation

Price Code S1

First Floor
3,458 sq. ft.

Second Floor
2,097 sq. ft.

Hobby room!

Photo, above: Right off the kitchen, a full wet bar stands ready to serve guests or to simply whip up some pre-dinner cocktails. Creating a stylish and inviting interior, recessed lighting puts a modern twist on the traditional wood floor and paneling.

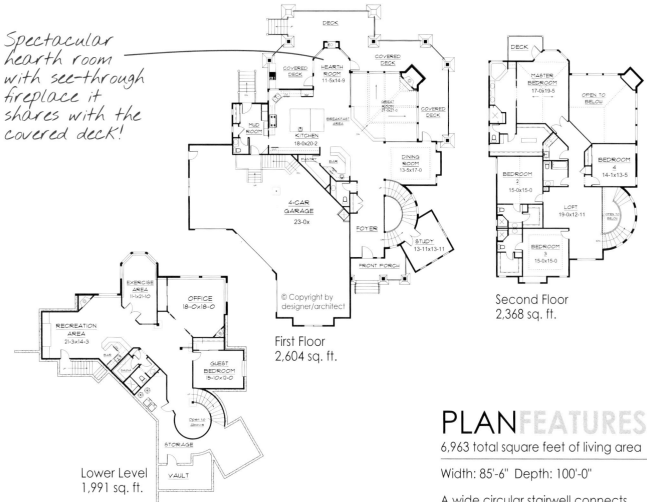

Spectacular hearth room with see-through fireplace it shares with the covered deck!

DECK

COVERED DECK

HEARTH ROOM
11-5x14-9

COVERED DECK

COVERED DECK

GREAT ROOM
21-0x21-0

MUD ROOM

BREAKFAST AREA

KITCHEN
18-0x20-2

DINING ROOM
13-5x17-0

PANTRY

BAR

4-CAR GARAGE
23-0x

FOYER

STUDY
13-11x13-11

FRONT PORCH

© Copyright by designer/architect

First Floor
2,604 sq. ft.

DECK

MASTER BEDROOM
17-0x19-5

OPEN TO BELOW

BEDROOM 2
15-0x15-0

BEDROOM 4
14-1x13-5

LOFT
19-0x12-11

OPEN TO BELOW

BEDROOM 3
15-0x15-0

Second Floor
2,368 sq. ft.

EXERCISE AREA
11-1x21-10

OFFICE
18-0x18-0

RECREATION AREA
21-3x14-3

BAR

SAUNA

GUEST BEDROOM
15-10x12-0

Open to Above

STORAGE

VAULT

Lower Level
1,991 sq. ft.

Photo, below: Immediately off the foyer, this simple and yet striking stairwell leads to the second floor loft and bedrooms, separating these private spaces from the rest of the home.

PLANFEATURES

6,963 total square feet of living area

Width: 85'-6" Depth: 100'-0"

A wide circular stairwell connects all floors, and accesses the privately situated study

Luxurious amenities are found throughout, including a gourmet kitchen, two fireplaces, a bar, walk-in pantry and enormous deck with kitchenette

The lower level has many options for everyday use, including a home office, recreation area complete with wet bar, an exercise area and bath with sauna

5 bedrooms, 5 full baths, 2 half baths, 4-car side entry garage

Basement foundation

Price Code S2

houseplansandmore.com

PLANFEATURES

4,532 total square feet of living area

Width: 96'-10" Depth: 75'-10"

The hearth room is surrounded by windows and has a 3-sided fireplace warming the breakfast room and kitchen

The secluded study features a bay window and private porch

The breakfast room opens onto the spacious lanai making impromptu meals easy

3 bedrooms, 3 full baths, 2 half baths, 3-car side entry garage

Slab or crawl space foundation, please specify when ordering

Price Code S1

Second Floor
800 sq. ft.

Amazing master suite!!

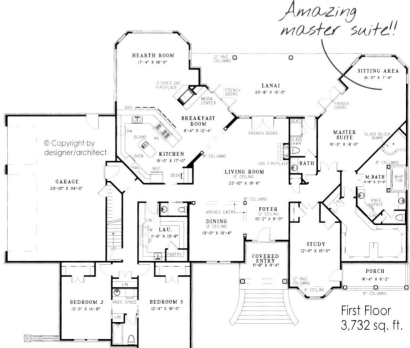

First Floor
3,732 sq. ft.

PLANFEATURES

2,563 total square feet of living area

Width: 61'-0" Depth: 52'-0"

Energy efficient home with 2" x 6" exterior walls

A distinctive see-through fireplace connects and warms the hearth and living rooms

The living room boasts an impressive 17' ceiling and beautiful high windows

The front porch wraps around the outside of the dining room

4 bedrooms, 3 1/2 baths, 2-car side entry garage

Basement foundation

Price Code F

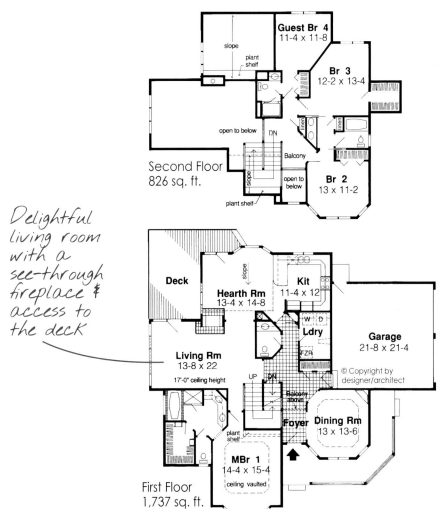

Delightful living room with a see-through fireplace & access to the deck

Guest Br 4
11-4 x 11-8

Br 3
12-2 x 13-4

slope

plant shelf

open to below

DN

Balcony

Second Floor
826 sq. ft.

linen

linen

Br 2
13 x 11-2

open to below

plant shelf

Deck

slope

Kit
11-4 x 12

Hearth Rm
13-4 x 14-8

W D

Ldry

FZR

Garage
21-8 x 21-4

© Copyright by designer/architect

Living Rm
13-8 x 22
17'-0" ceiling height

UP DN

Balcony above

plant shelf

Foyer

Dining Rm
13 x 13-6

MBr 1
14-4 x 15-4
ceiling vaulted

First Floor
1,737 sq. ft.

houseplansandmore.com

VANDERVILLE

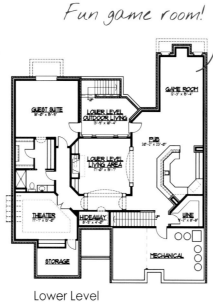

PLANFEATURES
4,779 total square feet of living area

Width: 57'-6" Depth: 109'-10"

A stylish stone exterior gives this ranch house European flair

Double doors off the entry hall lead to a private and spacious den with enough space to create a substantial home office

Enormous his and hers walk-in closets grace the entry into the plush master bath from the master bedroom

3 bedrooms, 3 1/2 baths, 3-car side entry garage

Walk-out basement foundation

Price Code F

Fun game room!

Lower Level
2,113 sq. ft.

© Copyright by
designer/architect

First Floor
2,666 sq. ft.

Beautiful master bath!

Second Floor
1,435 sq. ft.

BEDROOM 2
11'-0" x 12'-10"

W.I CLO.

MSTR. BATH
9'-2" x 11'-10"

TRAY VAULT

BEDROOM 3
13'-2" x 10'-3"

BATH

W.I CLO.
9'-2" x 8'-2"

MASTER BEDRM.
15'-2" x 16'-4"

BONUS ROOM
13'-0" x 31'-6"

DN

BATH

BEDROOM 4
10'-6" x 13'-4"

W.I CLO.   DESK

OPT. SCREEN PORCH:
11'-0" x 11'-6"

VAULT RIDGE

CASUAL DINING
11'-0" x 8'-0"

KITCHEN
13'-0" x 17'-10"

GREAT ROOM
17'-0" x 17'-0"

STUDY
10'-0" x 10'-10"

W.I. CLO.

MUDROOM

BATH

GARAGE
23'-6" x 32'-2"

LAUNDRY   OFFICE

HUTCH SPACE

DINING
10'-6" x 12'-8"

FOYER
10'-10" x 10'-6"

UP   DN

COVERED PORCH:
38'-3" x 8'-2"

First Floor
1,474 sq. ft.

© Copyright by designer/architect

PLAN FEATURES

2,909 total square feet of living area

Width: 74'-0" Depth: 52'-6"

The exciting open floor plan is highly functional for entertaining as well as day-to-day living

The convenient mud room features "cubbies" with storage shelves and a large walk-in closet

Nestled at the end of the hall on the second floor is the master bedroom with a dramatic vaulted tray ceiling, spa-style bath and walk-in closet

The bonus room on the second floor has an additional 497 square feet of living area

4 bedrooms, 3 1/2 baths, 3-car side entry garage

Walk-out basement foundation

Price Code E

houseplansandmore.com

STOCKARD

PLANFEATURES

4,204 total square feet of living area

Width: 83'-0" Depth: 70'-4"

Palladian windows and fluted pilasters grace the entry of this extraordinary home

The bold two-story foyer has an arched opening into the family room that is warmed by a fireplace and accesses the terrace/deck area

The master bedroom enjoys a private master bath with whirlpool tub, shower with seat and ample amounts of closet space

The future recreation room above the garage has an additional 485 square feet of living area

4 bedrooms, 4 full baths, 2 half baths, 2-car side entry garage

Partial basement/crawl space foundation

Price Code F

houseplansandmore.com

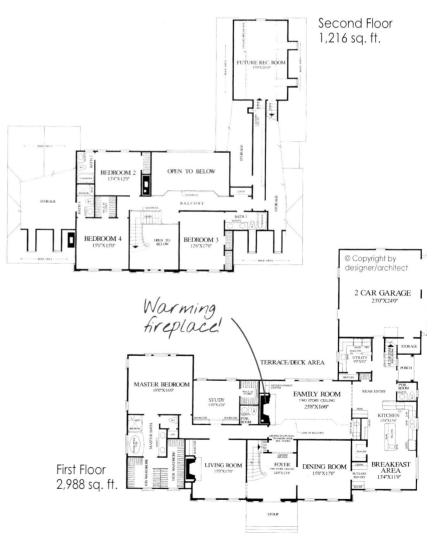

Second Floor
1,216 sq. ft.

Warming fireplace!

First Floor
2,988 sq. ft.

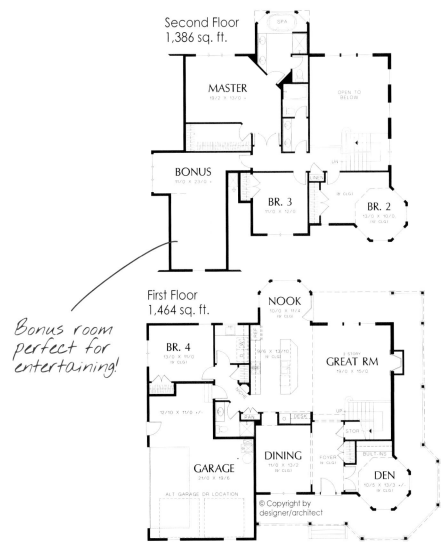

Second Floor
1,386 sq. ft.

SPA

MASTER
19/2 X 13/0

OPEN TO BELOW

BONUS
11/0 X 23/0 +

BR. 3
11/0 X 12/0

LINEN

BR. 2
13/0 X 10/0
(9' CLG)

Bonus room perfect for entertaining!

First Floor
1,464 sq. ft.

NOOK
10/0 X 11/4
(9' CLG)

BR. 4
13/0 X 11/0
(9' CLG)

9/6 X 13/10
(9' CLG)

GREAT RM
19/0 X 15/0
2 STORY

12/10 X 11/0 +/-

NICHE

DESK

UP

STOR

DINING
11/0 X 13/2
(9' CLG)

FOYER
(9' CLG)

BUILT-INS

GARAGE
21/0 X 19/6

DEN
10/5 X 13/3 +/-
(9' CLG)

ALT GARAGE DR LOCATION

© Copyright by designer/architect

PLANFEATURES

2,850 total square feet of living area

Width: 59'-0" Depth: 51'-6"

Energy efficient home with 2" x 6" exterior walls

An enormous wrap-around porch surrounds the home on one side creating a lot of outdoor living area

A double-door entry leads to the master bedroom which features a private bath with spa tub

Extra space in the garage allows for storage or work area

The bonus room is included in the second floor square footage

4 bedrooms, 3 baths, 2-car side entry garage

Crawl space foundation

Price Code F

houseplansandmore.com

PLANFEATURES

2,826 total square feet of living area

Width: 57'-0" Depth: 41'-0"

The breakfast area has windows on all exterior walls and access to a patio/deck

The fifth bedroom is located conveniently off the living area and could easily convert to a home office

The living area has an 11' ceiling

The master bedroom has a window seat and stepped ceiling

5 bedrooms, 3 baths, 2-car side entry garage

Walk-out basement foundation

Price Code G

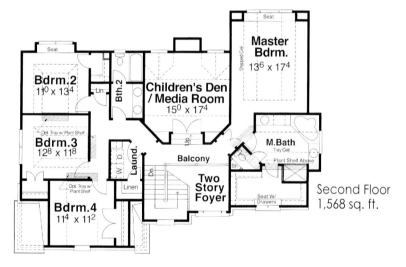

Second Floor
1,568 sq. ft.

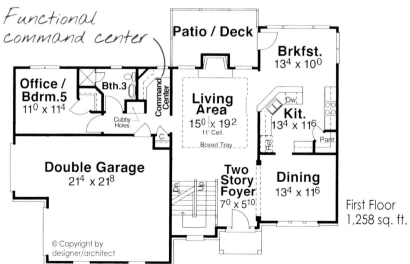

Functional command center

First Floor
1,258 sq. ft.

© Copyright by designer/architect

PLANFEATURES

1,370 total square feet of living area

Width: 36'-0" Depth: 46'-6"

Energy efficient home with 2" x 6" exterior walls

An enormous sundeck surrounds the rear of this home providing plenty of space for relaxing and dining outdoors

The second floor vaulted master bedroom has a private covered balcony and interesting interior windows that provide additional light and distinction

The great room is open and bright with a partial two-story ceiling topped with skylights

3 bedrooms, 2 baths

Crawl space or basement foundation, please specify when ordering

Price Code B

Plenty of deck space

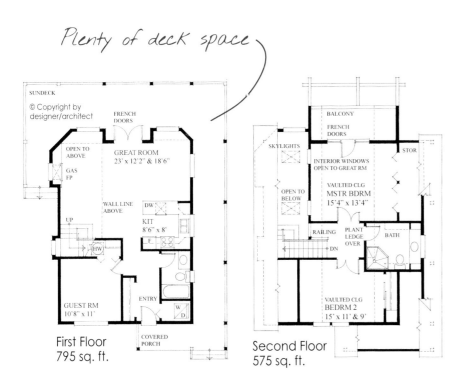

First Floor
795 sq. ft.

Second Floor
575 sq. ft.

Photo, above: The center island has space for two people to casually dine right within the kitchen, but for more formal dining, homeowners can move beyond the space into the dining area overlooking the outdoor patio. Plus, the kitchen is just steps from the great room, perfect when entertaining.

Photo, right: An amazing vaulted great room promises a feeling of openness thanks to its vaulted ceiling and two sets of double sliding doors that lead to a large screened porch.

houseplansandmore.com

Enchanting rear screened porch perfect for gatherings!

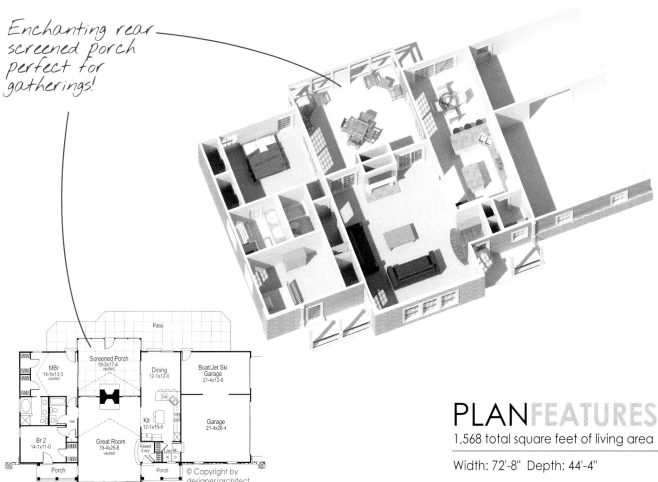

Photo, below: This angle shows off the open floor plan of the kitchen and how close the dining space is to where the cooking will happen.

PLANFEATURES

1,568 total square feet of living area

Width: 72'-8" Depth: 44'-4"

Multiple entrances from three porches help to bring the outdoors in

The lodge-like great room features a vaulted ceiling, stone fireplace, step-up entrance foyer and opens to a huge screened porch

The kitchen has an island and peninsula, a convenient laundry area and adjoins a spacious dining area that leads to a screened porch and rear patio

The master bedroom has two walk-in closets, a luxury bath and access to the screened porch and patio

2 bedrooms, 2 baths, 3-car side entry garage

Crawl space foundation

Price Code B

houseplansandmore.com

PLANFEATURES

3,968 total square feet of living area

Width: 65'-0" Depth: 57'-11"

The cozy sitting room is perfect for a game room, home theater or other hobby space

The amazing two-story great room is illuminated by a wall of windows and warmed by a convenient double-sided fireplace

The lovely study located just off the entry provides plenty of shelf space for books and other collections

The unfinished lower level has an additional 2,045 square feet of living area

4 bedrooms, 3 1/2 baths, 3-car garage

Walk-out basement or basement foundation, please specify when ordering

Price Code S1

Second Floor
1,896 sq. ft.

Handsome office

First Floor
2,072 sq. ft.

© Copyright by designer/architect

PLANFEATURES

2,241 total square feet of living area

Width: 68'-4" Depth: 56'-0"

11' ceilings can be found in the entry, great room, kitchen and dining area

The large kitchen island with breakfast bar also includes a table extension providing enough dining space for up to seven people

The elegant master bedroom is topped with a coffered ceiling and enjoys amenities such as two walk-in closets and a private bath

4 bedrooms, 2 1/2 baths, 2-car side entry garage

Basement foundation

Price Code C

Charming master bedroom with bay window

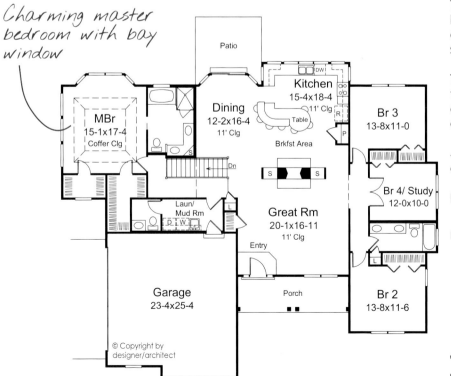

houseplansandmore.com

PLANFEATURES

3,266 total square feet of living area

Width: 57'-4" Depth: 41'-7"

The screen porch has two double-door entrances from the living room

The sunny breakfast room has lots of windows for a cheerful atmosphere

All of the bedrooms on the second floor have spacious walk-in closets

The multimedia room makes a great casual family room near the secondary bedrooms

5 bedrooms, 3 1/2 baths, 2-car drive under side entry garage

Two-story pier foundation

Price Code S1

Inviting wrap-around covered front porch

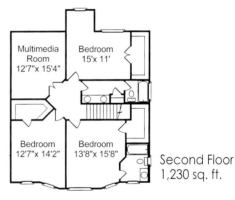

Second Floor
1,230 sq. ft.

Multimedia Room
12'7"x 15'4"

Bedroom
15'x 11'

Bedroom
12'7"x 14'2"

Bedroom
13'8"x 15'8"

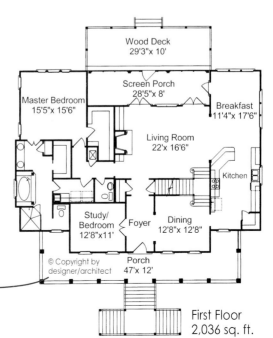

Wood Deck
29'3"x 10'

Screen Porch
28'5"x 8'

Master Bedroom
15'5"x 15'6"

Living Room
22'x 16'6"

Breakfast
11'4"x 17'6"

Kitchen

Study/Bedroom
12'8"x11'

Foyer

Dining
12'8"x 12'8"

© Copyright by designer/architect

Porch
47'x 12'

First Floor
2,036 sq. ft.

PLANFEATURES

2,250 total square feet of living area

Width: 40'-0" Depth: 50'-0"

Enter through the front door into a stunning foyer, which soars to the roofline with a decorative plant shelf and skylight

The vaulted living and dining rooms are open to the foyer and outlined by handsome columns

Vaulted ceilings highlight bedroom #3 and the master bedroom

4 bedrooms, 3 baths, 3-car garage

Crawl space foundation

Price Code D

Vaulted master bedroom with a private bath & walk in closet

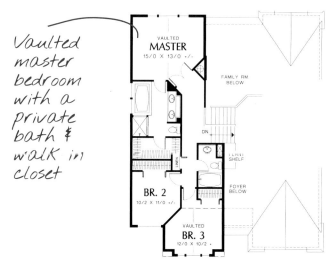

Second Floor
848 sq. ft.

First Floor
1,402 sq. ft.

© Copyright by designer/architect

houseplansandmore.com

EVELYN

PLANFEATURES

2,100 total square feet of living area

Width: 56'-8" Depth: 59'-0"

The spacious great room features a vaulted ceiling, fireplace and a staircase to the atrium below

The efficient kitchen has seating for quick and easy meals next to the sunny breakfast area

A bay window, private bath and walk-in closet are some of the amenities of the master bedroom

3 bedrooms, 2 baths, 2-car garage

Walk-out basement foundation

Price Code B

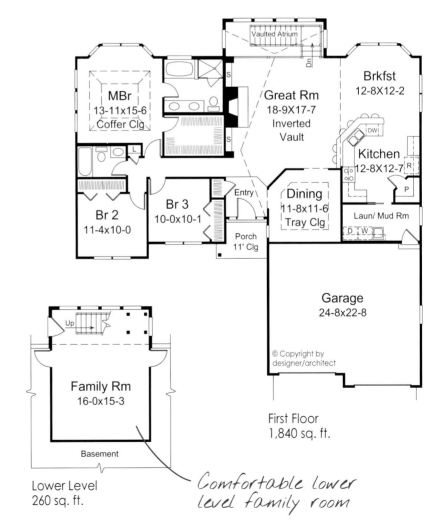

Vaulted Atrium

Dn

MBr
13-11x15-6
Coffer Clg

Great Rm
18-9X17-7
Inverted
Vault

Brkfst
12-8X12-2

Kitchen
12-8X12-7

DW

Entry

Dining
11-8X11-6
Tray Clg

Laun/ Mud Rm

D   W

Br 2
11-4x10-0

Br 3
10-0x10-1

Porch
11' Clg

Garage
24-8x22-8

© Copyright by
designer/architect

First Floor
1,840 sq. ft.

Up

Family Rm
16-0x15-3

Basement

Lower Level
260 sq. ft.

Comfortable lower level family room

MAYLAND
PLAN #651-001D-0031

1,501 total square feet of living area

Price Code B

Width: 48'-0" Depth: 66'-0"

3 bedrooms, 2 baths, 2-car side entry garage

Basement foundation, drawings also include crawl space and slab foundations

GREENBAY PARK
PLAN #651-053D-0010

1,983 total square feet of living area

Price Code A

Width: 50'-0" Depth: 30'-0"

3 bedrooms, 2 1/2 baths, 2-car side entry drive under garage

Walk-out basement foundation

PAIGE
PLAN #651-121D-0016

1,582 total square feet of living area

Price Code A

Width: 42'-4" Depth: 54'-0"

3 bedrooms, 2 baths, 2-car detached garage

Basement foundation

SYDNEY
PLAN #651-121D-0025

1,368 total square feet of living area

Price Code AA

Width: 50'-0" Depth: 34'-6"

3 bedrooms, 2 baths, 2-car detached garage

Basement foundation

SARAH
PLAN #651-121D-0032

2,392 total square feet of living area

Price Code C

Width: 68'-6" Depth: 74'-0"

4 bedrooms, 2 1/2 baths, 2-car side entry garage

Basement foundation

AUBREY
PLAN #651-121D-0033

944 total square feet of living area

Price Code AAA

Width: 32'-0" Depth: 34'-0"

2 bedrooms, 1 bath, 2-car detached garage

Basement foundation, drawings also include crawl space or slab foundation

VANDEMARK PLAN #651-007D-0006

2,624 total square feet of living area — Price Code E

Width: 70'-0" Depth: 46'-4"

4 bedrooms, 2 1/2 baths, 2-car side entry garage

Basement foundation

MEADVILLE PLAN #651-011D-0182

2,328 total square feet of living area — Price Code D

Width: 57'-2" Depth: 58'-7"

4 bedrooms, 2 1/2 baths, 2-car garage

Crawl space foundation

WATERSTONE PLAN #651-013S-0009

4,398 total square feet of living area — Price Code S1

Width: 62'-0" Depth: 66'-0"

4 bedrooms, 3 1/2 baths, 3-car side entry garage

Walk-out basement foundation

DUTCH HILL PLAN #651-032D-0469

1,440 total square feet of living area — Price Code E

Width: 40'-0" Depth: 32'-0"

3 bedrooms, 2 baths, 1-car garage

Basement foundation

FELIPE PLAN #651-106S-0052

5,743 total square feet of living area — Price Code S1

Width: 63'-10" Depth: 59'-11"

5 bedrooms, 5 full baths, 2 half baths, 3-car garage

Slab foundation

DERBY PLACE PLAN #651-129S-0003

5,469 total square feet of living area — Price Code S2

Width: 79'-4" Depth: 91'-0"

4 bedrooms, 4 full baths, 2 half baths, 2-car side entry garage

Walk-out basement foundation

PLAN FEATURES

2,973 total square feet of living area

Width: 108'-6" Depth: 59'-0"

Energy efficient home with 2" x 6" exterior walls

This stunning home has a large vaulted great room designed for elegant entertaining

A private double-doored study offers an entire wall of built-ins

The bonus room above the garage has an additional 417 square feet of living area

3 bedrooms, 3 1/2 baths, 3-car side entry garage

Crawl space foundation

Price Code E

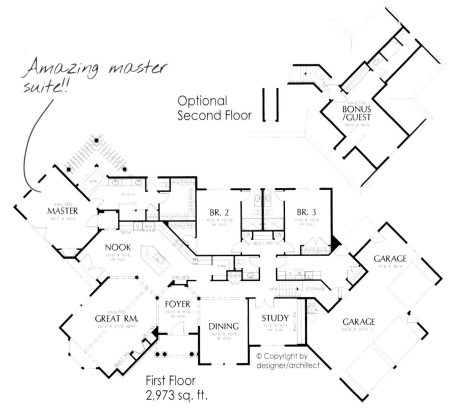

Amazing master suite!!

Optional Second Floor

First Floor
2,973 sq. ft.

© Copyright by designer/architect

Photo, above: Naturally cheerful, the great room has a tremendous amount of light from the large wall of windows and a warm glow from the fireplace.

Photo, right: A spacious great room boasts a vaulted ceiling, dining area, atrium with elegant staircase, and feature windows.

houseplansandmore.com

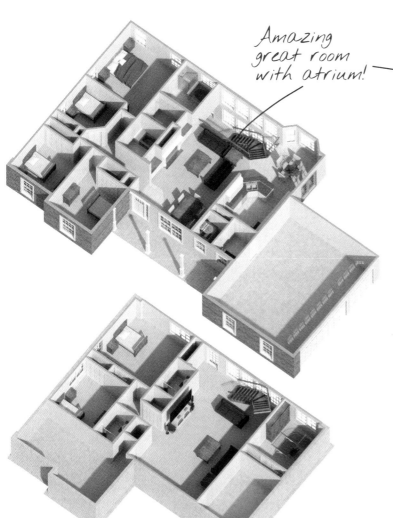

First Floor
1,978 sq. ft.

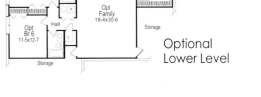

Optional Lower Level

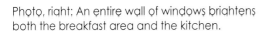

Photo, right: An entire wall of windows brightens both the breakfast area and the kitchen.

Photo, below: Plenty of cabinets and a wrap-around counter for dining are two great features of this home's kitchen.

Amazing great room with atrium!

PLAN FEATURES

1,978 total square feet of living area

Width: 76'-8" Depth: 47'-4"

This home's classic traditional exterior is always in style

The spacious great room boasts a vaulted ceiling, dining area, an atrium with an elegant staircase and feature windows

The lower level has an additional 1,295 square feet of optional living area that consists of a family room, two bedrooms, two baths and a study

2" x 6" exterior walls available, please order plan #651-007E-0077

4 bedrooms, 2 1/2 baths, 3-car side entry garage

Walk-out basement foundation

Price Code C

PLANFEATURES

6,495 total square feet of living area

Width: 109'-0" Depth: 84'-6"

A stand-alone fireplace warms the great room that is brightened by windows

The stunning kitchen features an uncommon center island with an eating bar, a walk-in pantry and a large walk-in wine closet

The view from the second floor is spectacular, showcasing an expansive loft area

Entertaining is a breeze on the stately lower level complete with a bar and home theater

5 bedrooms, 5 1/2 baths, 3-car side entry garage, 1-car garage

Walk-out basement or basement foundation, please specify when ordering

Price Code S4

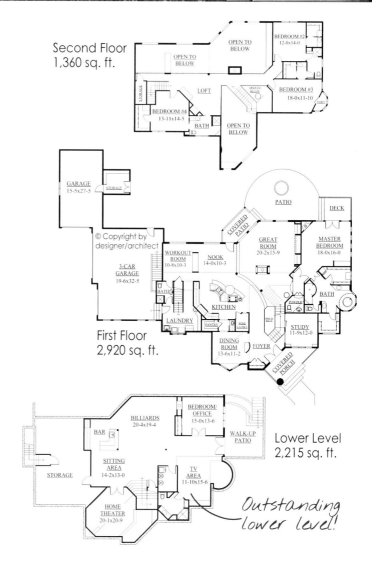

Second Floor
1,360 sq. ft.

First Floor
2,920 sq. ft.

© Copyright by designer/architect

Lower Level
2,215 sq. ft.

Outstanding lower level!

houseplansandmore.com

DELLVIEW

PLAN #651-011D-0030

2,476 total square feet of living area

Price Code E

Width: 60'-0" Depth: 52'-0"

3 bedrooms, 2 1/2 baths, 3-car garage

Crawl space foundation

ELKGROVE

PLAN #651-016D-0064

4,027 total square feet of living area

Price Code H

Width: 69'-0" Depth: 48'-0"

5 bedrooms, 4 1/2 baths, 3-car side entry garage

Crawl space foundation, basement foundation available for an additional fee

EVELINE

PLAN #651-038D-0006

2,281 total square feet of living area

Price Code D

Width: 76'-4" Depth: 45'-10"

3 bedrooms, 2 1/2 baths, 3-car side entry garage

Basement, crawl space or slab foundation, please specify when ordering

RIVERPARK

PLAN #651-053D-0012

2,356 total square feet of living area

Price Code B

Width: 49'-0" Depth: 38'-0"

4 bedrooms, 2 1/2 baths, 2-car side entry garage

Basement foundation

ACKERMAN PLACE

PLAN #651-071D-0183

4,300 total square feet of living area

Price Code G

Width: 105'-4" Depth: 53'-0"

4 bedrooms, 3 1/2 baths, 3-car side entry garage, 1-car garage

Crawl space foundation

GLYN CAGNY

PLAN #651-051S-0018

4,295 total square feet of living area

Price Code S1

Width: 102'-8" Depth: 48'-10"

4 bedrooms, 4 1/2 baths, 3-car side garage

Basement foundation

PLANFEATURES

1,826 total square feet of living area

Width: 48'-0" Depth: 35'-4"

Energy efficient home with 2" x 6" exterior walls

Quaint and charming, this home has a lovely cottage feel loaded with curb appeal

A radiant dining room is filled with sunlight from windows all around

Enter double-doors on the second floor to find a lovely master bedroom location with an enormous walk-in closet

3 bedrooms, 2 baths, 1-car garage

Basement foundation

Price Code F

Second Floor
908 sq. ft.

Glorious dining area!

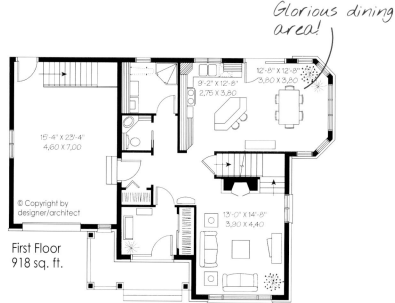

First Floor
918 sq. ft.

© Copyright by designer/architect

houseplansandmore.com

RANDOLPH LAKE PLAN#651-011D-0172

2,516 total square feet of living area — Price Code E

Width: 60'-0" Depth: 53'-0"

3 bedrooms, 2 1/2 baths, 3-car garage

Crawl space foundation

WARSAW PLAN#651-013S-0003

3,291 total square feet of living area — Price Code S1

Width: 76'-0" Depth: 86'-6"

4 bedrooms, 3 1/2 baths, 3-car side entry garage

Walk-out basement foundation

WEMBLETON PLAN#651-020S-0004

5,560 total square feet of living area — Price Code S2

Width: 94'-0" Depth: 68'-0"

4 bedrooms, 4 full baths, 2 half baths, 3-car side entry garage

Slab foundation, drawings also include crawl space foundation

GLACIERHILL POINT PLAN#651-011S-0022

3,542 total square feet of living area — Price Code S1

Width: 71'-0" Depth: 58'-6"

4 bedrooms, 3 1/2 baths, 3-car garage

Crawl space foundation

CARWINE RIDGE PLAN#651-055S-0024

3,914 total square feet of living area — Price Code S1

Width: 71'-0" Depth: 55'-0"

3 bedrooms, 3 1/2 baths, 3-car side entry garage

Slab or crawl space foundation, please specify when ordering

GRASS VALLEY MANOR PLAN#651-011S-0008

3,557 total square feet of living area — Price Code S1

Width: 87'-6" Depth: 56'-0"

3 bedrooms, 2 1/2 baths, 3-car garage

Partial slab/walk-out basement foundation

PLANFEATURES

3,339 total square feet of living area

Width: 80'-0" Depth: 68'-4"

A truly dramatic whirlpool tub is free-standing and the main focal point of the master bath

Bedroom #3 features a charming built-in window seat

The family room is filled with sunlight from an entire wall of windows and also features the conveniences of a fireplace and built-in media shelves

4 bedrooms, 4 baths, 3-car side entry garage

Slab foundation

Price Code G

Second Floor
441 sq. ft.

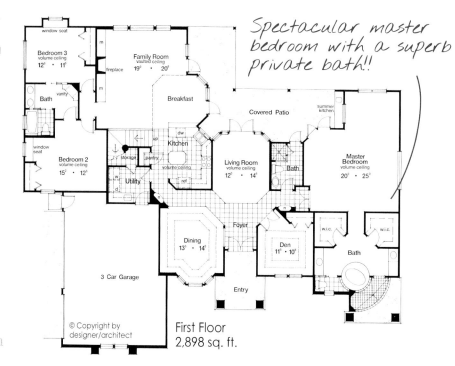

Spectacular master bedroom with a superb private bath!!

First Floor
2,898 sq. ft.

© Copyright by designer/architect

COUNTRYVIEW
PLAN #651-007D-0015

2,828 total square feet of living area — Price Code F

Width: 76'-10" Depth: 57'-10"

5 bedrooms, 3 1/2 baths, 2-car side entry garage

Basement foundation, drawings also include crawl space and slab foundations

GRANDBORO
PLAN #651-011D-0169

2,458 total square feet of living area — Price Code D

Width: 54'-6" Depth: 54'-0"

3 bedrooms, 2 1/2 baths, 3-car side entry garage

Crawl space foundation

PLEASANT HILL
PLAN #651-024D-0047

2,205 total square feet of living area — Price Code C

Width: 54'-6" Depth: 45'-0"

3 bedrooms, 2 baths, 2-car drive under carport

Pier foundation

RIDGEPEAK
PLAN #651-038D-0059

3,903 total square feet of living area — Price Code H

Width: 60'-0" Depth: 82'-6"

4 bedrooms, 3 baths, 2-car side entry garage, 2-car drive under rear entry garage

Walk-out basement foundation

ECHO GLEN
PLAN #651-055D-0530

2,237 total square feet of living area — Price Code D

Width: 37'-8" Depth: 71'-6"

3 bedrooms, 2 1/2 baths, 2-car rear entry garage

Crawl space or slab foundation, please specify when ordering

WENDELL BAY
PLAN #651-072D-0026

2,307 total square feet of living area — Price Code E

Width: 61'-4" Depth: 45'-0"

3 bedrooms, 3 baths, 2-car side entry garage

Basement foundation

PARKLAWN

PLANFEATURES

4,457 total square feet of living area

Width: 76'-0" Depth: 59'-4"

Energy efficient home with 2" x 6" exterior walls

A unique blend of stone and stucco siding, columns and arches creates a facade that will stand out in any neighborhood

The entry leads into the great room that features a see-through fireplace, built-in cabinets and a beamed ceiling

Entertain in style with the lower level recreation room, media room and nearby wine room

4 bedrooms, 3 1/2 baths, two 2-car side entry garages

Walk-out basement foundation

Price Code S1

First Floor
2,262 sq. ft.

© Copyright by designer/architect

Unique wine room!

Lower Level
2,195 sq. ft.

houseplansandmore.com

414

GRAPEVINE PARK PLAN #651-011D-0148

2,517 total square feet of living area   Price Code E

Width: 73'-0" Depth: 42'-0"

3 bedrooms, 2 1/2 baths, 2-car side entry garage

Crawl space foundation

COVENTRY PLAN #651-023D-0001

3,149 total square feet of living area   Price Code E

Width: 66'-0" Depth: 47'-0"

4 bedrooms, 3 1/2 baths, 2-car detached garage

Slab foundation, drawings also include crawl space foundation

APPLE HILL PLAN #651-032D-0027

2,281 total square feet of living area   Price Code G

Width: 58'-0" Depth: 40'-0"

3 bedrooms, 2 1/2 baths, 2-car garage

Basement foundation

TRENTON PARK PLAN #651-047D-0168

3,338 total square feet of living area   Price Code G

Width: 77'-4" Depth: 94'-0"

4 bedrooms, 3 1/2 baths, 2-car side entry garage

Slab foundation

CAROL JUNCTION PLAN #651-072D-0428

2,763 total square feet of living area   Price Code F

Width: 53'-0" Depth: 55'-8"

3 bedrooms, 2 1/2 baths, 2-car side entry garage

Basement foundation

KINARD PLAN #651-106S-0047

4,984 total square feet of living area   Price Code S1

Width: 75'-0" Depth: 74'-0"

5 bedrooms, 5 baths, 3-car garage

Slab foundation

FOREST PATH

PLANFEATURES

3,374 total square feet of living area

Width: 95'-0" Depth: 47'-9"

An enchanting courtyard surrounding the garage leads to a patio area that has access to the breakfast room

Relax in the master bath that includes two large walk-in closets and a lovely vaulted ceiling

The vaulted foyer leads into an open and airy first floor

The bonus room on the second floor has an additional 250 square feet of living area

3 bedrooms, 2 1/2 baths, 3-car side entry garage

Crawl space or slab foundation, please specify when ordering

Price Code S1

Striking hearth room with corner fireplace!

Second Floor
714 sq. ft.

First Floor
2,660 sq. ft.

© Copyright by designer/architect

houseplansandmore.com

JOSHBURY
PLAN#651-007D-0047

2,730 total square feet of living area   Price Code E

Width: 62'-0" Depth: 51'-8"

4 bedrooms, 2 1/2 baths, 3-car side entry garage with storage area

Basement foundation

FLAGSTAFF
PLAN#651-023D-0002

2,869 total square feet of living area   Price Code E

Width: 62'-4" Depth: 53'-0"

4 bedrooms, 3 baths, 2-car rear entry garage

Slab foundation, drawings also include crawl space foundation

FOURCHON
PLAN#651-072D-0994

3,265 total square feet of living area   Price Code G

Width: 69'-0" Depth: 65'-8"

4 bedrooms, 2 1/2 baths, 2-car side entry garage

Basement foundation

COUNTRY POND
PLAN#651-011D-0153

2,539 total square feet of living area   Price Code E

Width: 56'-0" Depth: 40'-0"

5 bedrooms, 2 1/2 baths, 2-car garage

Crawl space foundation

RUBYVILLE
PLAN#651-032D-0310

2,336 total square feet of living area   Price Code G

Width: 58'-0" Depth: 40'-0"

3 bedrooms, 2 1/2 baths, 2-car garage

Basement foundation

LAKE HARBOR
PLAN#651-106S-0044

5,445 total square feet of living area   Price Code S1

Width: 61'-8" Depth: 75'-0"

6 bedrooms, 6 1/2 baths, 2-car garage

Slab foundation

PLANFEATURES

3,816 total square feet of living area

Width: 90'-0" Depth: 69'-10"

A beautifully designed master bedroom enjoys a lavish dressing area as well as access to the library

The second floor computer loft is centrally located and includes plenty of counterspace

The two-story great room has an impressive arched opening and a beautiful beamed ceiling

The outdoor covered deck has a popular fireplace

The lower level has an additional 1,186 of optional living area

4 bedrooms, 3 1/2 baths, 3-car side entry garage

Walk-out basement foundation

Price Code F

Second Floor
1,091 sq. ft.

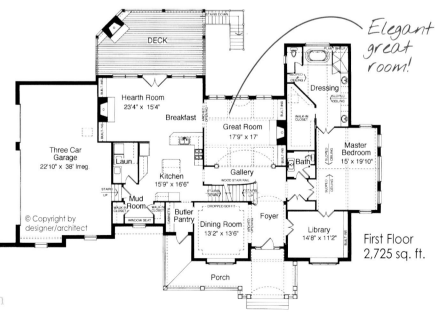

Elegant great room!

First Floor
2,725 sq. ft.

© Copyright by designer/architect

GLOUCHESTER

PLAN#651-011D-0035

6,088 total square feet of living area

Price Code H

Width: 117'-6" Depth: 63'-6"

6 bedrooms, 5 baths, 3-car side entry detached garage

Crawl space foundation

LEHIGH ACRES

PLAN#651-047D-0213

3,446 total square feet of living area

Price Code F

Width: 68'-0" Depth: 83'-4"

4 bedrooms, 4 baths, 3-car side entry garage

Slab foundation

MERALDA

PLAN#651-055D-0305

2,252 total square feet of living area

Price Code D

Width: 36'-0" Depth: 69'-0"

4 bedrooms, 3 baths, 2-car rear entry garage

Slab or crawl space foundation, please specify when ordering

OUTLOOK

PLAN#651-011S-0050

5,560 total square feet of living area

Price Code S1

Width: 72'-0" Depth: 63'-0"

4 bedrooms, 3 1/2 baths, 3-car garage

Crawl space foundation

TRAMMELLI

PLAN#651-055D-0051

1,848 total square feet of living area

Price Code C

Width: 38'-0" Depth: 79'-6"

3 bedrooms, 2 baths, 2-car rear entry garage

Crawl space or slab foundation, please specify when ordering

MACHENS LAKE

PLAN#651-065D-0154

1,897 total square feet of living area

Price Code C

Width: 48'-0" Depth: 38'-0"

3 bedrooms, 2 1/2 baths, 2-car garage

Basement foundation

LUCA

PLANFEATURES

3,808 total square feet of living area

Width: 80'-0" Depth: 99'-10"

The elegant foyer is flanked by formal living and dining rooms that are perfect for entertaining

A luxurious see-through fireplace warms both the master bedroom and bath

The great room is flooded with warm, natural light and has access to the outdoors

Bedrooms #2 and #3 share a Jack and Jill bath while bedroom #4 enjoys its own private bath

The loft area on the second floor has 456 square feet of living area and is included in the total square footage

4 bedrooms, 3 1/2 baths, 3-car side entry detached garage

Basement foundation

Price Code G

houseplansandmore.com

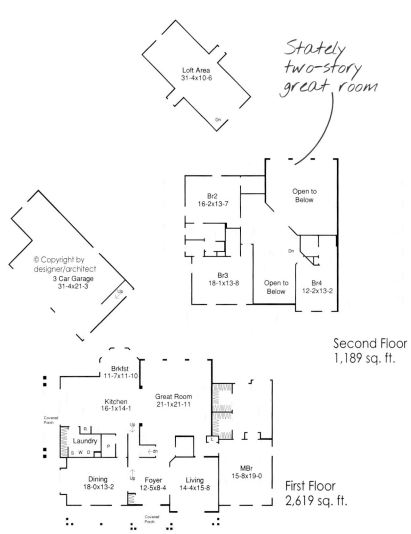

Loft Area
31-4x10-6

Dn

Stately two-story great room

Br2
16-2x13-7

Open to Below

Dn

Br3
18-1x13-8

Open to Below

Br4
12-2x13-2

Second Floor
1,189 sq. ft.

© Copyright by designer/architect
3 Car Garage
31-4x21-3

Up

Brkfst
11-7x11-10

Kitchen
16-1x14-1

Great Room
21-1x21-11

Covered Porch

Laundry
S W D

R
P

Up

dn

L

MBr
15-8x19-0

Dining
18-0x13-2

Up

Foyer
12-5x8-4

Living
14-4x15-8

Covered Porch

First Floor
2,619 sq. ft.

CHADINGTON
PLAN#651-007D-0059

3,169 total square feet of living area

Price Code F

Width: 55'-8" Depth: 51'-8"

4 bedrooms, 2 1/2 baths, 3-car side entry garage

Basement foundation

PRAIRIERUN
PLAN#651-011D-0134

2,995 total square feet of living area

Price Code E

Width: 70'-0" Depth: 53'-0"

3 bedrooms, 2 1/2 baths, 3-car side entry garage

Crawl space foundation

CROSS HILL
PLAN#651-024D-0062

4,257 total square feet of living area

Price Code H

Width: 85'-10" Depth: 88'-10"

4 bedrooms, 5 baths, 3-car side entry garage

Slab foundation

LOCKPORT
PLAN#651-032D-0024

2,350 total square feet of living area

Price Code G

Width: 58'-0" Depth: 33'-0"

3 bedrooms, 2 1/2 baths, 2-car side entry garage

Basement foundation

MOHALA
PLAN#651-038D-0077

1,738 total square feet of living area

Price Code C

Width: 68'-6" Depth: 42'-8"

3 bedrooms, 2 baths, 2-car side entry garage

Basement foundation

SOLANA
PLAN#651-106S-0042

5,204 total square feet of living area

Price Code S1

Width: 78'-6" Depth: 65'-2"

5 bedrooms, 4 1/2 baths, 3-car garage

Slab foundation

PLANFEATURES

5,464 total square feet of living area

Width: 87'-9" Depth: 113'-8"

A large vaulted hearth room extends off the kitchen

Sliding glass doors in the family room and master bedroom lead to the large rear deck

The lower level offers plenty of entertaining space featuring a wine cellar, unique wet bar, media room, billiards area and an exercise room

5 bedrooms, 4 1/2 baths, 3-car side entry garage

Basement or walk-out basement foundation, please specify when ordering

Price Code S1

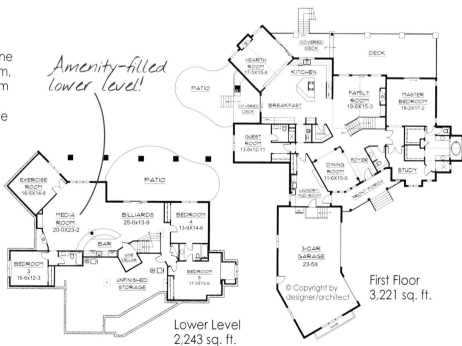

Amenity-filled lower level!

Lower Level
2,243 sq. ft.

First Floor
3,221 sq. ft.

© Copyright by designer/architect

CHASEPARK   PLAN#651-007D-0063

3,138 total square feet of living area   Price Code E

Width: 56'-4" Depth: 57'-8"

4 bedrooms, 3 1/2 baths, 2-car side entry garage

Basement foundation

TYSONHILL   PLAN#651-011S-0058

4,080 total square feet of living area   Price Code S1

Width: 112'-0" Depth: 76'-0"

4 bedrooms, 3 1/2 baths, 3-car side entry garage

Crawl space foundation

TARRYTOWN   PLAN#651-053D-0019

2,282 total square feet of living area   Price Code B

Width: 50'-0" Depth: 32'-0"

4 bedrooms, 2 1/2 baths, 2-car drive under side entry garage

Walk-out basement foundation

HARRISBURG LAKE   PLAN#651-011D-0043

2,196 total square feet of living area   Price Code E

Width: 50'-0" Depth: 56'-0"

4 bedrooms, 2 1/2 baths, 3-car garage

Crawl space foundation

WALKER SPRINGS   PLAN#651-024D-0350

2,011 total square feet of living area   Price Code C

Width: 43'-0" Depth: 69'-0"

3 bedrooms, 2 1/2 baths, 2-car side entry carport

Slab foundation

HUNTSMOOR   PLAN#651-101S-0016

4,656 total square feet of living area   Price Code S1

Width: 122'-6" Depth: 74'-4"

5 bedrooms, 4 1/2 baths, 3-car side entry garage

Walk-out basement or basement foundation, please specify when ordering

HOME PLANS INDEX

OUR BLUEPRINT PACKAGES INCLUDE...

Quality plans for building your future, with extras that provide unsurpassed value, ensure good construction and long-term enjoyment. A well-structured home is the result of outstanding blueprints - the actual plans and specifications that tell the builder exactly how to build your home.

And with our BLUEPRINT PACKAGES you get the absolute best. A complete set of blueprints is available for every design in this book. These "working drawings" are highly detailed, resulting in two key benefits:

- *Better understanding by the contractor of how to build your home and . . .*
- *More accurate construction estimates.*

Below is a sample of the plan information included for most of the designs in this magazine. Specific details may vary with each designer's plan. While this information is typical of most plans, we cannot assure the inclusion of all the following referenced items. Please contact customer service for plan specific information, including which of the following items are included.

1. Cover Sheet:

The cover sheet features the artist's rendering of the exterior of the home and is included with many of the plans. It will give you an idea of how your home will look when completed and landscaped.

2. Foundation:

The foundation plan shows the layout of the basement, crawl space, slab or pier foundation. All necessary notations and dimensions are included. See the plan page for the foundation types included. If the home plan you choose does not have your desired foundation type, our Customer Service Representatives can advise you on how to customize your foundation to suit your specific needs or site conditions.

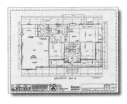

3. Floor Plans:

The floor plans show placement of walls, doors, closets, plumbing fixtures, electrical outlets, columns, and beams for each level of the home.

4. Interior Elevations:

Views of special interior elements such as fireplaces, kitchen cabinets, built-in units and other features of the home are included in the interior elevations.

5. Exterior Elevations:

Exterior elevations illustrate the front, rear and both sides of the house, with all details of exterior materials and the required dimensions.

6. Sections:

Sections show detail views of the home or portions of the home as if it were sliced from the roof to the foundation. This sheet shows important areas such as load-bearing walls, stairs, joists, trusses and other structural elements, which are critical for proper construction.

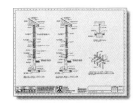

7. Details:

Details show how to construct certain components of your home, such as the roof system, stairs, deck, etc.

A quality home - one that looks good, functions well, and provides years of enjoyment - is a product of many things - design, materials, and craftsmanship.

WHAT KIND OF PLAN PACKAGE DO YOU NEED?

Now that you've found your dream home design, you are ready to order the type of plans that fit your particular situation. Here are your choices to get started . . .

The One-Set Study Package:

We offer a One-set plan package so you can study your home in detail. This one set is considered a study set and is marked "not for construction." It is a copyright violation to reproduce blueprints.

The Minimum 5-Set Package:

If you're ready to start the construction process, this 5-set package is the minimum number of blueprint sets you will need. It will require keeping close track of each set so they can be used by multiple subcontractors and tradespeople.

The Standard 8-Set Package:

For best results in terms of cost, schedule and quality of construction, we recommend you order eight (or more) sets of blueprints. Besides one set for yourself, additional sets of blueprints will be required by your mortgage lender, local building department, general contractor and all subcontractors working on foundation, electrical, plumbing, heating/air conditioning, carpentry work, etc.

Reproducible Masters:

If you wish to make some minor design changes, you'll want to order reproducible masters. These drawings contain the same information as the blueprints but are printed on reproducible paper and clearly indicates your right to alter, copy or reproduce. This will allow your builder or a local design professional to make the necessary drawing changes without the major expense of redrawing the plans. This package also allows you to print copies of the modified plans as needed. The right of building only one structure from these plans is licensed exclusively to the buyer. You may not use this design to build a second or multiple dwelling(s) without purchasing another blueprint. Each violation of the Copyright Law is punishable in a fine.

Mirror Reverse Sets:

Plans can be printed in mirror reverse. These plans are useful when the house would fit your site better if all the rooms were on the opposite side than shown. They are simply a mirror image of the original drawings causing the lettering and dimensions to read backwards. Therefore, when ordering mirror reverse drawings, you must purchase at least one set of right-reading plans. Some of our plans are offered mirror reverse right-reading. This means the plan, lettering and dimensions are flipped but read correctly. See the Home Plans Index on pages 424-426 for availability.

PDF File Format:

A complete set of construction drawings in an electronic format that allows you to resize and reproduce the plans to fit your needs. Since these are electronic files, we can send them to you within 24 hours (Mon-Fri, 8-5 CST) via email and save you shipping costs. They also offer printing flexibility by allowing you to print the size and number of sets you need. Note: These are not CAD files and cannot be altered electronically.
Note: PDF files are non-refundable and not returnable.

CAD Packages:

A CAD package is a complete set of construction drawings in an electronic file format. They are especially beneficial if you have a significant amount of changes to make to the home plan you have selected or if you need to make the home plan fit your local codes. If you purchase a CAD Package, you have the option to take the plan to a local design professional who uses AutoCAD or DataCAD and they can modify the design much easier and quicker than with a paper-based drawing, which will help save you time and money. Just like our reproducible masters, with a CAD package you will receive a one-time build copyright release that allows you to make changes and the necessary copies needed to build your home. For more information and availability, please call our Customer Service Department at 1-800-373-2646.
Note: CAD files are non-refundable and not returnable.

Additional Sets:

Additional sets of the plan ordered are available for an additional cost of $45.00 each. Five-set, eight-set, and reproducible packages offer considerable savings.
Note: Available only within 90 days after purchase of plan package or reproducible masters of the same plan.

MAKING CHANGES TO YOUR PLAN

We understand that it is difficult to find blueprints that will meet all your needs. That is why HDA, Inc. is pleased to offer plan modification services.

Thinking About Customizing Your Plan?

If you're like many customers, you may want to make changes to your home plan to make it the dream home you've always wanted. That's where our expert design and modification team comes in. You won't find a more efficient and economic way to get your changes done than by using our design services.

Whether it's enlarging a kitchen, adding a porch or converting a crawl space to a basement, we can customize any plan and make it perfect for your family. Simply create your wish list and let us go to work. Soon you'll have the blueprints for your new home and at a fraction of the cost of hiring an architect!

Easy steps for Fast service

1. Visit houseplansandmore.com to print the modification request form, complete the form and email it to customize@hdainc.com.

2. Fax the completed modification form to 651-602-5050.

3. Call 888-355-5728 for your free estimate.

If you are not able to access the internet, please call 1-800-367-0921 (Monday-Friday, 8am-5pm CST).

The HDA Modification Advantage:

We can customize any of the thousands of plans on houseplansandmore.com.

FREE cost estimates for your home plan modifications within 24 hours (Monday-Friday, 8am-5pm CST).

Average turn-around time to complete the modifications is 2-3 weeks.

One-on-one design consultations.

Customizing Facts:

The average cost for us to customize a house plan is typically less than 1 percent of the building costs — compare that to the national average of 7 percent of building costs.

The average modification cost for a home is typically $800 to $1,500 (this does not include the cost of the reproducible blueprint, which is required to make plan changes).

The average cost to modify a project plan is typically between $200-$500.

Other Helpful Information:

Feel free to include a sketch, or a specific list of changes you'd like to make.

One of our designers will contact you within 24 hours with your free estimate.

Upon accepting the estimate, you will need to purchase the reproducible set of plans.

A contract, which includes a specific list of changes and fees will be sent to you for approval.

Upon approving the contract, our designers will keep you up to date by emailing or faxing sketches throughout the project.

Plan can be converted to metric.

Barrier Free Conversion (accommodating a plan for special needs, transferring your living space for everyone).

Customizing is also available for project plans, such as sheds, garages, apartment garages and more.

Below are a few terrific products sure to help the beginner as well as the experienced builder.

Your Blueprint Package will contain the necessary construction information to build your home. We also offer the following products and services to save you time and money in the building process.

The Legal Kit™

Home building can be a complicated process with many legal regulations being confusing. This Legal Kit was designed to help you avoid many legal pitfalls and build your home with confidence using the forms and contracts featured in this kit. Included are request for proposal documents, various fixed price and cost plus contracts, instructions on how and when to use each form, warranty statements and more. Save time and money before you break ground on your new home or start a remodeling project. Instructions are included on how to use the kit and since the documents are universal, they are designed to be used with all building trades. Since review by an attorney is always advised before signing any contract, this is an ideal way to get organized and started on the process. Plus, all forms are reproducible making it a terrific tool for the contractor and home builder. At a price of $35.00, this kit is ideal.

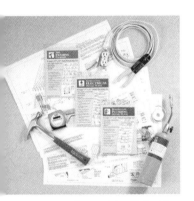

Detail Plan Packages:

Framing, Plumbing and Electrical Plan Packages

Three separate packages offer home builders details for constructing various foundations; numerous floor, wall and roof framing techniques; simple to complex residential wiring; sump and water softener hookups; plumbing connection methods; installation of septic systems, and more. Packages include 3-dimensional illustrations and a glossary of terms. These drawings do not pertain to a specific home plan making them perfect for your building situation. Each package is $20 or purchase all three for $40 making it a great bargain.

Material List:

Material lists are available for many of the plans in this magazine. Each list gives you the quantity, dimensions and description of the building materials necessary to construct your home. You'll get faster and more accurate bids from your contractor while saving money by paying for only the materials you need. See the Home Plans Index on pages 424-426 for availability. Cost: $125

NOTE: Material lists are not refundable. A material list can only be sold when at least one set of blueprints has been purchased. They cannot be purchased separately. Material lists are designed with the standard foundations only and will not include alternate or optional foundations.

Express Delivery:

Most orders are processed within 24 hours of receipt. Please allow 7-10 business days for delivery. If you need to place a rush order, please call us by 11:00 a.m. Monday through Friday, 8am-5pm CST and ask for express service (allow 1-2 business days).

Technical Assistance:

If you have questions, call our technical support line at 1-314-770-2228 Monday through Friday, 8am-5pm CST. Whether it involves design modifications or field assistance, our designers are extremely familiar with all of our designs and will be happy to help you. We want your home to be everything you expect it to be.

To order any of the products on this page, please see the Home Plan Order Form on page 432.

BEFORE YOU ORDER

Exchange Policies:

Since blueprints are printed in response to your order, we cannot honor requests for refunds. However, if for some reason you find that the plan you have purchased does not meet your requirements, you may exchange that plan for another plan in our collection within 90 days of purchase. At the time of the exchange, you will be charged a processing fee of 25% of your original plan package price, plus the difference in price between the plan packages (if applicable) and the cost to ship the new plans to you.

NOTE: Reproducible drawings can only be exchanged if the package is unopened. PDF and CAD files are not returnable and non-refundable.

Building Codes & Requirements:

At the time the construction drawings were prepared, every effort was made to ensure that these plans and specifications meet nationally recognized codes. Because building codes vary from area to area, some drawing modifications and/or the assistance of a professional designer or architect may be necessary to comply with your local codes or to accommodate specific building site conditions. We advise you to consult with your local building official for information regarding codes governing your area.

Blueprint Price Schedule

Price Code	1-Set	5-Sets SAVE $80	8 Sets SAVE $115	PDF File/ Reproducible Masters	CAD
AAA	$310	$410	$510	$610	$1,000
AA	$410	$510	$610	$710	$1,250
A	$470	$570	$670	$770	$1,370
B	$530	$630	$730	$830	$1,490
C	$585	$685	$785	$885	$1,600
D	$635	$735	$835	$935	$1,700
E	$695	$795	$895	$995	$1,820
F	$750	$850	$950	$1,050	$1,930
G	$1,000	$1,100	$1,200	$1,300	$2,130
H	$1,100	$1,200	$1,300	$1,400	$2,320
I	$1,150	$1,250	$1,350	$1,450	$2,420
J	$1,200	$1,300	$1,400	$1,500	$2,650
K	$1,250	$1,350	$1,450	$1,550	$2,900
S1	N/A	N/A	N/A	$2,500	$3,500
S2	N/A	N/A	N/A	$3,000	$4,000
S3	N/A	N/A	N/A	$3,500	$4,500
S4	N/A	N/A	N/A	$4,000	$5,000
S6	N/A	N/A	N/A	$5,000	$6,000
S7	N/A	N/A	N/A	$6,000	$7,000

Plan prices are subject to change without notice.
Please note that plans and material lists are not refundable.

Shipping & Handling Charges

U.S. Shipping - (AK and HI express only)	1-4 Sets	5-7 Sets	8 Sets or Reproducibles
Regular (allow 7-10 business days)	$15.00	$17.50	$25.00
Priority (allow 3-5 business days)	$35.00	$40.00	$45.00
Express* (allow 1-2 business days)	$50.00	$55.00	$60.00

Canada Shipping (to/from)** - Plans with suffix 032D - see index			
Standard (allow 8-12 business days)	$35.00	$40.00	$45.00
Express* (allow 3-5 business days)	$75.00	$85.00	$95.00

Overseas Shipping/International

Call, fax, or e-mail (plans@hdainc.com) for shipping costs.
 * For express delivery please call us by 11:00 a.m. Monday-Friday CST
** Orders may be subject to custom's fee and/or duties/taxes.

NOTE: Shipping and handling charges do not apply on PDF files. Orders will be emailed within 24 hours (Mon-Fri., 8-5 CST) of purchase.

Questions?
Call Our Customer Service Number
1-314-770-2228

HOME PLAN ORDER FORM

1.) **CALL** toll-free 1-800-373-2646 for credit card orders.
   Mastercard, Visa, Discover and American Express are accepted.

2.) **FAX** your order to 1-314-770-2226.

3.) **MAIL** the Order Form to: **HDA, Inc.**
   944 Anglum Road
   St. Louis, MO 63042
   attn: Customer Service Dept.

4.) **ONLINE** visit houseplansandmore.com

For fastest service,
Call Toll-Free
1-800-DREAM HOME
(1-800-373-2646)
day or night

Please send me -

PLAN NUMBER **651-**_____

PRICE CODE_____ (see page 424-426)

Specify Foundation Type (see plan page for availability)

☐ Slab   ☐ Crawl space   ☐ Pier

☐ Basement ☐ Walk-out basement ☐ Floating slab

☐ CAD Package (call for availability) $ _____

☐ Reproducible Masters $ _____

☐ PDF File (call for availability) $ _____

☐ Eight-Set Plan Package $ _____

☐ Five-Set Plan Package $ _____

☐ One-Set Study Package (no mirror reverse) $ _____

Additional Sets* (see page 428)

   ☐ ____ (Qty.) at $45 each $ _____

Mirror Reverse* (see page 428)

   ☐ Right-reading $150 one-time charge
      (see index for availability) $ _____

   ☐ Additional foundation option - $250
      (see plan page for availability) $ _____

   ☐ Print in Mirror Reverse
      (where right-reading is not available)
      ____ (Qty.) at $15.00 each $ _____

☐ Material List* $125 (see index for availability) $ _____
   (see page 430 for more information)

☐ Legal Kit (002D-9991, see page 430) $ _____

Detail Plan Packages: (see page 430)

   ☐ Framing   ☐ Electrical   ☐ Plumbing $ _____
   (002D-9992) (002D-9993)   (002D-9994)

                    SUBTOTAL $ _____

Sales Tax (MO residents add 8.425%) $ _____

☐ Shipping / Handling (see page 431) $ _____

TOTAL (US funds only - sorry no CODs) $ _____

*Available only within 90 days after purchase of plan package
   or reproducible masters of the same plan.

I hereby authorize HDA, Inc. to charge this purchase
to my credit card account (check one):

☐ MasterCard   ☐ VISA   ☐ DISCOVER   ☐ AMERICAN EXPRESS Cards

Plan prices are subject to change without notice. Please
note that plans and material lists are not refundable.

Credit Card number _____

Expiration date _____

Signature _____

Name_____
             (Please print or type)

Street Address_____
             (Please do not use a PO Box)

_____

City_____

State_____

Zip _____

Daytime phone number (____) -_____

E-mail address _____

I am a   ☐ Builder/Contractor
         ☐ Homeowner
         ☐ Renter

I ☐ have ☐ have not selected my general contractor.

Thank you for your order!

Note: Shipping and handling does not apply for PDF files.
Orders will be emailed within 24 hours
(Mon.-Fri., 8am-5pm CST) of purchase.